edexcel
advancing learning, changing lives

Edexcel A2 Geography

Peter Byrne   Sally Garrington   Paul Guinness
Garrett Nagle   Viv Pointon

STUDENT BOOK

A PEARSON COMPANY

We are grateful to the following for permission to reproduce copyright material:

Figures

Figure 1.3 'The regional Pattern of energy consumption 2007'; Figure 1.5 'Increase in world energy consumption, 1982-2007'; Figure 1.9 'Distribution of proved oil reserves: 1987, 1997 and 2007'; Figure 1.10 'The reserves-to-production ratio, 2008'; Figure 2.1 'Map showing the major trade movements for oil, 2007'; Figure 2.3 'Major oil-producing countries, 2007'; Figure 2.4 'Natural gas production, 2007'; and Unit 3, Section A Exam Practice Figure 'Consumption per capita 2007' from *BP Statistical Review of World Energy*, June 2008, pp 6-8, 21, 42, copyright © BP; Figure 1.7 'Energy use by economic sector' from *Monthly Update: China's Future in an Energy-Constrained World*, December 2008; Figure 29.2 'The earth's drylands' source: Millennium Ecosystem Assessment; Figure 37.8 'Air pollution trends in developed and developing countries 1990-2000' Earth Trends 2005; Unit 3, Section B Resources Figures 4 'GDP growth compared: China and India 1960-2005'; Figure 5 'China's consumers: 1998, 2003'; Figure 6 'Services in India and China' and Figure 8 'Socio-economic characteristics of the population: India, China' WRI Earthtrends 2003, copyright © World Resources Institute www.earthtrends.wri.org; Figure 2.5 'Gas imports to Europe' from "Russia: Oil and gas giant", *Geo Factsheet No 217* p3; Figure 14.3 'The constituents of urban poverty' from "Slum housing: Global Patterns and Case Studies" by Paul Guinness, *Geo Factsheet No 180*, p2; Exam Practice Figure 4.1 'The complex causes of desertification' from "Environmental issues in the Sahel" by Simon Norman from *Geo Factsheet No 116*, p3, copyright © Curriculum Press; Figure 2.7 'The Arctic Oil Rush' from "The Great Arctic Circle Oil Rush" by Telis Demos, published in *Fortune Magazine*, 8 Aug 2007 copyright © International Mapping Associates; Figure 2.10 The top ten companies from the FORTUNE Global 500 listing, 21 July 2008 issue, www.money.cnn.com, copyright © Time Inc. All rights reserved; Figure 2.8 'OPEC share of world crude oil reserves, 2007' www.opec.org/home/PowerPoint/Reserves/images/Slide6.gif; and Figure 12.4 'OPEC Member Countries and the Secretariat' http://www.opec.org/library/what%20is%20OPEC/FAQ.pdf, reproduced with permission of OPEC; Figure 3.1 'Peak oil production' by Colin Campbell, *The Association of Peak Oil and Gas Newsletter* No 77 - May 2007, reproduced by permission of Colin Campbell and Association for the study of Peak Oil&Gas (ASPO); Figure 3.3 'The number of nuclear power reactors worldwide' and Figure 3.4 'The number of nuclear power reactors worldwide' from *AS Geography for OCR Student Book* by Nagle et al, Heinemann, copyright © Pearson Education Limited; Figure 3.6 'Garrisoning the global gas station' www.tomdispatch.com/post/174943 Tomgram: Michael Klare, The Pentagon as Energy Insecurity Inc, reproduced with permission of Professor Michael T. Klare; Figure 3.7 'Oil price volatility' from "Western Economies are Flailing on an oil price rollercoaster" by Halligan, L. *The Sunday Telegraph* 14 December 2008 copyright © Telegraph News & Media 2008; Figure 4.4 adapted from 'Comparing global models of terrestrial net primary productivity (NPP): the importance of water availability', *Global Change Biology*, V5, Supplement 1, pp46-55 (Churkina, G.; Running, S. W.; Schloss, A. L.; Intercomparison, The Participants of the Potsdam NpP. Model April 1999), Blackwell Publishing, reproduced with permission from Galina Churkina and Blackwell Publishing; Figure 4.6 'Water resource use by sector in the UK 1997/1998' Office for National Statistics www.statistics.gov.uk; Figure 14.10 'Total GDP for China, India and Britain 1978-2006'; Figure 36.3 'Neonatal mortality rates, major causes by socio-economic group of father' Causes of death, England and Wales 2002-04; and 'Post-neonatal mortality rates, major causes by socio-economic group of father' Causes of death, England and Wales 2002-04, Office for National Statistics www.statistics.gov.uk Crown © copyright © 2009. Crown Copyright material is reproduced with permission under the terms of the Click-Use License; Figure 4.7 'How water is used in the production chain' by Hoekstra, A. Y., 2008 and Figure 4.9 'Footprint data', www.waterfootprint.org copyright © Water Footprint Network; Figure 4.9 data from CIA Central Intelligence Agency and NationMaster.com, copyright © CIA Central Intelligence Agency and NationMaster.com; Figure 4.9 data from 2006-2007 population from http://unstats.un.org/unsd/demographic/products/vitstats/serATab2.pdf; Figure 6.2. 'The areas thought most likely to suffer water scarcity or stress in 2025' Predicted water scarcity and stress in 2025, UNEP; Figure 7.9 'Map of global diversity by country' adapted from "World Atlas of Biodiversity" (Earth's Living Resources in the 21st Century) Published in association with UNEP-WCMC by University of California Press, Berkeley and Los Angeles, California and University of California Press Ltd. London England. Copyright UNEP World Conservation Monitoring centre. 2002; Figure 14.4 'The world's megacitie's from UN. World Urbanization Prospects: The 2005 Revision. Working Paper No. ESA/P/WP/200, from http://www.un.org/esa/population/publications/WUP2005/2005WUP_FS7.pdf; Figure 14.7 'Indians and blacks – poorly represented in parliament' UGI Briefing 136 Winds of Change in Latin America; Figure 15.8 'ODA by world region' Human Development Report 2007/2009, UNDP data from http://hdrstats.undp.org/indicators/; Figure 3AEP Figure 6 'The Geography of technological Innovation and Achievement' UNDP HDR Review 2001, p 45 'technologies work for human development', UNDP; and Unit 3, Study & Revision Skills Figure 'World income distributed by percentiles of the population 2000. Regional share of the population for each 20% of income (%)' undp.org/Dikhanov 2005 copyright © UN; Figure 4.10 'Map of the World showing water scarity' published on http://news.bbc.co.uk/1/hi/sci/tech/5269296.stm#graphic copyright © International Water Management Institute http://www.iwmi.org; Figure 5.1 Sources of water' from *Geology and Environment in Britain and Ireland*, by Woodcock, N. p.47 (1994); Figure 5.6 'International river basins' 'Number of countries that share a basin' Figure 6.3 'State-to-State Water Interactions in Transboundary Basins, 1946-1999' adapted from 'International River Basins of the World' by Wolf, Yoffe and Giordano *International Journal of Water Resources Development*, Vol. 15 No. 4, December 1999; and Figure 15.1 'Model of cumulative causation' from Myrdal's process of cumulative causation by Keeble in *Socio-economic Models in Geography*, eds Chorley, R.J. and Haggett, P. Methuen 1967, reprinted by permission of the publisher Taylor & Francis Ltd Books UK, http://www.informaworld.com; Figure 5.3 'The frequency that particular contaminants occur in groundwater in England and Wales' http://www.groundwateruk.org/images/illustrations/gwf043.jpg, Reproduced with the permission of the British Geological Survey © NERC. All rights Reserved, IPR/112-33CT; Figure 7.7 'Table of Net Primary Production and plant biomass for different types of ecosystems' from *Ecosystems and Biodiversity*, by Holmes, D. 2006; Figure 21.4 'The Response Curve is a model used to demonstrate how communities deal with and recover from disaster' from *Natural Hazards & Disasters* by Holmes, D. and Warn, S. 2008; and Figure 35.5 'World map showing the areas affected by malaria' from "Will there ever be a Malaria Vaccine" by Pearson, F. *Biological Sciences Review*, September 2006, reproduced by permission of Philip Allan Updates; Figure 10.3 'Regional shares in world merchandise exports, 2000 and 2007', International trade statistics 2008 from http://www.wto.org/english/res_e/statis_e/its2008_e/its08_charts_e.htm, copyright © World Trade Organization; Figure 10.6 'Global core and periphery' from Figure 18 *Development (Access to Geography)* by Nagle, G. Hodder Stoughton 2005; Figures 13.4 'The Rostow model'; 13.5 'The Frank model', and 14.15 'Relationship between GDP and pollution' from *Advanced Geography: Concepts and Cases (Access to Geography)* by Guinness, P. and Nagle, G. p190, 192, 176, Hodder and Stoughton, 2002; Figure 13.6 'The WTO view of the world trading system' from *Globalisation (Access to Geography)* by Guinness, P. p31, Hodder & Stoughton, 2003. Data source WTO; and Figure 15.2 'The polarisation of growth in the core region and the spread of the periphery' from *Brazil: Advanced Case Studies* by P. Guinness, Hodder and Stoughton, 1998. Reproduced by permission of Hodder & Stoughton Ltd; Figure 11.3 'Map of Russia natural gas and pipelines to Europe' from *Russian Analytical Digest*, no. 29, 16 October 2007, p.6, http://www.res.ethz.ch/analysis/rad/ copyright © University of Basel; Figure 12.1 'Emerging superpowers'; and Figure 13.3 'Human development index values' source: The Wikipedia Foundation www.wikipedia.org; Figure 13.1 'Top 15 and bottom 15 countries in GDP (PPP) per capita' from *The World Factbook* source: Central Intelligence Agency; Figure 14.8 'The indigenous/non-indigenous schooling gap' and Figure 14.9 'The income gap between the formal and informal economy' from 'Measures of Well-being: a case study of Bolivia' – Bjorn-Soren Gigler, *Missing Dimensions of Poverty Data*, OPHI, May 29 2007, Figure 15.7: 'The share of people living in poverty and projections for 2015' (by world region) http://siteresources.worldbank.org/INTGLOMONREP2008/Images, Figure 18.4 'Wide gaps persist in the use of many technologies in 2004' http://siteresources.worldbank.org/INTGEP2008/Resources/; Figure 3AEP.5 'The Education Gap' Education attendance rates OECD; Unit 3, Section B Resources, Figure 14 'Projected Premature Annual Deaths due to Urban Air Pollution, Total and by Economic Group or Region, 2001-2020' http://www.worldwatch.org/node/1811; and Unit 3, Section B Resources: figure 9 'Economy Ratings' 2009 http://www.doingbusiness.org/EconomyRankings/ copyright © World Bank; Figure 15.11 "List of Countries that have Qualified to Receive HIPC Initiative Assistance" March 2008, www.imf.org, copyright © International Monetary Fund; Figure 16.1 'Access to Electricity' map No. 346; and Figure 18.1 'The world's ecological footprint' map No. 322, http://www.worldmapper.org/, copyright © 2006 SASI Group (University of Sheffield) and Mark Newman (University of Michigan); Figure 16.3 'The Shipping Lanes' from "Domesticated Nature: Shaping Landscapes and Ecosystems for Human Welfare" by Kareiva, P., Watts, S., McDonald, R. and Boucher, T. published in *Science* 1 June 2007, copyright © The American Association for the Advancement of Science; Figure 16.5 data from 'World Air Travel by Distance and Passenger Volume, 1950–2005' from International Civil Aviation Organization, "Development of World Scheduled Revenue Traffic," at www.ICAOdata.com. Published in *THE WORLDWATCH INSTITUTE Vital Signs 2007-2008*, granted with permission of ICAO; Figure 16.6 'The distribution of internet hosts in 1999' adapted from *Geographies of Development* by Potter, Binns, Elliott & Smith, 2004; and Figure 36.5 from *The Geography of Health* by Bob Digby, Longman, 1994, copyright © Pearson Education Limited; Figure 16.6 'Distribution of Broadband subscribers by region, 2004, in present' and Figure 17.3 'Telephone subscribers and Internet Users World, Millions' http://www.itu.int/ITU-D/ict/publications/wtdr_06/index.html copyright © ITU World Telecommunication/ICT Indicators Database; Figure 17.1 'Country of registration of patents in force in 2002' source UNdata http://data.un.org; Figure 17.2 'relationship between population, resources and technology' from *New Patterns: Process and Change in Human Geography* by Michael Carr, Figure 4.6, p,38, 1997; Figure 35.2 'Differences in type of disease between less and more developed countries' *Geography: An Integrated Approach, 3rd Edition* by Waugh, D. p. 645; Figure 40.4 'Carrying capacity' based on Kim Adam's diagram in *Geofile Online* January 2008. No. 561 "Recreation, tourism and carrying capacity: a case study of the impacts of visitors in a rural/wilderness area: Macchu Picchu"; and Figure 41.7 "Butler Model" *Tourism Focus on Geogrpahy - Leisure and Tourism* by Nagle, G. 1999, p21, copyright © Nelson Thornes; Figure 17.9 'World cereals production and yields' UN Food and Agriculture Organization published on http://news.bbc.co.uk/1/hi/in_depth/6496585.stm; Figure 27.2 'Food Security, The Four Dimensions' published by the United Nation's Food and Agriculture Organization, http://www.rlc.fao.org/progesp/pesa/caricom/images/Food%20Security.gif; Figure 27.3 'Regions and Countries requiring Emergency Food Assistance in late 2008' from *Crop Prospects and Food Situation*, No 4, October 2008 http://www.fao.org/docrep/011/ai473e/ai473e00.HTM; Figure 27.5 'Hunger Map: Undernourished population' http://www.fao.org/es/ess/faostat/foodsecurity/FSMap/map14.htm; Figure 28.1 'Population estimates and medium-variant projections, 1950-2100' http://www.fao.org/sd/wpdirect/WPimages/tokyo1.gif; Chapter 30, image from http://www.fao.org/docrep/u8480e/U8480E2t.jpg; Figure 30.3 'Project undernourishment in the developing world', and Figure 30.4 'Agricultural GDP and undernourishment in 2001–03' from *The State of Food Insecurity in the World 2006*, ftp://ftp.fao.org/docrep/fao/009/a0750e/a0750e00.pdf copyright © FAO; Figure 20.1 "Magma chambers below the earth's surface are the source of the material which helps to create the generally conical shape of volcanoes" http://www.georesources.co.uk/volgen.htm copyright © David Rayner (GeoResources); Figure 20.2 "Types of volcanos" Colin Solomon copyright © Dorling Kindersley; Figure 20.3 'Intrusive landforms', source: U.S. Geological Survey http://pubs.usgs.gov/of/2004/1007/images/volcanic.gif; Figure 21.5 "Maps to understand the spatial patterns of disaster due to earthquakes and volcanoes" from *Number of Occurrences of Earthquake Disasters by country: 1974-2003 and Number of Occurrences of Volcano Disasters by country: 1974-2003*, EM-DAT The OFDA CRED International Disaster Database www.emdat.be Universite Catholique de Louvain - Brussels – Belgium, copyright © EMDAT; Figure 24.2 Data compiled into a temperature graph for Yellowknife, copyright © Her Majesty The Queen in Right of Canada, Environment Canada, 2009; Figure 24.2 Data compiled into a temperature graph for Vardø, from The Weather Network www.theweathernetwork.com, copyright © Pelmorex Media Inc, reproduced by permission; Figure 24.3 adapted from "Climate Impact of Increasing Atmospheric Carbon Dioxide" by Hansen, J., Johnson, D., Lacis, A., Lebedeff, S., Lee, P., Rind, D., and Russell, G. Science, 213, 28 August 1981, p957-966 copyright © The American Association for the Advancement of Science; Figure 24.5 'Examples of cold climates - Vostok, Antarctica' source: "British Antarctic Survey Schools Pack 1999", copyright © British Antarctic Survey; Figure 27.5 'The first four patterns of the 'nutrition transition', as described by Popkin, The American Journal of Clinical Nutrition http://www.ajcn.org/ permission conveyed through Copyright Clearance Center; Figure 31.6 'The gaeltacht areas of Ireland' from *AS and A Level Geography for Edexcel Specification B*, by Nagle, G. OUP, 2003; and Figure 35.10 'The cycle of deprivation' from *British Inner Cities* by Matthews, H. OUP, 1991, copyright © Oxford University Press, granted by permission of Oxford University Press, www.oup.com; Figure 32.5 'Israel and disputed territories' http://www-tc.pbs.org/frontlineworld/stories/israel502/images/501israel_map.gif map courtesy of Frontline/World; Figure 33.1 from *Geographies of globalization* by Murray, W, 2006, p. 37, copyright © Routledge; Figure 35.1 'Exposure Time Frames' and Figure 36.2 'How exposure to pollution can affect human health' www.in.gov/idem/4144.htm copyright © IDEM and U.S. EPA; Figures 35.4 'Different categories of disease' and 35.5 'Methods of transmission of some infectious diseases' from *Human Health and Disease* by University of Cambridge Local Examinations Syndicate, Cambridge University Press 1997, reproduced with permission; Figure 35.6 'The epidemiological transition' from *Health and Welfare (Access to Geography)* by Lloyd, J. p51, Hodder Murray, 2002. Original source "The Epidemiologic Transition" International Encyclopedia of Population, Volume 1, by Omran, A.R. 1971, The Free Press. Reproduced by permission of John Murray (Publishers) Ltd; Figure 36.2 'The most hazardous persistent organic pollutants [POPs]' source US Environmental Protection Agency / Diabetics Case, Vol 29, p1638 www.epa.gov; Figure 36.4 'Vadodara City' from "Development, Environment and Urban Health in India-Jayasree", *Geography 2007*, pp.159-160; Figures 36.7 'Kilbourne's model: the spread of influenza'; 36.8 'The core-periphery model' and Figure 36.6 'The four Hamer-Sopel models' from "Teaching about the Geography of Disease" by Steve Jenkins *Teaching Geography* pp111, 114, July 1999, www.geography.org.uk copyright © The Geographical Association; Figures 37.1 'Global distribution of deaths from urban air pollution', 37.4 'Major sources and health and environmental effects of air pollutants' from *August 2008 Monthly Update: Air Pollution's Causes, Consequences and Solutions* by Kallman, M. 20 August 2008 http://earthtrends.wri.org/updates/node/325; Figure 38.1 'The relationship between health care and income group' *The World Health Report 2008* p.10; and Figure 38.4 'GDP per capita and life expectancy at birth, 1975 and 2005 [The Preston curve]' *The World Health Report 2008* p.4 copyright © World Health Organization; Figure 37.7 'The relationship between skin latitude in the USA and Canada' from *Health and Welfare (Access to Geography)* by Lloyd, J. p18, Hodder Murray, 2002. Reproduced by permission of Edward Arnold (Publishers) Ltd; Figure 38.3 'The UK: causes of disability and incapacity benefit recipients' from *The Depression Report: A New Deal for Depression and Anxiety Disorders* June 2006, p.7, http://cep.lse.ac.uk/textonly/research/mentalhealth/depression_report_layard.pdf copyright © Centre for Economic Performance, London School of Economics; Figure 38.5 'Resources to fight AIDS' from "From Symptom to System" by Jack, A., *Financial Times* 28 September 2007 copyright © Financial Times 2007; Figure 39.1 'Graph of growth in number of international tourists' adapted from http://www.unwto.org/facts/eng/vision.htm, World Tourism Organization, copyright © UNWTO, 9284401809; Figure 41.9 'Village Ways – a walking company in northern India', copyright © Village Ways – Community based responsible tourism, www.villageways.com; Unit 3, Section A Exam Practice Figure 5, Education for rich and poor: "average years of education for richest and poorest 20% of 17- to 22-year-olds" *Demographic and Health Surveys*, Harttgen et al 2000, reproduced with permission of Kenneth Harttgen; Unit 3, Study & Revision Skills Figure p.15, 'Living Planet Index 1970-2000'; and Unit 3, Section B Resources Figure 13, 'Biocapacity and Ecological footprints in Asia' data from *WWF Living Planet Report 2008*, WWF–World Wide Fund For Nature, Switzerland, copyright © 2008 WWF, UNEP-WCMC. All Rights reserved; Unit 3, Study & Revision Skills Figure p.16, 'Stabilisation levels and probability ranges for temperature increases' *Stern Review on the Economics of Climate Change*, Office of Climate Change (OCC) Stern Review, 2005, Executive Summary, © Crown copyright 2006; Unit 3, Section B Resources Figure 7, 'Hourly Labour costs in manufacturing in US$: Asia 2001, 2003' Oxford Economic Forecasting www.oef.com copyright © Oxford Economics Ltd; Unit 3, Section B Resources Figure 10, 'FDI Inflows, $bn' copyright © Economist Intelligence Unit; *and* Unit 3, Section B Resources Figure 10, 'Chinese oil supply and demand', Source: Energy Information Administration, Oct 2008 www.eia.doe.gov.

Text

Extract on page 25, "About Peak Oil" by Colin J Campbell, p12, www.peakoil.net/about-peak-oil reproduced by permission of Colin Campbell and Association for the study of Peak Oil&Gas (ASPO); Extract on page 128 'Oxfam's 'Make Trade Fair' campaign' from http://www.oxfam.ca/what-we-do/campaigns/make-trade-fair, 2009, reproduced with the permission of Oxfam GB, Oxfam House, John Smith Drive, Cowley, Oxford OX4 2JY, UK www.oxfam.org.uk. Oxfam GB does not necessarily endorse any text or activities that accompany the materials; Extract on p139 'Case study: Kenya connected' adapted from *Why Africa?* http://eprom.mit.edu/whyafrica.html copyright © EPROM Program for Developmental Entrepreneurship, Massachusetts Institute of Technology; Extract on p216 about LEAF from http://www.leafuk.org/leafuk/organisation/ifm.asp, reproduced with permission of LEAF; Extract on page 228 reference The FAO in Mozambique copyright © FAO; Extract on p227 from 'Sustainability: the way forward' http://www.who.int/nutrition/topics/policies/en/index.html, 2009 copyright © World Health Organization; and Extract on p271 from "Is our water being poisoned with a cocktail of drugs?" by Derbyshire, D., *Daily Mail*, p18, 30 September 2008 copyright © Solo Syndication 2008.

In some instances we have been unable to trace the owners of copyright material and we would appreciate any information that would enable us to do so.

CONTENTS

018638

ABOUT THIS BOOK

Written by a team of experts, including experienced examiners and teachers, this Edexcel A2 Geography Student Book and CD-ROM provides all of the content, tools and exam guidance you need to study for Edexcel's Advanced GCE in Geography.

Divided into two units – Contested Planet and Geographical Research – the Student Book contains a number of features that are designed to help your learning and exam preparation.

The Student Book

Learning objectives ───────────
At the beginning of each chapter, these provide a clear overview of what you need to learn in the chapter.

Learning objectives

After studying this chapter, you will be able to discuss these ideas and concepts and provide located examples of them:
- The use of the concept of maximum sustainable yield in planning resource extraction from an ecosystem.
- The roles that different groups and individuals play in managing biodiversity.
- The conflicts that can arise from different roles within management.
- There is a range of strategies and policies for managing biodiversity and each has advantages and disadvantages.
- The tension between economic development and conservation of biodiversity will cause problems in the future unless difficult choices are made.

Key terms ───────────
At the beginning of each chapter, these list the important terms and concepts that are explored in the chapter. Some key terms are defined in margin boxes when they first appear in the text.

Key terms

Carrying capacity
Ecological footprint
Global orchestration
Maximum sustainable yield

Case study ───────────
Real-life case studies feature throughout the Student Book, allowing you to apply the theory to actual events.

Case study: Kangaroos in Australia

This case study looks at different views of sustainable yield within the rangelands of Australia.

The red kangaroo, an indigenous species of Australia, grazes the same semi-arid lands that farmers use for extensive sheep rearing. It is regarded as a pest by the farmer because of the competition with sheep for vegetation. They would prefer much lower densities of kangaroos across these lands. However, sheep farming is barely sustainable in these locations because of the long-term drought that Australia is experiencing at present. It is thought that it will decline rapidly over the next decade.

Conservationists would like to see fewer kangaroos killed (some would like a complete ban on all hunting), but there are towns that are dependent on this resource. Kangaroo hides and meat are harvested and currently this is thought

▲ **Figure 9.3:** Kangaroos with sheep ranching in evidence.

to be at MSY level, about 10–20% of the red kangaroo population in any year. If more were culled, above the MSY, to appease the farmers, there would be fewer to harvest in the future and the leather and meat industries would suffer. In the long term it is felt that the kangaroo is a better 'crop' than sheep if harvested at MSY as it is uniquely adapted to the drought-prone climate of the Australian interior.

Taking it further ───────────
Provides stretch and challenge content and activities for further study beyond the Student Book. Some of these are found on the page while others take you to your Student CD-ROM.

Taking it further

Access the following website www.jncc.gov.uk and then search for the UK Biodiversity Indicators In Your Pocket publication. This is produced annually by DEFRA and will give you lots of information about the UK's biodiversity and how it can be used to measure the health of the natural world.

Examiners' tips

Benefit from reading top tips from the examiners for added exam success.

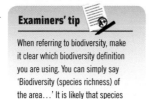

Examiners' tip

When referring to biodiversity, make it clear which biodiversity definition you are using. You can simply say 'Biodiversity (species richness) of the area…' It is likely that species richness is the definition you will use

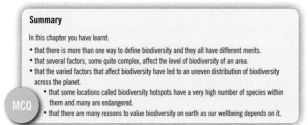

Summary

In this chapter you have learnt:
* that there is more than one way to define biodiversity and they all have different merits.
* that several factors, some quite complex, affect the level of biodiversity of an area.
* that the varied factors that affect biodiversity have led to an uneven distribution of biodiversity across the planet.
* that some locations called biodiversity hotspots have a very high number of species within them and many are endangered.
* that there are many reasons to value biodiversity on earth as our wellbeing depends on it.

MCQ

Summary

An end-of-chapter summary reviews the main concepts and learning points.

Exam practice

At the end of each chapter or topic, practice what you've learnt with Edexcel exam-style questions.

Exam practice

Study the diagrams below which compare the impact of six major hazard types over a 30-year period.

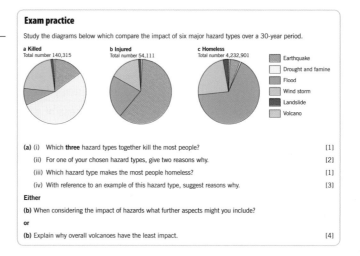

a Killed
Total number 140,315

b Injured
Total number 54,111

c Homeless
Total number 4,232,901

- Earthquake
- Drought and famine
- Flood
- Wind storm
- Landslide
- Volcano

(a) (i) Which **three** hazard types together kill the most people? [1]

(ii) For one of your chosen hazard types, give two reasons why. [2]

(iii) Which hazard type makes the most people homeless? [1]

(iv) With reference to an example of this hazard type, suggest reasons why. [3]

Either

(b) When considering the impact of hazards what further aspects might you include?

or

(b) Explain why overall volcanoes have the least impact. [4]

The CD-ROM

Study and revision skills Advice and guidance on how to get the most out of your study and revision to ensure exam success.

MCQ Test your learning and monitor your progress with the interactive **Multiple-Choice Question** function. With any incorrect answers, you will be directed back to the relevant section of the Student Book for further revision.

Taking it Further Ideas for further study to challenge the concepts and ideas explored in the Student Book.

Glossary Full definitions of useful geographical terms and concepts.

Exam Practice Resource booklet containing answers and commentary to Unit 3 Exam practice and Unit 4 sample questions and answers.

Introduction to Unit 3

Moving on from AS level

You will find that A2 level Geography builds from AS level. One of the exams is longer, there is more extended writing in examinations and in Unit 4 you have to develop research skills. There are new topics to study and they are investigated in a little more depth than at AS level.

Importantly, there is a strong link between AS level and A2. You will find your AS level work helps you understand some A2 topics, as it provides a foundation to build on. The strongest links are between AS Unit 1 and A2 Unit 3 (Figure 0.1).

AS Unit 1 Global Challenges		A2 Unit 3 Contested Planet
Global hazards and hazard trends	→	• The link between deforestation and reef destruction and increasing risk of landslides and floods (Biodiversity Under Threat). • The impact of frequent natural disasters on the development process (Bridging the Development Gap)
Climate change and global warming	→	• The impact of global water on water supplies (Water Conflicts). • The need to tackle global warming by switching to renewable energy resources (Energy Security).
Globalisation and Global networks	→	• How the process of globalisation contributes to increasing wealth and power (Superpower Geographies). • The role of TNCs and governments in developing and using technology and communications (The Technological Fix?).
On the move and World cities	→	• How urbanisation and migration might help poorer countries to develop (Bridging the Development Gap). • How ageing population and economic change might undermine the most powerful countries (Superpower Geographies).

▲ **Figure 0.1:** Links between AS Unit 1 and A2 Unit 3.

It is important to keep your AS work, as you may need to refer back to it. This is especially the case when it comes to the Synoptic investigation in Unit 3 (see Synopticity on page 7).

The six topics

Unit 3, Contested Planet, involves the in-depth study of six core topics. These topics link together under three broad headings (Figure 0.2). Topics 1–3 focus on contests over resource use and the conflicts that these can produce. It examines ways in which increasing demand for resources can threaten sustainability and increase the risk of environmental degradation.

Topics 4 and 5 focus on the development of the rich and poor. Superpower Geographies explores the reasons for the concentration of wealth and power in the USA and EU, as well as the growing wealth in the emerging powers of China, India and others. The plight of the poor, and how they might develop, is the focus of Bridging the Development Gap.

Finally topic 6 assesses the range of solutions available to make the contested planet a more environmentally sustainable world – from bottom-up intermediate technology to cutting-edge biotechnology.

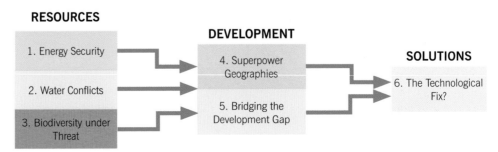

▶ **Figure 0.2:** The six topics of Unit 3, Contested Planet.

Within Unit 3 there are three synoptic themes which crop up repeatedly. These are:

- **players** – the views of different people and groups (governments, NGOs, individuals, businesses, environmentalists) and their role in creating problems and finding solutions
- **actions** – the different strategies and methods that could be used to try to solve problems and the different scales of action (local, regional, national, global)
- **futures** – what different futures might look like if we continue to live in a 'business as usual' way, or switch to a more sustainable lifestyle or even go for a more radical model such as 'green growth'.

You will find that investigating these themes will help you to 'be synoptic'.

The Unit 3 examination

Unit 3 carries 60% of the A2 marks. There is a 2½-hour Unit 3 examination. This is split into two sections (A and B). It is marked out of 90 marks (Figure 0.3).

Section A	50 marks
• Two 25-mark resource-based longer essay-style questions from a choice of five. • Each question will be split into part (a) worth 10 marks and (b) worth 15 marks. The part (a) question will be a data stimulus question.	
Section B	40 marks
• A synoptic issues analysis taking the form of three linked essay-style questions. • Four working weeks prior to the exam a synoptic resource booklet will be given to you to work on in class.	

Figure 0.3 shows that Section B of the Unit 3 examination is a synoptic issues analysis. This is based on a five-page resource booklet you will receive four working weeks before the exam.

▲ **Figure 0.3:** The Unit 3 assessment model.

You can study these resources before the exam, and work on them with your teacher in class. In each exam series the pre-release resources will be based on one of the six Unit 3 topics. They also focus on a particular location, for instance:

- **The Technological Fix?:** GM crops in Latin America
- **Superpower Geographies:** Emerging power of India and China
- **Bridging the Development Gap:** Development in Sri Lanka

There will not be a Section A question on the topic used for the Section B pre-release materials. This is why there are five questions, not six, in Section A of the exam paper.

Synopticity

Section B of the Unit 3 exam is synoptic. Synopticity in Geography is often not very well understood by students. It means:

1. Making links between different topics within a unit, and between units.
2. Using the three Unit 3 themes – players, actions and futures.
3. Linking a situation to a global theme such as climate change, or the development gap.
4. Using models and theories.
5. Comparing one situation with another – sometimes called using parallel examples.

Figure 0.4 shows how these synoptic ideas work using the AS topic of Environmental threats in the Arctic as an example. You will practise how to do this when you have received your pre-release materials before the Unit 3 exam.

1 Link between Units	Environmental Threats in the Arctic	3 Links to global themes
Link to Biodiversity under Threat as Arctic species and ecosystems suffer or become extinct. Link to Energy Security as Arctic oil is exploited.		Global climate change is a key theme, as it affects the entire planet. The world's relentless demand for resources (oil, gas, minerals) is another.
2 Players, Actions and Futures	**4 Model and Theories**	**5 Parallel examples**
Role of governments (USA, Canada, Russia) in protecting the Arctic; role of TNCs in exploiting resources; views of indigenous people.	Sustainability stool or quadrant might be used as basis for an 'Arctic Future' plan, or the UNSECO biosphere model to protect vulnerable ecosystems.	Threats and management options in the Arctic could be compared and contrasted with those in the Antarctic.

▲ **Figure 0.4:** Illustrating synopticity.

CHAPTER 1 To what extent is the world 'energy secure' at present?

Learning objectives

After studying this chapter, you will be able to discuss these ideas and concepts and provide located examples of them:
- The types of energy resources, their classification and environmental impact.
- The distribution of fossil fuel resources and renewable energy potential.
- Trends in global energy supply and demand by source, type of economy and economic sector.
- The growing concerns about energy security because there is so little excess capacity to ease pressure on energy resources.

Energy classification and environmental impact

There are many energy sources that can be classified in different ways. The main distinction is between renewable energy, non-renewable energy and recyclable sources. Non-renewable sources of energy are the fossil fuels and nuclear fuel. These are finite so that as they are used up the supply that remains is reduced. Resource depletion can occur relatively quickly and eventually these non-renewable resources could become completely exhausted. Non-renewable resources are sometimes referred to as stock resources.

Renewable energy can be used over and over again. These resources are mainly forces of nature that are sustainable and which usually cause little or no environmental pollution. Renewable energy includes hydro-electric, biomass, wind, solar, geothermal, tidal and wave power.

◀ **Figure 1.1:** Renewable resources such as solar thermal power do not need regeneration and are in constant supply.

Renewable resources which do not need regeneration are often termed flow resources. Such resources are in constant supply. They include solar, wind and tidal power. Biomass requires regeneration, as vegetation matter must grow again, and thus would not constitute a flow resource.

Recyclable energy resources are defined as those where fuel that has been used once can be used again to generate power. At present, only nuclear power is classed as a recyclable resource. Here, nuclear reprocessing can make uranium waste reusable.

Renewable resources, apart from hydro-electricity, have been utilised to only a limited extent so far due to problems regarding technology and cost. However, the use of such resources will undoubtedly increase significantly in the future as fossil fuel deposits become further depleted and environmental concerns about nuclear power persist.

At present, non-renewable resources dominate global energy. The challenge is to transform the global energy mix to achieve a better balance between renewable and non-renewable sources of energy. This is the only way that many countries will be able to meet energy demand and reduce emissions of greenhouse gases.

Environmental impact

Environmental impact has become a major factor in energy decision-making. Many energy decisions made 30 or 40 years ago would not be made now because the balance between economic gain and environmental cost has shifted considerably in favour of the latter. For virtually every country, all projects above a certain size require an environmental impact assessment which looks in detail at all the ways the environment will be affected. Figure 1.2 summarises the main environmental impacts associated with the production and use of the different sources of energy.

Key terms

Energy mix — the relative contribution of different energy sources to a country's energy production/consumption.

Environmental impact assessment — a document required by law detailing all the impacts on the environment of an energy type or another project above a certain size.

Energy source	Environmental impact: production and use
Coal	Coal is the most polluting source of energy. Opencast mining can scar the landscape of large areas and require costly remedial work. Burning coal is the major cause of climate change. Environmental legislation in a number of countries has required coal-burning power plants to reduce pollutants such as nitrogen oxides and sulphur dioxide by installing building-size scrubbers and catalytic units. However, at present, all the carbon dioxide produced is still released into the atmosphere. This amounts to nearly two billion tons each year from US coal power plants alone.
Oil	Where large oil fields occur the infrastructure can cover a very large area. Oil spills at production sites and along pipeline and tanker routes are major hazards. Oil-fired power stations create greenhouse gases although significantly less than coal-fired power stations.
Natural gas	Natural gas, composed mainly of methane, is the least polluting of all the fossil fuels. However, it can create major environmental problems when it is flared off as a waste product at oilfields. This occurs when there is no infrastructure present to pipe the gas to customers.
Nuclear	No other source of energy creates such heated discussion as nuclear power. The main concerns are: (1) power plant accidents, which could release radiation into air, land and sea (2) radioactive waste storage/disposal (3) rogue state or terrorist use of nuclear fuel for weapons (4) the possible increase in certain types of cancer near nuclear plants.
Hydro-electricity	Although HEP is generally seen as a clean form of energy it is not without its problems which include: (1) large dams and power plants can have a huge negative impact on the environment (2) the obstruction of the river for aquatic life (3) deterioration in water quality (4) large areas of land may be flooded (5) submerging large forests without prior clearance can release significant quantities of methane, a greenhouse gas.
Wind	The visual impact of wind farms can have a very significant effect on landscapes. There are also concerns about the hum of turbines disturbing both people and wildlife. Turbines can kill birds. Migratory flocks tend to follow strong winds but wind companies argue they steer clear of migratory routes.
Solar	Both central receivers and photovoltaic cells require large areas of land to produce a significant amount of power. Some people object to the visual impact of such installations.
Geothermal	Geothermal steam causes some degree of pollution because it contains impurities such as hydrogen sulphide. Geothermal hot water can have a high brine content. This can corrode and clog piping and has to be disposed of once brought to the surface.
Biomass	Clearing vegetation for firewood can lead to desertification. The use of biomass for cooking and heating in developing countries causes indoor pollution which is a major health hazard.
Tidal	There is concern that tidal barrages may have a significant impact on the regional environment, as they are often in estuaries of high ecological value.
Waves	The main environmental concerns are noise pollution and visual impact.

▲ **Figure 1.2:** Energy sources and their environmental impacts.

The distribution of energy resources

The fossil fuels dominate the global energy situation. Their relative contributions are: oil 36%, coal 28%, natural gas 24%. In contrast, hydro-electricity and nuclear energy account for about 6% each. The main data source used in this chapter is the *BP Statistical Review of World Energy*. It includes commercially traded fuels only. It excludes fuels such as wood, peat and animal waste which, though important in many countries, are unreliably documented in terms of production and consumption statistics.

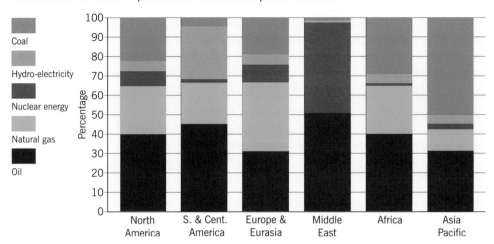

▶ **Figure 1.3:** The regional pattern of energy consumption, 2007.

Figure 1.3 shows the regional pattern of energy consumption for 2007. Consumption by type of fuel varies widely by world region:

- **Oil:** Nowhere is the contribution of oil less than 30% and it is the main source of energy in four of the six regions shown in Figure 1.3. In the Middle East it accounts for approximately 50% of consumption.
- **Coal:** Only in the Asia Pacific region is coal the main source of energy. In contrast it accounts for less than 5% of consumption in the Middle East and South and Central America.
- **Natural gas:** Natural gas is the main source of energy in Europe and Eurasia and it is a close second to oil in the Middle East. Its lowest share of the energy mix is 11% in Asia Pacific.
- **Hydro-electricity:** The relative importance of hydro-electricity is greatest in South and Central America (28%). Elsewhere its contribution varies from 6% in Africa to less than 1% in the Middle East.
- **Nuclear energy:** Nuclear energy is not presently available in the Middle East and it makes the smallest contribution of the five energy sources in Asia Pacific, Africa and South and Central America. It is most important in Europe, Eurasia and North America. The USA and its Western allies in particular are very concerned about countries such as Iran developing nuclear electricity in case they use this as a 'front' or pretence for developing nuclear weapons.

Non-renewable energy

Oil

In 2007, the Middle East accounted for 30.8% of oil production, followed by Europe and Eurasia (22.0%), North America (16.5%) and Africa (12.5%). Within the Middle East, Saudi Arabia dominates production, alone accounting for 12.6% of the world total. The Russian Federation accounts for over half the total production of Europe and Eurasia.

The global distribution of oil consumption is markedly different, being led by Asia Pacific (30%), North America (28.7%) and Europe and Eurasia (24%). In contrast to its dominant production position the Middle East accounted for only 7.4% of world oil consumption.

Natural gas

Production of natural gas is dominated by Russia and the USA, together accounting for almost 40% of the world total. There is a much stronger correlation between consumption and production of natural gas than for oil due mainly to the different ways these two energy products are transported. Most natural gas is transported by pipeline. Only a relatively small amount is moved by sea in the form of liquefied natural gas (LNG). Global consumption of natural gas is led by Europe and Eurasia (39.4%), North America (27.6%) and Asia Pacific (15.3%).

Coal

Coal production is dominated by the Asia Pacific region with over two-thirds of the latter accounted for by China. China produced 41.1% of global coal in 2007. The next largest producing countries were the USA (18.7%), Australia (6.9%), India (5.8%) and the Russian Federation (4.7%). As for natural gas, there is a strong relationship between the production and consumption of coal by world region. Consumption is led by Asia Pacific (59.7%), North America (19.3%) and Europe and Eurasia (16.8%).

Nuclear power

With 103 operating reactors, the USA leads the world in the use of nuclear electricity. This amounts to a quarter of the world's total, producing 20% of the USA's electricity.

Other countries, deeply concerned about their ability to satisfy demand, are going ahead with plans for new nuclear power plants. China currently produces 6,600 megawatts (MW) of power from nine reactors. It aims to increase this to 40,000 MW. India already has 15 operating nuclear power plants with eight more under construction. France obtains 78% of its electricity from nuclear power. As some uranium is recycled, nuclear power is not absolutely non-renewable.

Renewable energy

Hydro-electricity dominates renewable energy production. The newer sources of renewable energy which make the largest contribution to global energy supply are wind power and biofuels.

Hydro-electric power

Of the traditional five major sources of energy, HEP is the only one which is renewable. The 'big four' HEP nations of China, Canada, Brazil and the USA account for over 46% of the global total.

Wind power

The worldwide capacity of wind energy is approaching 100,000 MW. Global wind energy is dominated by a relatively small number of countries. Germany is currently the world leader with 23.6% of global capacity. Germany, the USA and Spain together account for almost 58% of the world total.

Biomass

Biofuels are the most technically advanced form of biomass. These are fossil fuel substitutes that can be made from a range of agri-crop materials including oilseeds, wheat, corn and sugar. They can be blended with petrol and diesel. In recent years, increasing amounts of cropland have been used to produce biofuels.

Ethanol is the most common biofuel globally, particularly in Brazil and the USA. It accounts for over 90% of total biofuel production. Many developing countries rely on traditional biomass for their energy needs through the collection of fuelwood for direct burning.

Geothermal electricity

By 2005 the global capacity of geothermal electricity had reached 8,900 MW, with considerable new development under way. The number of countries producing power from this source could rise from 21 in 2000 to 46 in 2010, with global capacity reaching 13,500 MW. The USA is the world leader in geothermal electricity with plants in Alaska, California, Hawaii, Nevada and Utah. Total production accounts for 0.37% of the electricity used in the USA.

Solar power

Installed capacity of solar power is at a much lower level than wind energy. By the end of 2002, 1500 MW of photovoltaic solar power had been installed globally. The leading countries were Japan (627 MW), Germany (295 MW) and the USA (212 MW). The alternative source is solar thermal power plants. The total global installed capacity at the end of 2002 was 364 MW, most in the form of nine power plants in the Mojave Desert in Southern California.

The reasons for variations in energy supply

As you might expect, global variations in energy supply occur for a number of reasons. These can be broadly subdivided into physical, economic and political factors. Technological change has had a major impact. For example, offshore oilrigs can now drill in much deeper water than 30 years ago. Public perception has become increasingly important.

▼ **Figure 1.4:** Factors causing energy supply to vary.

Factors	Why energy supply varies
Physical	• Deposits of fossil fuels are found in only a limited number of locations. • Large-scale hydro-electric development requires high precipitation, major steep-sided valleys and impermeable rock. • Large power stations require flat land and geologically stable foundations. • Solar power needs a large number of days a year with strong sunlight. • Wind power needs high average wind speeds throughout the year. • Tidal power stations require a very large tidal range. • The availability of biomass varies widely due to climatic conditions.
Economic	• The most accessible, and lowest-cost, deposits of fossil fuels are invariably developed first. • Onshore deposits of oil and gas are usually cheaper to develop than offshore deposits. • Potential hydro-electric sites close to major transport routes and existing electricity transmission corridors are more economical to build than those in very inaccessible locations. • In poor countries foreign direct investment is often essential for the development of energy resources. • When energy prices rise significantly, companies increase spending on exploration and development.
Political	• Countries wanting to develop nuclear electricity require permission from the International Atomic Energy Agency. • International agreements such as the Kyoto Protocol can have a considerable influence on the energy decisions of individual countries. • Potential HEP schemes on 'international rivers' may require the agreement of all countries that share the river. • Governments may insist on energy companies producing a certain proportion of their energy from renewable sources. • Legislation regarding emissions from power stations will favour the use, for example, of low-sulphur coal, as opposed to coal with a high sulphur content. • The cost of R & D is a significant factor, particularly in the development of newer forms of energy.

Taking it further

Working in groups, try to produce other examples for each of the three categories in Figure 1.4.

Trends in global energy supply and demand

Demand for energy is growing globally, and at regional and local scales, especially in developed and emergent countries such as China and India. Figure 1.5 shows a global increase of over 60% between 1982 and 2007 along with the changing contribution of the five major energy sources to global consumption.

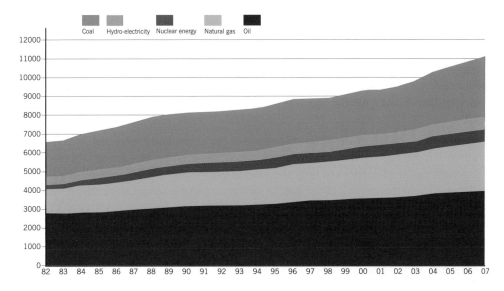

Figure 1.5: Increase in world energy consumption, 1982–2007.

MEDCs

Deindustrialisation and increasing energy efficiency in MEDCs in general has resulted in a relatively modest increase in demand compared with NICs (Figure 1.6). In fact, Germany and the UK actually show a decrease. This is partly due to higher efficiency rates but also due to the fact that the data includes only the five traditional sources of energy, which exclude renewable energy such as wind power. The other MEDCs illustrated in Figure 1.6 are the USA and Japan.

NICs

It is the newly industrialised countries that are increasing their energy demand by the fastest rate. China alone has accounted for one-third of the growth in global oil demand since 2000. China passed Japan as the world's second largest user of oil in 2004. Its average daily consumption of 6.63 million barrels is about twice its domestic production. Because of this situation, its oil imports doubled between 1999 and 2004. However, oil consumption per person is still only one-fifteenth of that in the USA. As this gap narrows it will have a considerable impact on global demand. The demand for oil in China is expected to increase by 5–7% a year. If this occurs, China will take over from the USA as the world's largest consumer of oil by 2025. Rising demand is concentrated on the large industrial cities which are located mainly in the eastern coastal zone.

Other newly industrialised countries such as India, Malaysia and South Korea (Figure 1.6) are also recording high increases in energy demand.

Country	1997 consumption	2007 consumption
USA	2204.8	2361.4
Japan	506.6	517.5
Germany	337.8	311.0
UK	220.4	215.9
South Korea	179.6	234.0
Malaysia	37.8	57.4
China	961.4	1863.4
India	260.6	404.4
Bangladesh	10.6	20.3
Pakistan	41.2	58.3
Peru	10.9	13.8
Algeria	26.5	34.7

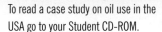

Taking it further

To read a case study on oil use in the USA go to your Student CD-ROM.

Key term

Supply shock — a significant interruption to supply due to an environmental, economic or political event.

Synoptic link

Look at Edexcel AS Geography page 90. Figure 4 and the accompanying text examines energy usage and ecological footprints for a range of developed countries.

Taking it further

For more information read 'Oil use in China' on your Student CD-ROM.

Figure 1.6: Primary energy consumption 1997–2007 (million tonnes oil equivalent).

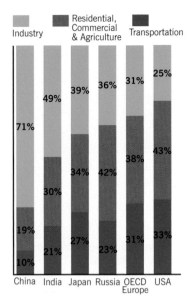

Industry | Residential, Commercial & Agriculture | Transportation

▲ Figure 1.7: Energy use by economic sector.

Developing countries

Most developing countries struggle to fund their energy requirements. In Figure 1.6 data is presented for Bangladesh, Pakistan, Peru and Algeria. As you might expect there is considerable variation in the rate of growth. Energy demand is influenced by a number of factors, two of which are the rate of economic development and the rate of population growth.

There is a strong positive correlation between GNP per capita and energy use. In poor countries it is the high- and middle-income groups that generally have enough money to purchase sufficient energy and they also tend to live in locations where electricity is available. Around the world 2 billion people lack access to household electricity. It has been estimated that connecting these people to electricity services would add only 1% extra to emissions of greenhouse gases. In the poorest countries of the world, traditional biomass often accounts for 90% or more of total energy consumption.

Variable energy patterns over time

The use of energy in all countries has changed over time due to a number of factors:
- Technological development: For example, nuclear electricity has been available only since 1954. Oil and gas can now be extracted from much deeper waters than in the past and renewable energy technology is advancing steadily.
- Increasing national wealth: As average incomes increase, living standards improve. This involves the increasing use of energy and the use of a greater variety of energy sources.
- Changes in demand: At one time all of Britain's trains were powered by coal and most people also used coal for heating in their homes. Before natural gas was discovered in the North Sea, Britain's gas was produced from coal (coal gas).
- Changes in price: The relative prices of the different types of energy can influence demand. Electricity production in the UK has been switching from coal to gas over the past 20 years mainly because power stations are cheaper to run on natural gas.
- Environmental factors/public opinion: Public opinion can influence decisions made by governments.

Resource availability

Energy security depends on resource availability, both domestic and foreign, and security of supply. It can be affected by geopolitics, and is a key issue for many economies. Because there is little excess capacity to ease pressure on energy resources, energy insecurity is rising, particularly for non-renewable resources.

Following the 1973 Arab–Israeli war, the Arab nations reduced the supply of oil to the USA and western Europe in an effort to reduce their support for Israel. This led to a serious energy shortage which became known as the 'Energy Crisis'.

Other less serious shortages of supply have occurred since then, which have pushed energy prices up and reminded us that we cannot take energy for granted. Figure 1.8 shows what happens at petrol stations when there is a shortage of oil.

The key energy issues for individual countries are the three Ss: Sustainability, Security and Strategy.

Figure 1.9 illustrates the spatial distribution of proved oil reserves. In the period 1987–2007 proved reserves rose considerably but much more in the earlier part of the period than in the later part. Here lies the problem with demand increasing at a faster rate than proved reserves. In 2007, the Middle East accounted for 61% of global proved reserves. The main countries contributing to the latter figure are: Saudi Arabia 21.3%; Iran 11.2%; Iraq 9.3%; Kuwait 8.2% and the United Arab Emirates 7.9%. Europe and Eurasia held the second largest proved reserves with 11.6% of the world total. The Russian Federation accounted for over half of the latter figure.

◄ Figure 1.8: A petrol shortage causing long queues at a US petrol station.

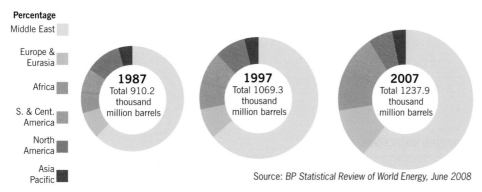

Source: *BP Statistical Review of World Energy, June 2008*

▲ **Figure 1.9:** Distribution of proved oil reserves: 1987, 1997 and 2007.

An important measure of resources is the reserves-to-production ratio. While the R/P ratio is over 82 years in the Middle East, it is less than 14 years in North America (Figure 1.10). BP estimates that the world R/P ratio is 41.6 years. However, this figure is seen as wildly over-optimistic by some experts. The Association for the Study of Peak Oil and Gas (ASPO) predicts that the peak of global oil production could come as early as 2011. If ASPO is correct and the oil peak is imminent it will not allow time to shift energy use to alternative sources.

Region	Reserves/production ratio (years)
North America	13.9
South and Central America	45.9
Europe and Eurasia	22.1
Middle East	82.2
Africa	31.2
Asia Pacific	14.2
World	41.6

▲ **Figure 1.10:** The reserves-to-production ratio, 2008 (Source: *BP Statistical Review of World Energy 2008*).

The USA, gravely concerned about the political leverage associated with imported oil, began in 1977 the construction of a Strategic Petroleum Reserve. The oil was to be stored in a string of salt domes and abandoned salt mines in southern Louisiana and Texas which could be easily linked up to pipelines and shipping routes. The initial aim was to store one billion barrels of oil which could be used in the event of supply discontinuation.

When Hurricane Katrina disrupted supplies of Gulf Coast petroleum in 2005 the US government said it would consider lending oil from the Strategic Petroleum Reserve, the country's emergency stockpile, to refiners that requested it. The loaned oil would be returned to the SPR when supplies got back to normal levels. The SPR currently holds 700 million barrels.

Summary

In this chapter you have learnt:

- about the classification of energy resources and the varying environmental impact of their production and use.
- about the distribution of fossil fuel resources and renewable potential.
- about the factors that affect access to and consumption of resources.
- about global trends in supply and demand by source, type of economy and economic sector.
- about the increase in energy insecurity, particularly for finite resources.

MCQ

Taking it further

Look at the World Energy Council's website (www.worldenergy.org) for more information on these issues. For a case study on the Energy Crisis in America read 'Energy Crisis America: a preview' on your Student CD-ROM.

Key terms

Energy crisis — a serious shortage of energy which interrupts domestic supplies and impacts on all sectors of the economy.

Proved reserves of oil — quantities of oil that geological and engineering information indicates with reasonable certainty can be recovered in the future from known reservoirs under existing economic and operating conditions.

Reserves-to-production (R/P) ratio — the reserves remaining at the end of any year are divided by the production in that year. The result is the length of time that those remaining reserves would last if production were to continue at that level.

Strategic Petroleum Reserve — the USA's reserve supply of oil which should last for about three months in the event of severe interruptions to imported oil.

Taking it further

Look at the latest *BP Statistical Review of World Energy* (www.bp.com/ statisticalreview). Use the energy charting tool to create custom charts for your own analysis of the global energy situation.

CHAPTER 2 What are the potential impacts of an increasingly 'energy insecure' world?

Key terms

Energy infrastructure
Energy pathway
Energy TNCs
Oil sands
OPEC
Resource nationalisation

Learning objectives

After studying this chapter, you will be able to discuss these ideas and concepts and provide located examples of them:
- Developments in energy infrastructure and supply pathways and the increasing level of risk associated with them.
- The risks in economic and political terms if energy supplies are disrupted.
- The stimulus to exploration in technically difficult and environmentally sensitive areas.
- The increasing economic and political power of energy TNCs and producer groups.

Key terms

Energy infrastructure — the built environment constructed for the exploration, development and production of energy, and all the networks that transport energy from points of production to consumers.

Energy pathways — supply routes between energy producers and consumers which may be pipelines, shipping routes or electricity cables. Figure 2.1 shows the major trade movements for oil in 2007. The map clearly shows that the Middle East is the major global focal point of oil exports.

Energy infrastructure and supply pathways

Infrastructure

Energy infrastructure includes:
- plant and machinery at points of resource exploitation
- energy terminals, pipelines and shipping (oil tankers, coal carriers, etc.)
- oil and other energy refineries
- power stations
- electricity grids.

Such infrastructure requires considerable initial investment and maintenance. Substantial costs may also be involved when infrastructure reaches the end of its life-cycle. The USA's Nuclear Regulatory Commission estimates that it costs $300 million or more to shut down and decommission a nuclear power plant.

Pathways

Energy pathways between producers and consumers can be complex, exhibiting considerable levels of risk. As major energy consumers have had to search further and further for reliable sources of power, supply lines have become longer and more vulnerable to economic, environmental, political and terrorist disruption. There are growing concerns about protecting the world's immense energy infrastructure. There are more than 160,000 miles of oil pipelines in the USA alone.

▶ **Figure 2.1:** Map showing the major trade movements for oil, 2007.

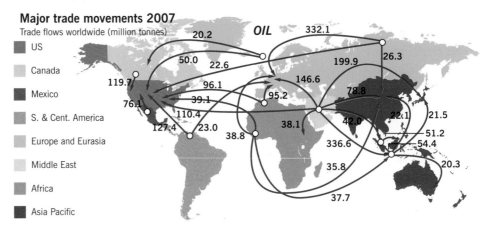

Major trade movements 2007
Trade flows worldwide (million tonnes)

- US
- Canada
- Mexico
- S. & Cent. America
- Europe and Eurasia
- Middle East
- Africa
- Asia Pacific

OIL

20.2 332.1 26.3
50.0 22.6 199.9
119.7 96.1 146.6 78.8
76.1 39.1 95.2
110.4 38.1 42.0 22.1 21.5
127.4 23.0 51.2
38.8 336.6 54.4
35.8 20.3
37.7

The long-running tensions that exist in the Middle East have at times caused serious concerns about the vulnerability of oil fields, pipelines and oil tanker routes. The destruction of oil wells and pipelines during the Iraq War showed all too clearly how energy supplies can be disrupted. Middle East oil exports are vital for the functioning of the global economy.

Most Middle East oil exports go by tanker through the Strait of Hormuz, a relatively narrow body of water between the Persian Gulf and the Gulf of Oman. At its narrowest, the strait is 55 km wide. Roughly 30% of the world's oil supply passes through the strait, making it one of the world's strategically important chokepoints. Iran has at times indicated that it could block this vital shipping route in the event of serious political tension. This could cause huge supply problems for many importing countries.

Pathways crossing difficult environments

Some major oil and gas pipelines cross some of the world's most inhospitable terrain. The trans-Alaskan pipeline crosses three mountain ranges and several large rivers. Much of the pipeline is above ground to avoid the permafrost problem. Here, the ground is permanently frozen down to about 300 m, apart from the top metre, which melts during the summer. Building foundations and the uprights which hold the pipeline above ground have to extend well below the melting zone (called the active layer). The oil takes about six days to make the 1,270 km journey. Engineers fly over the pipeline every day by helicopter to check for leaks and other problems. Problems such as subsidence have closed the pipeline for short periods.

The tensions between producers and consumers

Tensions can exist between energy producers and consumers. This can cause economic problems in terms of supply disruptions and rising costs. It can also result in political problems if sellers and buyers of energy seriously disagree. This has happened between energy-rich Russia and some of its customer countries.

Russia is one of the world's major producers and exporters of oil and gas. World Bank statistics show that oil and gas account for over 20% of Russia's GDP. The production of these fossil fuels is vital to the country's economic success. The high energy prices of recent years have been of massive benefit to the Russian economy. There is no shortage of demand for Russian oil and gas. To the west lies energy-hungry Europe. To the south and east are the rapidly expanding economies of India and China, along with the developed economies of South Korea and Japan. European countries in particular have become increasingly reliant on energy supplies from their giant neighbour.

Russian oil production has increased considerably over the last decade to put it alongside Saudi Arabia in the global league table (Figure 2.3). Russia vies with the USA as the world's number one gas producer (Figure 2.4).

▲ **Figure 2.2:** An oil tanker passes through the Strait of Hormuz: one of the world's strategically important chokepoints.

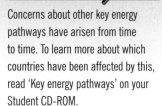

Taking it further

Concerns about other key energy pathways have arisen from time to time. To learn more about which countries have been affected by this, read 'Key energy pathways' on your Student CD-ROM.

Country	% of world total
Saudi Arabia	12.6
Russian Federation	12.6
USA	8.0
Iran	5.4
China	4.8

▲ **Figure 2.3:** Major oil-producing countries, 2007 (Source: *BP Statistical Review of World Energy*, June 2008).

Country	% of world total
Russian Federation	20.6
USA	18.8
Canada	6.2
Iran	3.8
Norway	3.0

▲ **Figure 2.4:** Natural gas production, 2007 (Source: *BP Statistical Review of World Energy*, June 2008).

Case study: Russia extends its energy influence

Russian gas is piped to a large number of countries via an extensive pipeline network (Figure 2.5). The pipeline networks for both oil and gas are owned by the state. Gas supplies by Gazprom (a state company with a monopoly on Russian gas exports) account for approximately 23% of gas consumption in the EU. Countries of central, eastern and southern Europe remain heavily dependent on imports from Russia. Some, such as the Baltic States, are 100% reliant. The largest buyer of Russian gas in absolute terms is Germany, followed by Ukraine and Italy. At present Russia does not export gas to eastern Asian countries or to the USA. The most important route for Russian gas exports is the pipelines crossing the Ukraine. These pipelines account for over 80% of all Russian gas sent beyond the CIS.

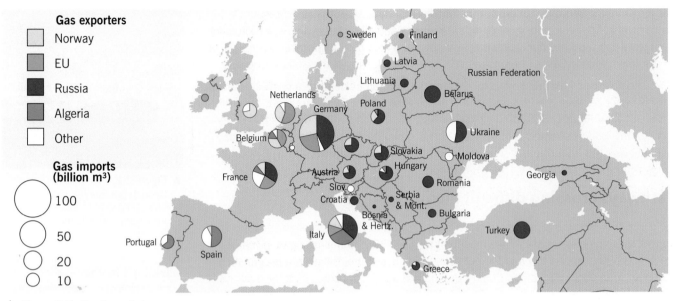

Gas exporters
- Norway
- EU
- Russia
- Algeria
- Other

Gas imports (billion m³)
- 100
- 50
- 20
- 10

▲ **Figure 2.5:** Gas imports to Europe.

Recent disputes between Russia and neighbouring countries

Russia has had a number of disputes with neighbouring countries over its exports of oil and gas. The following are some of the most recent:

- The 2006 'gas war' between Russia and the Ukraine was thought to be largely the result of Russia's displeasure with Ukraine due to its political shift towards the West after the 'Orange Revolution' in 2004. Russia increased the price of gas to the Ukraine considerably to put political pressure on the country (as well as increasing its revenue). In January 2009, Russia again halted gas supplies in pipelines passing through the Ukraine. Russia accused the Ukraine of 'stealing' gas destined for other European countries. The Ukraine denied this. The two-week dispute left a number of countries seriously short of energy.

- In January 2007 Belarus cut off a transit pipeline carrying Russian oil. The closure of the 2,500-mile Druzhba pipeline halted the movement of Russian oil supplies to a number of countries. The pipeline carries more than 1.2 million barrels of oil a day, providing almost a quarter of Germany's needs and 96% of Poland's imports as well as supplies to Hungary, Ukraine, the Czech Republic and Slovakia. This action was the latest round in the dispute between the two countries over the steep increases in the prices of Russian oil and gas. On 31 December 2006 Gazprom raised gas prices for Belarus from $47 per 1,000 m³ to $100. To counter the rising cost of Russian energy, Belarus announced it would charge an import duty of $45 a ton on Russian oil shipped across its territory to western Europe. When Belarus halted pumping, Russia accused Belarus of illegally siphoning off oil from the pipeline. Russia then closed the pipeline on its side of the border. Fortunately, a negotiated settlement was reached which allowed the pipeline to open again.

- In late 2006/early 2007 Azerbaijan was also in dispute with Russia. The former had suspended oil exports to Russia following a pricing dispute with Gazprom.

Such disputes have again raised EU fears about its increasing reliance on energy supplies from Russia. Critics argue that Russia has a habit of manipulating gas and oil supplies for political purposes. The German Chancellor Angela Merkel said that the dispute illustrated that Europe's energy sources needed to be more diverse. Thus the EU is looking to:

- build interconnecting pipelines and power lines, such as electricity hook-ups, between Germany, Poland and Lithuania and between France and Spain
- diversify supply. An important example is the Nabucco pipeline that will connect Europe with gas fields in the Middle East, Caucasus and central Asia via the Balkans and Turkey. The EU is also looking to build more terminals for the import of liquefied natural gas.

Serious doubts have been expressed about the management and efficiency of the energy industry in Russia. In May 2006, the head of the International Energy Agency (IEA) voiced concerns that Gazprom may not have enough gas to supply Europe over the next decade. An IEA study concluded that Gazprom was not reinvesting enough to ensure continued adequate supplies in the future. Gazprom relies on a very limited number of large gas fields and has so far failed to invest in developing new resources in the Arctic. Already Gazprom makes up the difference between its exports to Europe and its falling output from western Siberia by increasing imports from central Asia.

Russia has also taken a very tough line with foreign investors in the energy sector, making life difficult in a number of different ways. There is some concern that the country risks scaring off vital foreign investment as well as potential oil and gas customers. It is not just foreign investment that is needed to keep Russia's oil and gas sector on track, it is also the expertise of foreign firms.

According to the *Economist* (16 December 2006, page 13), 'In the early part of the decade new production from the former Soviet Union accounted for most of the growth in the world's supply of oil and gas. But when Mr Putin began his campaign to take control of Russia's resources, that growth stalled, just as China's demand for energy was taking off. The present high prices for oil and gas are the result. With exploration prospects drying up in most of the Western world, and with the countries of the Organisation of Petroleum Exporting Countries unwilling to open the taps, Russia is one of the few countries that could produce more oil – if only Mr Putin changed his thuggish ways.'

NATO warning

According to the *Financial Times* (13 November 2006), 'NATO advisers have warned the military alliance that it needs to guard against any attempt by Russia to set up an "Opec for gas" that would strengthen Moscow's leverage over Europe. The study warned that Russia could seek to construct a gas cartel including the countries of Central Asia, Algeria, Qatar, Libya and perhaps Iran.'

Exploiting new areas: the costs and benefits

Increasing energy insecurity has stimulated exploration of technically difficult and environmentally sensitive areas. Such exploration and development is economically feasible when energy prices are high but becomes less so when prices fall as the cost of production per barrel of oil is high in such areas.

Oil sands in Canada and Venezuela

Huge tar sand deposits in Alberta, Canada and in Venezuela could be critical over the next 50 years as the world's production of conventional oil falls. Such synthetic oil, which can also be made from coal and natural gas, could provide a vital bridge to an era of new technologies.

Examiners' tip

Keep an eye on the media for information on any more recent energy disputes involving Russia. Good recent information will be rewarded in the examination.

Key term

Oil sands — also known as tar sands or extra heavy oil. Naturally occurring mixtures of sand or clay, water and an extremely dense and viscous form of petroleum called bitumen.

▼ **Figure 2.6:** Squeezing oil from sand in Alberta, Canada.

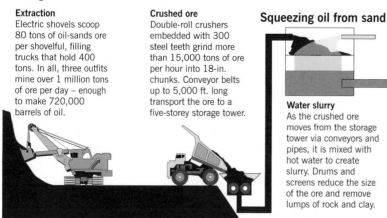

Extraction
Electric shovels scoop 80 tons of oil-sands ore per shovelful, filling trucks that hold 400 tons. In all, three outfits mine over 1 million tons of ore per day – enough to make 720,000 barrels of oil.

Crushed ore
Double-roll crushers embedded with 300 steel teeth grind more than 15,000 tons of ore per hour into 18-in. chunks. Conveyor belts up to 5,000 ft. long transport the ore to a five-storey storage tower.

Squeezing oil from sand

Water slurry
As the crushed ore moves from the storage tower via conveyors and pipes, it is mixed with hot water to create slurry. Drums and screens reduce the size of the ore and remove lumps of rock and clay.

Separation
Air and chemicals are added as the slurry is piped 1.2 miles to a separation vessel. There, sand sinks and bitumen froth floats to the surface. The sand and water tailings are sent to a holding basin.

Pre-refinery
The froth travels by pipeline to an upgrading facility where it is heated and distilled in natural gas-fired furnaces. Now, the synthetic oil is ready for refining into gasoline and other products.

The estimates of economically recoverable oil sand reserves in Canada vary considerably. *Oil & Gas Journal* estimates close to 180 billion barrels while the *BP Statistical Review of World Energy* puts the figure at about 17 billion barrels, based on oil sands under active development. The Canadian oil sands don't even turn up on the International Energy Agency's industry lists of the 10 countries with the largest proven oil reserves. Even the higher industry estimate is only about a six-year world supply, as the world now consumes close to 30 billion barrels of oil a year. At present about 33,000 employees work on the Alberta oil sands. Tar sands production reached 1 million barrels a day in 2005 and is projected to increase five-fold by 2030; still about half of Saudi Arabia's current output and less than 5% of estimated world production in 2030.

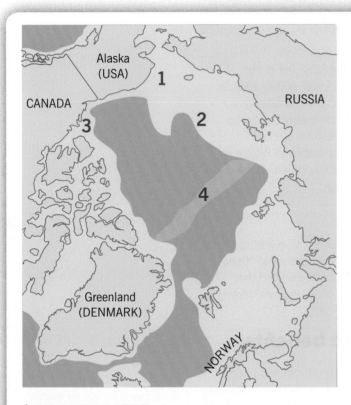

Case study: The Arctic Circle

As global warming causes the polar ice to recede, potentially oil-rich sea-beds are being uncovered beneath the Arctic Circle. This region has long been thought to hold substantial reserves. Some estimates say up to 25% of the world's undiscovered oil and natural gas may be located here.

The big issue is who can lay claim to which parts of the ocean. In June 2007, Russian scientists claimed they found evidence of 70 billion barrels of oil and natural gas reserves on the Lomonosov Ridge, a huge rock formation that extends through the North Pole from Siberia to Greenland.

Russia has claimed nearly half the Arctic – a territory of half a million square miles – and granted a monopoly to its own companies to exploit it. Denmark has objected, saying it, too, has rights to the ridge. Other interested countries, such as the USA, Canada and Norway, have failed to recognise the legitimacy of the Russian claim.

The US Geological Survey has calculated that a billion-barrel field would cost about $37 per barrel to extract, plus at least another $3 in exploration costs. By comparison, it costs about $2 per barrel to pump oil from the ground in Saudi Arabia, and $5 to $7 per barrel in Venezuela. Environmental groups want UN protection for Arctic wildlife and ecosystems. Oil spills would be a major concern in this fragile environment.

The Arctic National Wildlife Refuge (ANWR) is under threat from energy development. So far the environmental lobby has managed to hold the line under intense oil company pressure. However, as the USA becomes more and more concerned about its energy situation the ANWR will undoubtedly come under the threat of development again.

1 USA Continental Shelf
If the USA ratified the Law of the Sea treaty, it could claim territory here roughly half the size of Alaska.

2 Chukchi Sea
Shell has plans to explore here. But since Russia is claiming nearly half the Arctic Ocean, it may run into trouble.

3 Beaufort Sea
A 100-square-mile area in this body of water is said to be rich in oil and gas, but it's in dispute – so no one has bid on a drilling lease offered by both Canada and the USA.

4 Lomonosov Ridge
This giant undersea landmass extends from Russia to Greenland – and the two countries are fighting over it. In June, 2007 Russia said its scientists found evidence of a 70-billion-barrel deposit and claimed rights to the whole ridge.

◀ **Figure 2.7:** The Arctic oil rush.

However, there are serious environmental concerns about the development of tar sands:

* It takes two tons of mined sand to produce one barrel of synthetic crude, leaving lots of waste sand.
* It takes about three times as much energy to produce a barrel of Alberta oil-sands crude as it does a conventional barrel of oil. Thus, oil sands are large sources of greenhouse gas emissions.

Venezuela's heavy-oil production has not kept pace with Canada's, but is now about 500,000 barrels of synthetic crude a day, with plans to expand production to 1 million barrels a day by 2010 in the Orinoco tar belt.

South Atlantic: The Falkland Islands

The Falkland Islands are one of the latest energy frontier regions. Test wells have shown promising results and full-scale drilling should occur in 2009. This is a hostile physical environment where huge floating oilrigs will be used. Such rigs cost about $500,000 a day to hire. The remoteness of the Falkland Islands adds to the logistical problems associated with drilling. The British Geological Survey has estimated there is a 1 in 5 chance of finding commercially viable oil in the basin north of the Falklands, falling to a 1 in 10 chance in the basin to the south. Other major issues are:

* the prospect of interference from Argentina, which has a territorial claim to the Falkland Islands
* protecting the islands' pristine ecosystem.

The UK's Atlantic Frontier

In the UK the most isolated development is the oil fields approximately 150 km west of the Shetland Islands. This area is known as the 'Atlantic Frontier'. The wave and current conditions are stronger than in the North Sea and the water is also considerably deeper. The oil is extracted using floating production vessels, which are connected to sub-sea wells via flexible risers and sub-sea flowlines. Two oil fields have been brought into production: Foinaven in 1997 and Schiehallion in 1998.

Energy companies and producer groups

Energy TNCs, OPEC countries, other large producers and state energy corporations are increasingly powerful players in the global supply of energy.

Energy TNCs

Historically, the energy industry had been dominated by large TNCs such as Exxon, Royal Dutch Shell, BP and Texaco. Such companies figure among the largest corporations in the world. Figure 2.10 shows that energy companies comprise six of the ten largest global corporations. Their annual profits can be colossal, particularly when energy prices are high. Exxon Mobil, in second place overall in terms of revenue, was the most profitable company in the world ($39.5 billion) in 2007. However, the power of the energy TNCs has been challenged by, first, OPEC and, more recently, national energy companies.

The large energy companies have come under considerable attack from environmental groups in the past. Companies like BP and Shell have been working hard to foster a more positive public image. Investment in renewable energy has been an important part of this process. If the worst forecasts about non-renewable energy come to pass, the energy TNCs know they have to diversify to remain profitable.

Taking it further

Look at the Oil Sands Story website (www.oilsandsdiscovery.com/ oil_sands_story/story.html) to find out more about this potentially huge energy resource.

Key term

Energy TNCs — transnational corporations that specialise in the exploration, development, production and sale of energy products.

OPEC

OPEC is an intergovernmental organisation comprising 12 oil-producing nations. Recently Indonesia decided to leave the organisation. This was because the country had become a net importer of oil. OPEC was founded in 1960 after a US law imposed quotas on Venezuelan and Persian Gulf oil imports in favour of the Canadian and Mexican oil industries. OPEC's stated objective is 'to coordinate and unify the petroleum policies of Member Countries and ensure the stabilisation of oil markets in order to secure an efficient, economic and regular supply of petroleum to consumers, a steady income to producers and a fair return on capital to those investing in the petroleum industry'. Figure 2.8 shows OPEC's share of world crude oil reserves in 2007. Over the years, OPEC's decisions have had a substantial influence on oil prices.

OPEC has been heavily criticised at times for the allegedly political nature of some of its decisions. This has generally happened when the oil-rich Arab nations have wanted to put pressure on the USA and other Western countries with regard to the Israel–Palestinian issue. At an OPEC meeting in November 2007, Venezuela's President Hugo Chávez urged the organisation to take a 'stronger political and geopolitical role'. He argued that OPEC should ensure:

• the price of oil remained high at between $80 and $100 a barrel
• a method should be found to compensate the world's poorest countries for the high price
• affluent countries should pay a high price in order to combat climate change.

At the same conference, Iran also urged OPEC to take a tougher line with consumer countries.

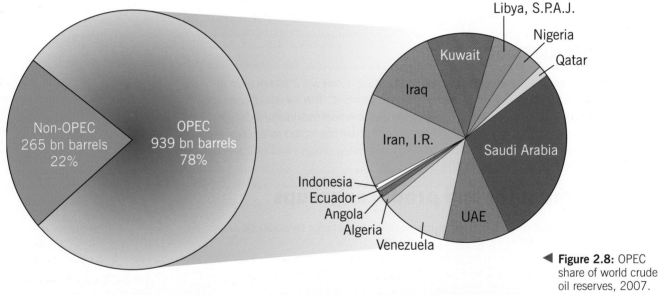

Figure 2.8: OPEC share of world crude oil reserves, 2007.

Figure 2.9: The November 2007 OPEC meeting.

	Company	Revenue ($ million)	Profits ($ million)
1	Wal-Mart Stores	351,139	11,284
2	Exxon Mobil	347,254	39,500
3	Royal Dutch Shell	318,845	25,442.0
4	BP	274,316	22,000
5	General Motors	207,349	−1,978
6	Toyota Motor	204,746	14,056
7	Chevron	200,567	17,138
8	DaimlerChrysler	190,191	4,049
9	ConocoPhillips	172,451	15,550
10	Total	168,357	14,765

▲ **Figure 2.10:** The top ten global corporations, 2008.

National companies

National (state) energy companies have become increasingly powerful as oil prices have risen and are a big challenge to the influence of the so-called oil 'majors'. National companies such as Russia's Gazprom, Saudi Aramco and Venezuela's PdVSA control about 80% of the world's oil reserves, 50% of the gas reserves and 80% of production. A number of these state energy companies have been formed as part of a process that has become known as resource nationalisation. This has resulted in the wholesale or partial exclusion of the major energy TNCs from a number of important producing areas. Where the major energy TNCs operate in countries with active national energy companies the former have been under pressure to accept harsher economic terms. Resource nationalisation has resulted in a significant shift of power within the energy industry.

Government taxation

It should not be forgotten that government taxation is an important component of the price of energy at the petrol pumps. Governments also get large tax revenues when companies produce crude oil and gas. According to OPEC, in 2007 national government taxes accounted for 61% of the price of a litre of petrol in the UK. This compared with 56% in Germany, 50% in France, 37% in Japan and 21% in the USA. When the price of petrol at the pump increases, drivers not only pay more to the oil companies, but also to the government.

Examiners' tip

Remember that there is a big difference between the price of crude (unrefined) oil, which is usually given in $ per barrel, and the refined product which is sold at petrol stations. The latter is much dearer because of the cost of refining, transport and retailing. Government tax also forms a significant part of the final price, although the amount of tax varies from country to country.

Summary

In this chapter you have learnt:

• that energy pathways between producers and consumers are complex and show increasing levels of risk.

• that there are economic and political risks if energy supplies are interrupted.

• that increasing energy insecurity has stimulated exploration in technically difficult and environmentally sensitive areas.

• that energy TNCs, OPEC countries and other large producers are increasingly powerful players in the global supply of energy.

MCQ

CHAPTER 3 What might the world's energy future be?

Learning objectives

After studying this chapter, you will be able to discuss these ideas and concepts and provide located examples of them:
• The uncertainty over both global energy supply and demand.
• The advantages and disadvantages of contrasting energy options.
• The geopolitical tension and the potential for conflict that can result from energy insecurity.
• Meeting future energy demands in countries at different levels of economic development in as sustainable a way as possible.

Economic growth and energy projections

There is uncertainty over global energy supply in terms of both reserves and energy demand. The latter is strongly affected by economic growth rates, conservation of resources and the pace with which the world can switch to renewable sources of power.

The future demand for energy will depend very much on the rate of global economic growth. The global recession that began in 2008 caused a significant decline in the demand for energy. While this economic downturn has been described as the most serious since the 1930s, most economists believe it is only a matter of time before economic conditions improve. As it does, the demand for energy will begin to rise again. The significant increase in the number of NICs in recent decades will be a major factor in future energy demand.

According to the International Energy Agency in 2005, world oil demand will grow by 32% by 2020 and global gas demand by 48%. This will be due to a combination of population growth and an increase in effective demand. This means that more and more people will be able to buy the supplies of energy they need for heat, light and mobility.

When will global peak oil production occur?

There has been growing concern about when global oil production will peak and how fast it will decline thereafter. For example, in the USA, oil production peaked in 1970. There are concerns that there are not enough large-scale projects under way to offset declining production in well-established oil production areas. The rate of major new oil field discoveries has fallen sharply in recent years. It takes six years on average from first discovery for a very large-scale project to start producing oil. There are widely varying estimates of when global peak oil production will occur:
• The International Energy Agency expects peak oil production somewhere between 2013 and 2037, with a fall by 3% a year after the peak.
• The United States Geological Survey predicts that the peak is at least 50 years away.
• However, in total contrast, the Association for the Study of Peak Oil and Gas (ASPO) predicts that the peak of global oil production would come as early as 2011, stating 'Fifty years ago the world was consuming 4 billion barrels of oil per year and the average discovery was around 30 billion. Today we consume 30 billion barrels per year and the discovery rate is now approaching 4 billion barrels of crude oil per year.' If ASPO is correct and the oil peak is imminent, it will not allow time to shift energy use to alternative sources.

Key term

Peak oil production — the year in which the world or an individual oil-producing country reaches its highest level of production, with production declining thereafter.

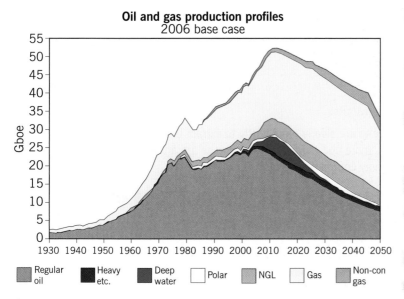

▲ **Figure 3.1:** Peak oil production.

ASPO has been criticised because it has changed its prediction a number of times as to the year when peak oil will occur. ASPO argues that this is understandable as new data becomes available. It also points out that hard information is often jealously guarded, making the true nature of the supply/demand balance difficult to judge. As Figure 3.2 illustrates, it is not pinpointing peak oil to an exact year that is important, but realising that this situation is imminent and developing sustainable policies to cope with it.

Extending the 'life' of fossil fuels

There are many technologies that can improve the use and prolong the life of fossil fuels. These include coal gasification, clean coal technologies and the extraction of unconventional natural gas. Such techniques may be very important in buying time for more renewable energy to come on-line.

Coal is the most polluting source of energy. Environmental legislation in a number of countries has required coal-burning power plants to reduce pollutants. Coal gasification is the technology that could transform the situation. At present, electricity from coal gasification is more expensive than that from traditional power plants but, if tougher pollution laws are passed in the future, this situation could change significantly.

The coal industry in a number of areas may be on the point of a limited comeback with the development of 'clean coal technologies'. This new technology has developed forms of coal that burn with greater efficiency and capture coal's pollutants before they are emitted into the atmosphere. The latest 'supercritical' coal-fired power stations, operating at higher pressures and temperatures than their predecessors, can operate at efficiency levels 20% above those of coal-fired power stations constructed in the 1960s. Existing power stations can be upgraded to use clean coal technology.

Conventional natural gas, which is generally found a few thousand metres or so below the surface, has accounted for most of the global supply to date. However, in recent years 'unconventional' deposits have begun to contribute more to supply.

About Peak Oil

Understanding Peak Oil

By Colin J. Campbell

The peak of oil discovery was passed in the 1960s, and the world started using more than was found in new fields in 1981. The gap between discovery and production has widened since. Many countries, including some important producers, have already passed their peak, suggesting that the world peak of production is now imminent. Were valid data available in the public domain, it would be a simple matter to determine both the date of peak and the rate of subsequent decline, but as it is, we find a maze of conflicting information, ambiguous definitions and lax reporting procedures. In short, the oil companies tended to report cautiously, being subject to strict Stock Exchange rules, whereas certain OPEC countries exaggerated during the 1980s when they were competing for quotas based on reported reserves. Despite the uncertainties of detail, it is now evident that the world faces the dawn of the Second Half of the Age of Oil, when this critical commodity, which plays such a fundamental part in the modern economy, heads into decline due to natural depletion. A debate rages over the precise date of peak, but rather misses the point, when what matters — and matters greatly — is the vision of the long, remorseless decline that comes into sight on the other side of it. The transition to decline threatens to be a time of great international tension. Petroleum Man will be virtually extinct this century, and Homo sapiens faces a major challenge in adapting to his loss. Peak Oil is by all means an important subject.

Source: http://www.peakoil.net/about-peak-oil

▲ **Figure 3.2:** Understanding peak oil.

Key term

Clean coal technology — power plant processes that both increase the efficiency of coal-burning and significantly reduce emissions.

Key terms

Coal gasification — a process which converts solid coal into a gas that can be used for power generation.
Unconventional natural gas — natural gas that is more difficult to access and therefore more expensive to extract than 'conventional' reserves.

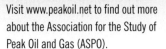

Taking it further

Visit www.peakoil.net to find out more about the Association for the Study of Peak Oil and Gas (ASPO).

Taking it further

To learn more about nuclear power use read 'Nuclear power in the USA and Ukraine' on your Student CD-ROM.

The main categories of unconventional natural gas are:
- deep gas
- tight gas
- gas-containing shales
- coal-bed methane
- geopressurised zones
- Arctic and sub-sea hydrates.

Unconventional deposits are clearly more costly to extract but, as energy prices rise and technology advances, more and more of these deposits are attracting the interest of governments and energy companies.

The advantages and disadvantages of contrasting energy options

There are different responses to increasing energy demands. The main options seem to be:
- 'business as usual' reliance on fossil fuels; the pitfalls of this approach have already been covered in the preceding chapters
- nuclear energy
- renewable energy with the emphasis on wind power
- energy-efficient savings.

Nuclear power: a global renaissance?

No other source of energy creates such heated discussion as nuclear power. (For information on the concerns relating to nuclear power refer to Figure 1.2.) The big advantages of nuclear power are:
- zero emissions of greenhouse gases
- reduced reliance on imported fossil fuels.

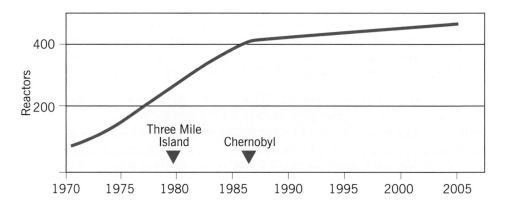

▶ **Figure 3.3:** The number of nuclear power reactors worldwide.

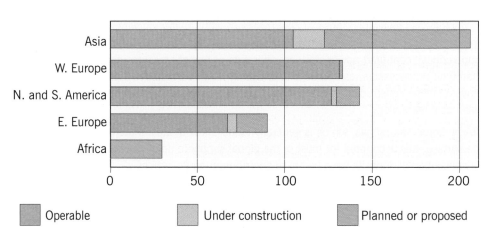

▶ **Figure 3.4:** Nuclear power by region.

Other countries, deeply concerned about their ability to satisfy demand, are going ahead with plans for new nuclear power plants (Figure 3.4). China currently produces 6,600 MW of power from nine reactors. It aims to increase this to 40,000 MW. India already has 15 operating nuclear power plants with eight more under construction. France obtains 78% of its electricity from nuclear power and is thinking about replacing its older plants with new ones.

A few countries have developed fast-breeder reactor technology. These reactors are very efficient at manufacturing plutonium fuel from their original uranium fuel load. This greatly increases energy production but it could prove disastrous if the plutonium got into the wrong hands as plutonium is the key ingredient for nuclear weapons.

▲ **Figure 3.5:** The nuclear power plant at Chernobyl.

Wind power

The costs of generating electricity from wind today are only about 10% of what they were 20 years ago, mainly due to advances in turbine technology. Thus, at well-chosen locations, wind power can now compete with conventional sources of energy. Wind energy operators argue that costs should fall further due to (a) further technological advances, and (b) increasing economies of scale. One large turbine manufacturer has stated that it expects turbine costs to be reduced by 3.5% a year for the foreseeable future.

Apart from establishing new wind energy sites, repowering is also beginning to play an important role. This means replacing first-generation wind turbines with modern multi-megawatt turbines, which give a much better performance. The advantages are:
- more wind power from the same area of land
- fewer wind turbines
- higher efficiency, lower costs
- enhanced appearance as modern turbines rotate at a lower speed and are usually more visually pleasing due to enhanced design
- better grid integration as modern turbines use a connection method similar to conventional power plants.

Issues relating to wind power
As wind turbines have been erected in more areas of more countries, the opposition to this form of renewable energy has increased.
- People are concerned that huge turbines located nearby could blight their homes and have a significant impact on property values.
- There are concerns about the hum of turbines disturbing both people and wildlife.
- Skylines in scenically beautiful areas might be spoiled forever.
- Turbines can kill birds. Migratory flocks tend to follow strong winds but wind companies argue they steer clear of migratory routes.
- Suitable areas for wind farms are often near the coast where land is expensive.
- Turbines can affect TV reception nearby.
- The opportunity cost of heavy investment in wind compared with the alternatives.

The recent rapid increase in demand for turbines has resulted in a shortage of supply. New projects now have to make orders for turbines in large blocks up to several years in advance to ensure firm delivery dates from manufacturers. Likewise, the investment from manufacturers is having to rise significantly to keep pace with such buoyant demand.

New developments in wind energy include:
- In 2008 a Dutch company installed the world's first floating wind turbine off the southern coast of Italy in water 110 m deep. The technology is known as the Submerged Deepwater Platform System.
- The Swedish company Nordic has recently brought a two-bladed turbine onto the market.

Key term

Fast-breeder reactor — a nuclear reactor in which the chain reaction is maintained mainly by fast neutrons. It is capable of producing more fissionable material than it consumes.

Wind energy has reached the 'take-off' stage both as a source of energy and a manufacturing industry. As the cost of wind energy improves further against conventional energy sources, more and more countries will expand into this sector. However, projections regarding the industry still vary considerably because of the number of variables that will impact upon its future.

Energy insecurity and increased geopolitical tension

Energy insecurity may lead to increased geopolitical tension and the potential for conflict as consumers attempt to secure supplies. This will be most likely within a 'business as usual' framework of reliance on fossil fuels. The best scenario is for major consumers in particular to invest in radical policies to diversify their energy mix, maximise energy conservation and reduce their reliance on imports as far as possible. If progress is slow in these respects, it is possible that current areas of tension, where energy supply is an issue, may edge closer to conflict in the future (Figure 3.6).

In an article entitled 'The G forces of energy insecurity' (www.energybulletin.net), published on 8 June 2006, Chris Ruppel discusses the period of energy security 1985–2003 and the new era of energy insecurity. He argues that after the two oil crises of the 1970s, followed by the end of the Cold War and the resolution of the 1990–91 (Iraq) Crisis, the world passed into a decade of lower oil prices and over-confidence about energy security. The general opinion among experts was that the long-term oil price would be $18–21 a barrel.

According to Ruppel the new era of energy insecurity has been brought about by:
- **growth:** the process of globalisation has significantly increased energy demand, particularly in the growing number of NICs
- **geology:** supply constraints have increased due to the end of the era of 'easy oil'. In many large oil fields only the more inaccessible oil is left to exploit
- **geopolitics:** production lost in the Iraq War and other disputes has highlighted the vulnerability of energy supplies. Countries such as Venezuela and Iran have shown they can use energy as political and economic weapons
- **guerrillas:** the actions of guerrilla and terrorist groups have shut down production in Iraq, Nigeria and other countries from time to time. Such actions can create a great deal of uncertainty in the global oil market
- **global warming:** significant risks of hurricane disruption, rising environmental compliance costs and a growing regulatory consensus on climate change have made global warming a major energy issue.

Oil price volatility

Oil-importing countries worry not only about the price of oil being high, but also about oil price volatility. In late 2008 oil price volatility hit a 22-year high. In mid-summer 2008, crude oil reached a high of $147 a barrel. By December 2008 it had dipped below $40; a staggering 72% drop. A high rate of volatility makes economic planning extremely difficult, particularly when a government's finances are already stretched.

Although the fall in the price of oil in late 2008 was welcomed by oil importers, there was underlying concern that refined oil inventories in the USA and in the West in general were extremely low. When inventories are low, oil industry analysts say that oil prices can 'turn on a dime' if global demand rises just slightly. At the same time in late 2008:
- OPEC was talking about 'severe' production cuts in order to push prices higher
- large exporters such as Saudi Arabia, Russia and the UAE had put major drilling projects 'under review', undermining future supplies of oil
- growing evidence was emerging that the world's largest oil fields were now seriously depleted.

Taking it further

To examine different countries' reliance on imported oil read 'Imported oil in the USA, Europe, Japan and China' on your Student CD-ROM.

Key terms

Oil price volatility — a measure of how rapidly and strongly traders think prices could move.
Refined oil inventories — stocks of refined oil.

posted June 12, 2008 2:07 pm

Tomgram: Michael Klare, The Pentagon as Energy Insecurity Inc.

Garrisoning the Global Gas Station

Challenging the Militarization of U.S. Energy Policy

By Michael T. Klare

American policymakers have long viewed the protection of overseas oil supplies as an essential matter of "national security", requiring the threat of -- and sometimes the use of -- military force. This is now an unquestioned part of American foreign policy.

On this basis, the first Bush administration fought a war against Iraq in 1990–1991 and the second Bush administration invaded Iraq in 2003. With global oil prices soaring and oil reserves expected to dwindle in the years ahead, military force is sure to be seen by whatever new administration enters Washington in January 2009 as the ultimate guarantor of our well-being in the oil heartlands of the planet. But with the costs of militarized oil operations -- in both blood and dollars -- rising precipitously isn't it time to challenge such "wisdom"? Isn't it time to ask whether the U.S. military has anything reasonable to do with American energy security, and whether a reliance on military force, when it comes to energy policy, is practical, affordable, or justifiable?

How Energy Policy Got Militarized

The association between "energy security" (as it's now termed) and "national security" was established long ago. President Franklin D. Roosevelt first forged this association way back in 1945, when he pledged to protect the Saudi Arabian royal family in return for privileged American access to Saudi oil. The relationship was given formal expression in 1980, when President Jimmy Carter told Congress that maintaining the uninterrupted flow of Persian Gulf oil was a "vital interest" of the United States, and attempts by hostile nations to cut that flow would be countered "by any means necessary, including military force".

To implement this "doctrine", Carter ordered the creation of a Rapid Deployment Joint Task Force, specifically earmarked for combat operations in the Persian Gulf area. President Ronald Reagan later turned that force into a full-scale regional combat organization, the U.S. Central Command, or CENTCOM. Every president since Reagan has added to CENTCOM's responsibilities, endowing it with additional bases, fleets, air squadrons, and other assets. As the country has, more recently, come to rely on oil from the Caspian Sea basin and Africa, U.S. military capabilities are being beefed up in those areas as well.

As a result, the U.S. military has come to serve as a global oil protection service, guarding pipelines, refineries, and loading facilities in the Middle East and elsewhere. According to one estimate, provided by the conservative National Defense Council Foundation, the "protection" of Persian Gulf oil alone costs the U.S. Treasury $138 billion per year -- up from $49 billion just before the invasion of Iraq.

Taking it further

Research the internet to see how oil prices have changed over the last six months. Try to identify reasons for any significant rises and falls in the price of oil.

▲ **Figure 3.6:** Garrisoning the global gas station.

► **Figure 3.7:** Oil price volatility.

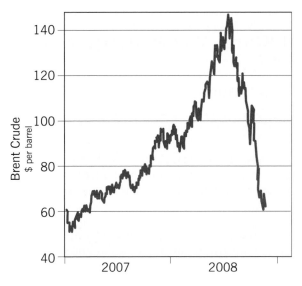

Key terms

Carbon credit — a permit that allows an organisation to emit a specified amount of greenhouse gases. Also called an emission permit.

Carbon trading — a company that does not use up the level of emissions it is entitled to can sell the remainder of its entitlement to another company that pollutes above its entitlement.

Green taxation — taxes levied to discourage behaviour that will be harmful to the environment.

Community energy — energy produced close to the point of consumption.

Microgeneration — generators producing electricity with an output of less than 50 KW.

Taking it further

For information on the increasingly sustainable energy strategies in Germany read 'Germany: Satisfying energy demand' on your Student CD-ROM.

▼ **Figure 3.8:** A small wind turbine – microgeneration in a school setting.

Radical policies and sustainability

Meeting future energy needs in developing, emergent and developed economies while avoiding serious environmental degradation will require increased emphasis on radical new approaches. These include the following:

- Much greater investment in renewable energy
- Conservation
- Recycling
- Carbon credits
- Green taxation.

To be effective in the long term, energy solutions must be sustainable.

In his acceptance speech for the presidency of the USA in August 2008, Barack Obama stated 'now is the time to end this addiction (to oil) and to understand that drilling is a stop-gap measure, not a long-term solution. As president, I will tap our natural gas reserves, invest in clean coal technology, and find ways to safely harness nuclear power. I'll help our auto companies re-tool, so that the fuel-efficient cars of the future are built right here in America. And I'll invest $150 billion over the next decade in affordable, renewable sources of energy.'

Energy management and conservation

Managing energy supply is often about balancing socio-economic and environmental needs. We have all become increasingly aware that this requires detailed planning and management.

Carbon credits and carbon trading are an important part of the EU's environment and energy policies. Under the EU's emissions trading scheme, heavy industrial plants have to buy permits to emit greenhouse gases over the limit they are allowed by government (carbon credits). However, this could be extended to other organisations such as banks and supermarkets. From 2008 onwards, the British government offered the free provision of visual display electricity meters so that people can see exactly how much energy they are using at any time.

Green taxation is steadily increasing in strength in the EU and other parts of the world. Examples are taxes on individuals for using air transport and pollution charges on companies.

Many countries are looking increasingly at the concept of community energy. Much energy is lost in transmission if the source of supply is a long way away. Energy produced locally is much more efficient. This will invariably involve microgeneration.

In March 2006, J.M. Barrosa took the European Commission's first shot at creating an EU energy policy. He argued that the EU can no longer afford 25 different and uncoordinated energy policies. Coordination of energy policies in the EU has the potential to create a more efficient energy market but it may be difficult to achieve. If the EU is successful in coordinating energy policies, this may well provide a model for other parts of the world to follow. This will be most likely where countries are already linked together in trade blocs such as NAFTA (the USA, Canada and Mexico).

Figure 3.9 summarises some of the measures governments and individuals can undertake to reduce the demand for energy and thus move towards a more sustainable situation.

Government	Individuals
• Improve public transport to encourage higher levels of usage. • Set a high level of tax on petrol, aviation fuel, etc. • Ensure that public utility vehicles are energy-efficient. • Set minimum fuel consumption requirements for cars and commercial vehicles. • Introduce congestion charging to deter non-essential car use in city centres. • Offer subsidies/grants to households to improve energy efficiency. • Encourage business to monitor and reduce its energy usage. • Encourage recycling. • Promote investment in renewable forms of energy. • Pass laws to compel manufacturers to produce higher-efficiency electrical products.	**Transport:** • Walk rather than drive for short local journeys. • Use a bicycle for short to moderate distance journeys. • Buy low-fuel consumption/low-emission cars. • Reduce car usage by planning more 'multipurpose' trips. • Use public rather than private transport. • Adopt car pooling. **In the home:** • Use low-energy light bulbs. • Install cavity wall insulation. • Improve loft insulation. • Turn boiler and radiator settings down slightly. • Wash clothes at lower temperatures. • Purchase energy-efficient appliances. • Don't leave appliances on standby.

▲ **Figure 3.9:** Examples of energy conservation measures.

Summary

In this chapter you have learnt:

• that there is uncertainty over both global energy supply and demand.

• that there are different possible responses to increasing energy demands.

• that energy insecurity may lead to increased geopolitical tension and the potential for conflict.

• that meeting new energy needs requires increased emphasis on radical new approaches.

MCQ

Taking it further

Work in groups to find out the latest developments across the world in (a) solar power, (b) wind energy, and (c) geothermal power.

Exam Practice – Section A

Energy Security

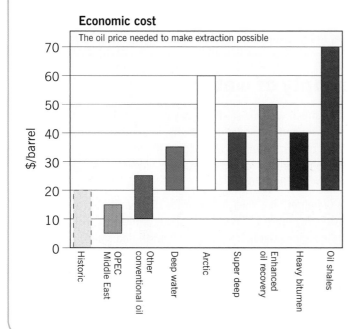

Economic cost

The oil price needed to make extraction possible

$/barrel — categories: Historic, OPEC Middle East, Other conventional oil, Deep water, Arctic, Super deep, Enhanced oil recovery, Heavy bitumen, Oil shales

(a) Explain how the world price of oil has a major impact on oil exploration by TNCs and governments. [10]

(b) Assess the potential environmental, economic and political risks in exploiting new energy resources. [15]

◀ **Figure 1:** The impact of oil prices on oil exploration.

CHAPTER 4 What is the geography of water supply and demand?

Key terms

Actual evapotranspiration
Arid and semi-arid
Drought
Potential evapotranspiration
Virtual water
Water footprint
Water scarcity
Water stress

Learning objectives

After studying this chapter, you will be able to discuss these ideas and concepts and provide located examples of them:

• Freshwater supply is a finite resource and its supply is controlled by physical factors such as climate, geology and surface processes.
• There is a growing mismatch between water supply and water demand that is being driven by economic growth.
• Water supply is also influenced by human actions such as water capture and diversion and over-abstraction and pollution can have detrimental effects on water supply and quality.
• Different groups, or players, are involved in the supply and use of water and their interests may conflict.

Location	Km³
Oceans	1,340,000,000
Ice caps and glaciers	27,000,000
Saline groundwater	12,900,000
Fresh groundwater (>1 km deep)	6,000,000
Fresh groundwater (<1 km deep)	4,000,000
Freshwater lakes	91,000
Saline lakes	85,000
Soil	16,000
Atmosphere	13,000
Marshes	12,000
Rivers	2,000
Biological	1,000
Total freshwater	**31,700,000**
Total water on earth	**1,390,000,000**

▲ **Figure 4.1:** The locations and volume of water on earth. The freshwater stores are identified in blue.

The earth is a blue planet: 71% of its surface is covered in water yet many parts of the world suffer acute water shortage. This section will explore the reasons for this and the consequences of and responses to the disparity in access to fresh water. Figure 4.1 shows how little water is actually available for human use: the main sources of water for human use are in the rivers, freshwater lakes and shallow groundwater and soil stores. This adds up to 0.296% of the total volume of water on earth; therefore freshwater is regarded as a finite resource.

It has been calculated that some 34,000 km³ of freshwater are available globally for human use every year. The global population, at the end of 2008, was around 6.8 billion so, if the water was shared equally, everyone would have about 5,000 m³ to use each year – that is 5,000,000 litres! But some 4 billion people live in areas receiving only one-quarter of the world's annual rainfall and, according to the United Nations, more than 1 billion people lack access to fresh drinking water. Meanwhile, the global population is increasing by about 80 million each year.

The supply of water

Climate primarily controls how much water is stored in any of the earth's natural reservoirs; the annual temperature and precipitation patterns in an area will determine the availability of water. The extent of storage will be affected by the local geology, namely the permeability and porosity of the underlying rocks. The surface processes that are operating will be the product of its climate and its geology.

The amount of precipitation (whether rain, sleet, snow or fog drip) varies according to latitude. Equatorial regions (roughly up to 15° north and south of the Equator) receive the greatest rainfall, temperate regions (latitudes 40° to 60° north and south) are also comparatively humid, whereas tropical and polar regions are arid or semi-arid. These are generalisations, of course, as other factors such as proximity to oceans and prevailing wind patterns distort simple latitudinal divisions.

Taking it further

Construct a pie diagram to illustrate the volumes of water in the different locations.

Seasonality is also very important for water supply as precipitation patterns vary throughout the year. Vancouver, on the west coast of Canada, receives about 1,100 mm of precipitation per year but, as Figure 4.2 shows, this falls mainly between October and March, with far less rainfall during the summer months when the temperature is higher. In summer, higher temperatures increase evaporation; in addition, plant growth throughout spring and summer increases rates of transpiration. Figure 4.3 illustrates the effect of these processes combined – evapotranspiration – upon the water balance of an area as the store of water in the soil is used in summer and refilled in winter.

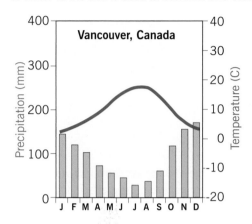

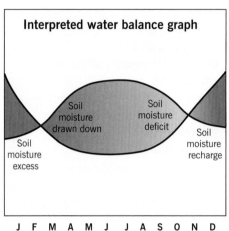

▲ **Figure 4.2:** The temperate maritime climate of Vancouver, located at 49°15' North 123°10' West, is clearly seasonal.

▲ **Figure 4.3:** The water balance graph showing how precipitation and evapotranspiration in a northern temperate climate affect the availability of water in the soil.

Globally, there are significant differences between annual precipitation and potential evapotranspiration. Figure 4.4 illustrates this well as the red, orange and yellow areas show deficits of up to 2,753 mm per year, while the green and blue areas show a surplus of precipitation over evapotranspiration of up to 5,237 mm per year. This map illustrates how areas experiencing water deficit spread far beyond low rainfall areas.

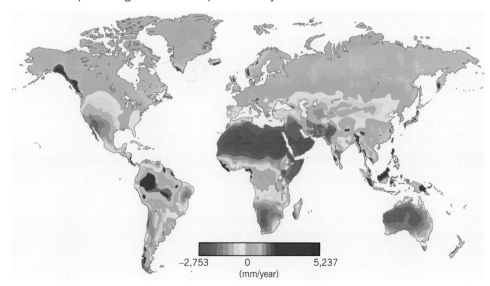

◀ **Figure 4.4:** The global water balance: the difference between precipitation and evapotranspiration.

While the amount of water available (and the temperature) will determine the ecology of an area, people have the technology to overcome the physical challenges of living in hostile environments, but this is limited by their ability to afford the required technology. Some of the areas that are most pressured in terms of water availability are also home to many poorer people and here people are much more reliant on seasonal rainfall and suffer greatly when these rains fail to arrive.

Most water supply systems are linked to the drainage basin system. Bounded by its watershed, the catchment area of a drainage basin will collect all of the precipitation within this boundary and water will be channelled towards the coastline (or a major lake). The relative sizes of the input (precipitation) and outputs (evaporation, transpiration and runoff, plus abstraction by people) vary hugely depending upon the location of the drainage basin.

The time it takes water that falls as precipitation to reach the main course of a river varies from a few hours to many years. The lag time, that is the time taken between the peak of a rainfall event and the peak discharge at a given point in a river, depends upon a number of factors that include:

- type of precipitation
- previous (antecedent) precipitation
- land use
- size and shape of the drainage basin
- relief of the catchment area
- drainage pattern
- underlying geology.

These factors combine to determine the rate of discharge and the availability of water in any one place. The nature of the underlying rocks is very important as it affects the amount of underground storage, the groundwater store that lies below the water table and feeds springs, streams and rivers as baseflow. Water is stored in porous rocks in the ground. The water table marks the surface of this water. The aeration zone above it is not saturated but it does contain enough water under normal conditions to support plants.

The type of rock or, more precisely, its permeability, is crucial. Granites and other igneous and metamorphic rocks are generally impermeable; they are aquicludes but cannot store water. Carboniferous limestone is pervious, that is, water can flow through cracks and joints in it, creating amazing caves and tunnels and striking landforms, but it does not make the best underground store. Sandstone and chalk are porous and so contain pore spaces within which water can be stored easily. The best stores are sands and gravels that are unconsolidated (not cemented together), so having high porosity, and which are bounded by impermeable rocks, containing the water.

The demand for water

People interrupt the hydrological cycle at several points, for example:
- land use changes affect interception and infiltration rates
- land use changes also affect surface storage
- flood management and dam construction affect channel flow and storage
- water abstraction affects groundwater storage.

River management is undertaken to control the flow of the water, to prevent flooding, to enable irrigation, to provide energy, to facilitate transport and to supply water.

Globally, two-thirds of water used is for agriculture, less than a quarter for industry and only 8% for domestic use, but the demand for water differs greatly in different parts of the world. Agriculture uses 88% of water in Africa compared with only 33% in Europe where industry consumes more than half of the supply; global water withdrawal for industry accounts for 22% of total water use, but this varies from 59% in high-income countries to 8% in low-income countries. The amount of water that people use depends not only on basic needs and how much water is available but also on levels of urbanisation and economic development.

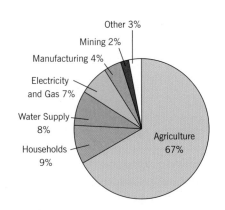

▲ **Figure 4.5:** World water use in 2005.

Figure 4.6 shows how water is used in the UK. Two-thirds of Britain's water comes from surface sources and one-third from groundwater, although these proportions vary by region: for example, groundwater accounts for around 70% of the total water supply in London and the South East. About 45% of all water abstraction in England and Wales is for the public water supply, half for domestic use and almost as much for power generation.

Population growth and economic development are driving a steadily increasing demand for new water supplies; in the last 70 years, the global population has tripled while water withdrawals have increased six-fold. As poorer countries develop, the volume of water used by industry is rising and, as the world becomes more urban, the demand for potable water (water that is fit to drink) for municipal use is exceeding the capacity of the local water companies to supply it. Agriculture, industry and the domestic sector use most of the water abstracted from rivers, lakes and aquifers, but larger volumes are being taken from finite sources and maintaining supplies to meet demand is becoming increasingly difficult.

Water use is more complex than simply measuring how much water is taken from the ground or rivers and delivered through our taps. Large quantities of water are used in agricultural and industrial processes, which means that every person in Britain effectively uses 4,645 litres a day. This means that Britain is dependent upon the water resources of other countries that are used in the production of imported food and other goods. The additional indirect water use is known as 'virtual water', that is, the amount of water used in the production of a good or service. Figure 4.7 shows how this concept works with reference to agricultural products. Water use is measured in terms of the volume of water consumed and/or polluted per unit of time and the consequent water footprint is divided into three elements:

- blue water is freshwater taken from surface water and groundwater resources
- green water is freshwater taken from rainwater stored in the soil as soil moisture
- grey water is polluted water, calculated as the volume of water that is required to dilute pollutants so that the quality of the water is above agreed water quality standards.

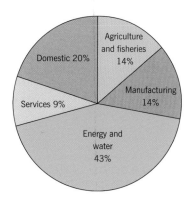

▲ **Figure 4.6:** Water resource use by sector in the United Kingdom 1997–1998.

Source: www.statistics.gov.uk

Taking it further

To find your water footprint take a look at the weblink on your Student CD-ROM.

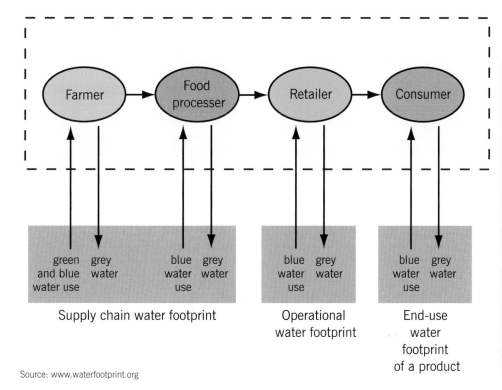

Source: www.waterfootprint.org

▲ **Figure 4.7:** How water is used in the production chain.

One sheet of A4 paper uses 10 litres

One slice of bread uses 40 litres

One apple uses 70 litres

One cup of coffee uses 140 litres

One pint of beer uses 160 litres

One bag of crisps (200 g) uses 185 litres

One litre of milk uses 1,000 litres

One burger uses 2,400 litres

One cotton T-shirt uses 4,100 litres

One kg of cheese uses 5,000 litres

One pair of jeans uses 10,600 litres

One car uses 120,000 litres

▲ **Figure 4.8:** Production costs in terms of water use.

The amount of water used is closely related to levels of economic activity. Comparison of the water footprints of different countries partly reflects this; as Figure 4.9 shows, there is a correlation between water use and economic level: the USA uses the most water and the Yemen, in the Middle East, the least. Global trade transfers this water use across national boundaries so that net importers of goods effectively have a greater water footprint than net exporters; more affluent countries use more water because they consume more goods and services. Considerable amounts of water are used in production processes for irrigation, cleaning, dying, cooling and heating – the production costs, in terms of water, just for your breakfast is over 250 litres!

▶ **Figure 4.9:** Water availability and water footprints for selected countries with comparative data on population and development.

Taking it further

One cubic kilometre is equal to one billion cubic metres and there are one thousand litres in one cubic metre. Use the data in Figure 4.9 to calculate how much water is available per capita in each country. Draw a scattergraph and carry out a Spearman rank correlation test to determine the strength of the relationship between water footprints and level of economic development.

Country	Population (2006-2007 estimates)	Water availability (km³/year)	Water footprint (m³/cap/yr)	GDP ($ per capita)	HDI
Argentina	38,970,611	814	1,404	13,244	0.869
Australia	21,017,222	398	1,393	34,882	0.962
Burkina Faso	13,730,258	18	1,529	1,213	0.370
China	1,311,020,000	2,830	702	5,345	0.777
Egypt	73,671,661	87	1,097	5,352	0.708
India	1,134,023,232	1,908	980	2,753	0.619
Namibia	2,088,669	46	683	5,172	0.650
Spain	44,873,567	111	2,325	31,312	0.949
UK	60,587,349	161	1,245	33,535	0.946
USA	299,398,484	3,069	2,483	45,790	0.951
Vietnam	84,155,800	891	1,324	2,600	0.733
Yemen	21,220,000	4	619	2,336	0.508

Sources: www.cia.gov/; http://unstats.un.org/; www.nationmaster.com; www.waterfootprint.org.

Water stress, water scarcity and drought

Global figures on water availability give a misleading impression as freshwater resources are not evenly distributed spatially or temporally. Locational, seasonal and annual variations can mean that the water is neither where it is wanted nor when it is wanted. The data for water availability given in Figure 4.9 are annual averages only; Spain and Australia have experienced significantly lower rainfall during the first decade of the 21st century and this has had severe regional impacts in both countries.

Water stress is measured as annual water supplies below 1,700 m³ per person. This involves the deterioration of freshwater resources in terms of quantity (aquifer depletion or dry rivers) and quality (eutrophication, pollution, or saline intrusion, for example). Water scarcity occurs when the shortage of freshwater threatens food production and damages ecosystems. This is measured as annual water supplies below 1,000 m³ per person.

Water scarcity may be divided into 'apparent scarcity', which exists when there is plenty of water but it is used wastefully, and 'real scarcity', which is caused by insufficient rainfall or too many people relying on a limited resource. A further classification of water scarcity is given in Figure 4.10.

Taking it further

Research 'The Great Dry', the drought that severely affected south-east Australia in the first decade of the 21st century, and compare the issues and consequences with the Yemen case study.

Physical water scarcity	More than 75% of river flows are allocated to agriculture, industries or domestic purposes (accounting for recycling of return flows). This definition of scarcity – relating water availability to water demand – implies that dry areas are not necessarily water-scarce, e.g. Mauritania.
Approaching physical water scarcity	More than 60% of river flows are allocated. These basins will experience physical water scarcity in the near future.
Economic water scarcity	Water resources are abundant relative to water use, with less than 25% of water from rivers withdrawn for human purposes, but malnutrition exists. These areas could benefit by development of additional blue and green water, but human and financial capacity are limiting.
Little or no water scarcity	Abundant water resources relative to use. Less than 25% of water from rivers is withdrawn for human purposes.

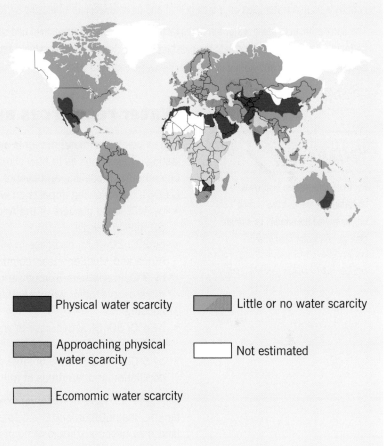

Physical water scarcity • Little or no water scarcity

Approaching physical water scarcity • Not estimated

Ecomomic water scarcity

▲ **Figure 4.10:** The extent and nature of water scarcity.

Places like south-east Australia and the Yemen are experiencing severe water shortages. The Yemen is naturally a semi-desert area on the edge of the Arabian Desert while the Murray-Darling basin in Australia is a relatively fertile area that should have rainfall all year round, but for several years since 2002 it has suffered below average rainfall that has progressively reduced its water resources. Both regions are suffering as a consequence of human activity.

Case study: The misuse of vital resources in the Yemen

The capital city of Yemen, Sana'a, is located in mountains to the north of the country and its inhabitants are finding that its dwindling water supply may not be able to sustain the ancient settlement. The old city is a UNESCO World Heritage Site; Sana'a is at least 2,500 years old and claims to be the world's oldest inhabited city. It is living on borrowed time but, for once, climate change is not the culprit, it is human behaviour.

There were over 21 million Yemenis in 2007 and the population is doubling every 17 years. The country imports most of its food, largely because it has too little water to feed itself; there is about one-fiftieth as much water per head as the world average. Insupportably large amounts of water go on a non-essential crop, khat, which is a shrub whose leaves, when chewed, can induce mild euphoria, excitement and hallucinations. It is increasingly popular in Yemen where almost half the people live on less than US$2 a day and people have little other amusement. Weaning Yemenis off khat will be like breaking the tobacco habit. Growing khat earns farmers 20 times as much as growing potatoes but 40% of the country's scarce water goes on irrigating khat and its cultivation is increasing by 10 to 15% a year.

The Sana'a basin is using water ten times faster than it is being replenished and soon there will be insufficient water to drink. One solution would be to encourage people to move to the coast on the Red Sea where renewable energy could be used to desalinate water. This is considered to be a cheaper option than attempting to increase the water supply in Sana'a.

Taking it further

For more information visit www.wateraid.org and use the search engine to find documents on climate change and water resources.

Water resources and climate change

With a warmer climate, droughts and floods could become more frequent, severe and long-lasting. Suggestions as to how climate change will affect regional water resources are based on computer modelling and cannot be precisely predicted, but, according to the Stern Review (2006), the following impacts on water resources are anticipated as temperatures rise:

- by 1°C: small glaciers in the Andes disappear completely, threatening water supplies for 50 million people
- by 2°C: 20–30% decrease in water availability in vulnerable regions such as southern Africa and Mediterranean countries
- by 3°C: in southern Europe serious droughts occur once every 10 years; 1 to 4 billion more people suffer water shortages, while 1 to 5 billion gain water, increasing the risk of flooding
- by 4°C: 30–50% decrease in water availability in southern Africa and Mediterranean countries
- by 5°C: disappearance of large glaciers on Himalayas affecting one-quarter of China's population and hundreds of millions in India.

Droughts can have devastating effects on agriculture, livestock and water supplies, causing famine, malnutrition and the displacement of populations from one area to another. The land may become starved of nourishment or contaminated with mineral salts, so that even when it does rain the ground cannot support much vegetation growth. With climate change expected to reduce rainfall in some places and cause droughts in others, some regions could become 'economic deserts', of no use to people or agriculture.

Taking it further

Look up www.dmcn.org, which is the website for the Drought Monitoring Centre for the Greater Horn of Africa (GHA) covering Burundi, Djibouti, Eritrea, Ethiopia, Kenya, Rwanda, Somalia, Sudan, Tanzania and Uganda.

Droughts are classified in different ways:
- Meteorological drought occurs when there is a prolonged period with less than average precipitation.
- Hydrological drought occurs when water reserves in aquifers, lakes and reservoirs fall below average levels.
- Agricultural drought can result from a reduction in precipitation levels but also may occur when inappropriate agricultural activity causes a shortfall in water available to the crops.

Some of the most dramatic examples of water shortages in 2008 included the drying up of Lake Faguibine in Mali, on which 200,000 mostly nomadic people depended, and fatal clashes over drying boreholes in northern Kenya. Oxfam estimated that 25 million people were affected by drought in Ethiopia. Even in rich nations, water shortages exacerbated by over-use of rivers and aquifers were causing serious problems. California declared a state of emergency over water shortages, Australia spent billions of dollars to cope with drought and governments in Europe had to ship in water to prevent communities running dry.

Identifying the players

Unsustainable use is threatening the future of water supply in many areas. Demand has risen as, in the last 70 years, the global population has tripled and water withdrawals have increased six-fold. There is increased competition for available water as living standards rise and groundwater reserves are abstracted faster than they are recharged. In some countries, urban populations are rising rapidly while, in others, old water mains and sewers are no longer fit for purpose. Pollution from urban, industrial and agricultural sources has affected water quality, and over-extraction in many places has reduced the ability of supplies and suppliers to meet demand. The threat of climate change, affecting the amount and reliability of rainfall in many parts of the world, compounds this unsustainable situation. There is also an environmental obligation to maintain fragile wetlands and water courses.

The people whose activities affect water supply and demand are the players: they control access to water or are affected by others' control of the water supply. They include water companies, governments, agriculture, industry and business, recreation and tourism, domestic users, charities and nature conservation. Vulnerable populations stand to suffer the most because access to water is controlled by those with wealth and power, especially in the developing and emerging economies where the lack of access to clean drinking water is a vital issue.

Summary

In this chapter you have learnt:

- Freshwater supply is a finite resource and its supply is controlled by physical factors such as climate, geology and surface processes.
- There is a growing mismatch between water supply and water demand that is being driven by economic growth.
- Water supply is also influenced by human actions such as water capture and diversion and over-abstraction and pollution can have detrimental effects on water supply and quality.
- Different groups, or players, are involved in the supply and use of water and their interests may conflict.

MCQ

CHAPTER 5 What are the potential implications of an increasingly 'water insecure' world?

Key terms

Fossil water
International river basins
Potable water
Strategic resource

Learning objectives

After studying this chapter, you will be able to discuss these ideas and concepts and provide located examples of them:
- The development, extraction and use of water sources can have social, economic and environmental implications.
- Water supply is increasingly a geopolitical issue, with competition for natural resources across international and interregional borders.
- Conflict can arise where demand exceeds supply and where different users use the same source of water.
- The development of water transfers from regions of surplus to regions of scarcity has political and environmental implications.

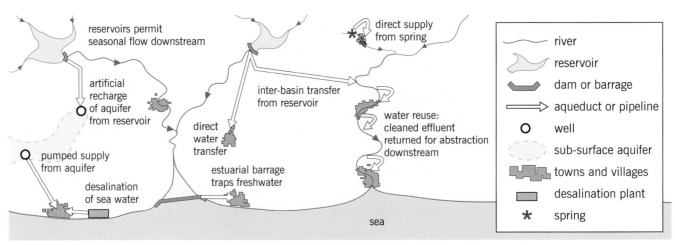

▲ **Figure 5.1:** The management of surface water.

Sources of water

The development of water resources depends upon the availability of easily accessible reserves. There are several sources of water for human use; these include surface stores, groundwater stores and rainwater. Surface stores in springs, streams, rivers and lakes are the most accessible sources, provided that the water is sufficiently clean to use. Narrow valleys in upland areas may be dammed to create reservoirs to store water and control flooding. Springs emerging directly from ground sources are generally potable (or drinkable). Other water courses may contain pollutants from adjacent natural and human land uses and need to be treated prior to use.

Groundwater sources are stored in aquifers usually within sandstones and limestones. Confined aquifers are those sandwiched between layers of impermeable rock called aquicludes. Wells are sunk to extract the water from aquifers but they have been over-exploited in some places and removal of the water is lowering water tables. The Ogallala aquifer lies under the central states of the USA from South Dakota to Texas and supplies water for agriculture, but the water is being pumped out faster than it is recharged and in places the water table is falling by over a metre per year. Most of the water in this aquifer is thought to have collected when the glaciers melted 15,000 years ago and it is described as fossil water; this means that it is now being recharged at a much slower rate.

Coastal well before excessive pumping

Coastal well after excessive pumping

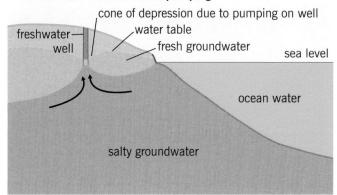

▲ **Figure 5.2:** The impacts of taking too much water from wells sited near coastlines.

Modification of the groundwater system can have long-lasting consequences. Lowering the water table by abstracting water faster than it is replenished causes wells to dry up. This can lead to subsidence as the previously water-bearing sediments may become compacted and the added weight of buildings can increase this effect. Near coasts, saltwater seeps naturally into permeable rocks. Normally freshwater in the ground floats on the denser saltwater but, when too much water is taken from the groundwater store, saltwater can be drawn up towards the well, contaminating the supply. Also, as water is taken from a well, a cone of depression in the water table is formed around the well.

Groundwater is vulnerable to pollution from landfill sites, to leakage from underground storage tanks and sewerage and to surface pollution spills where the ground above is permeable. Residues from agro-chemicals leach into groundwater stores. In some areas, such as East Anglia, Nitrate Sensitive Areas have been set up, restricting the use of nitrates to protect water supplies. Pollution is increasingly damaging the supply of freshwater; almost two million tonnes of waste are dumped daily into lakes, rivers and streams.

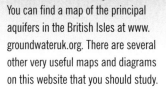

Taking it further

You can find a map of the principal aquifers in the British Isles at www.groundwateruk.org. There are several other very useful maps and diagrams on this website that you should study.

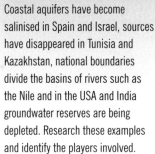

Taking it further

Coastal aquifers have become salinised in Spain and Israel, sources have disappeared in Tunisia and Kazakhstan, national boundaries divide the basins of rivers such as the Nile and in the USA and India groundwater reserves are being depleted. Research these examples and identify the players involved.

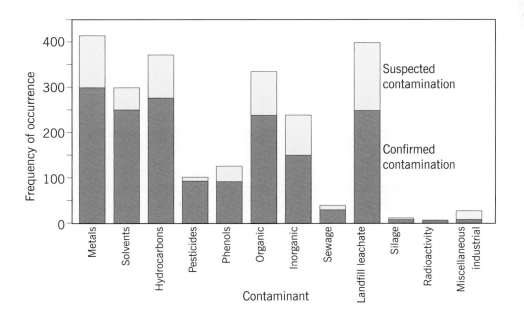

▲ **Figure 5.3:** The frequency with which particular contaminants occur in groundwater in England and Wales.

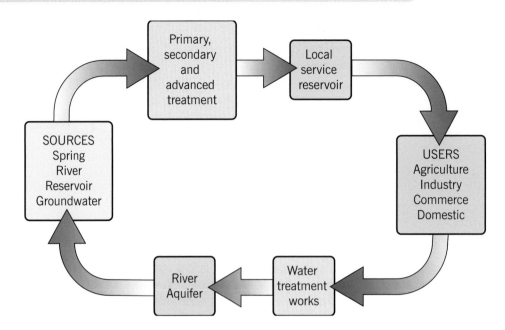

▲ **Figure 5.4:** The water supply cycle. In some places, waste water is returned to aquifers to enable their recharge.

Supplying clean water

While industries such as power generation may use untreated water, river water needs to be treated prior to domestic use. Water purification involves a series of physical, chemical and biological processes including settling, coagulation, disinfection, filtration through sand and aeration to encourage benign bacteria. Industry and agriculture may release waste water directly into rivers but this is strictly controlled in advanced countries to ensure that pollution is minimised. A water supply cycle such as that operating in the UK is illustrated in Figure 5.4. Waste water, cleaned of all significant pollutants, is returned to rivers or in some places, such as the Lea Valley in North London, used to artificially recharge an aquifer.

Access to a clean water supply is fundamental to human health with vital implications for human welfare. The minimum requirement is about five litres per day to prevent dehydration but 30 litres per day is regarded as the minimum needed for cooking and cleanliness as well as drinking. In many poorer countries up to 25 litres of water may be carried for several kilometres. It is the female members of the community who normally collect the water and it can take more than half of their time, causing young girls to give up formal education. Carrying water over long distances is a health hazard, especially during childhood and pregnancy. In urban areas water may be bought from private water-carrying services or from public standpipes.

Contaminated water is a major health risk in developing countries: water-borne diseases cause around 2 million deaths a year, mainly of children in poorer countries where there is inadequate or non-existent public sanitation. About 1 billion people in the world do not have access to safe water and 2.5 billion people do not have access to adequate sanitation. Water-related diseases prevent many people from leading healthy lives and undermine development efforts. Around 2.3 billion people in the world suffer from diseases caused by protozoa, viruses, bacteria and intestinal parasites acquired from water. In developing countries, diarrhoea is the leading cause of childhood death. Providing clean supplies of water and ensuring proper sanitation facilities would save millions of lives by reducing the prevalence of water-related diseases, so finding solutions to these problems should become a high priority for developing countries and aid agencies.

In September 2000, world leaders met at the United Nations headquarters in New York to adopt the Millennium Declaration setting out the eight Millennium Development Goals (MDGs) to be achieved by 2015. (see page 106)

MDG 7 is intended to ensure environmental sustainability and includes the aim to 'reduce by half the proportion of people without sustainable access to safe drinking water'. This should be achieved by increasing the proportion of total water resources used, the proportion of population using an improved drinking water source and the proportion of population using improved sanitation facilities.

People need a potable water supply and freedom from disease so they can work to support their families, and industry needs water for production processes. In developing countries seeking to improve their standard of living, restricted access to a reliable water supply has severe implications for economic activity, but they cannot always afford the infrastructure that is essential for sustainable economic growth. The challenge is amplified in countries where rainfall is low or very seasonal and temperatures are high, causing high rates of evaporation.

Reliable supplies and efficient water and waste treatment technology need to be installed to achieve MDG 7. In poorer countries, appropriate technology can enable improvements in water supply and sanitation and local people need training to ensure that it is sustainable. The charity WaterAid works with people in 17 countries in Africa, Asia and the Pacific region to improve their quality of life through lasting improvements to water, sanitation and hygiene education using local skills and practical, sustainable technologies.

In Burkina Faso, nearly 200 projects funded by international organisations are ongoing to improve water supply and sanitation with investments ranging from just a few thousand to many millions of dollars. These range from the provision of simple boreholes and hand pumps to restoring the Ziga reservoir north of Ouagadougou. Many small dams have been constructed to trap surface water, but widespread damming of rivers heavily reduces the region's limited water resources through losses to evaporation and seepage and increases susceptibility to microbiological hazards such as schistosomiasis or bilharzia.

Increasingly in drier climates, the capture and storage of rainwater is a viable option, particularly in remoter regions. Rainfall on roofs and other impermeable surfaces can easily be channelled to storage tanks. In Australia, for example, homes in the Southern Highlands are constructed with basement storage tanks, which in normal circumstances can provide sufficient water for a family throughout the year, requiring little treatment before use. In Bermuda, by law, all houses must have clean roofs to catch rainwater and underground cisterns for storage; hotels there have large rain-catchment areas.

The politics of water

UNEP (United Nations Environment Programme) has calculated that enough rain falls on Africa to supply the needs of 13 billion people and has called for a continent-wide programme of rainwater harvesting. UNESCO (2003) has suggested that globally the volume of water available per person will decrease by 30% by 2025, but

> 'One part of the world sustains a designer bottled-water market that generates no tangible health benefits, another part suffers acute public health risks because people have to drink water from drains or from lakes and rivers shared with animals and infected with harmful bacteria.' (Human Development Report, UNDP, 2006)

Water supply is increasingly a geopolitical issue. Water politics, sometimes called hydropolitics, have emerged internationally as a series of treaties, and agreements have been made between states and countries sharing water resources. Several major river systems cross international boundaries and tensions can arise over the use of the water as demand for water increases.

Taking it further

Look up the UNDP (United Nations Development Programme) MDG site (www.un.org/millenniumgoals/index.shtml) and follow the progress of different countries in achieving the MDGs. What does this tell you about the commitment and ability of rich nations to help poor nations achieve these goals?

▲ **Figure 5.5:** A girl pumps water at a local well in Burkina Faso

Key term

Strategic resource — a resource that is considered to be essential to the maintenance of an economy.

Water is a strategic resource and increasingly an important feature of many political conflicts. Some have suggested that water will become a tradable commodity as important as oil, benefiting water-rich countries such as Greenland, Canada and Colombia. Those who hold vital resources also hold power over those who do not have access to those resources. Where water resources cross international or state boundaries, the challenges for integrated watershed management are compounded and political cooperation may be compromised. The potential for conflict is high: water and its use may strain relations between and within countries. The authorities responsible for the sources and major upstream tributaries of river systems are able to control the flow downstream, possibly depriving other states and nations of valuable water resources. It has been calculated that there are 261 international rivers, namely rivers whose boundaries cross international borders, covering 45.3% of the earth's land surface. Nineteen basins are shared by five or more riparian countries (that is, those situated on a river bank).

▶ **Figure 5.6:** International river basins and the number of countries the rivers flow through.

International basins	Number of countries
Danube	17
Congo and Niger	11
Nile	10
Rhine and Zambezi	9
Amazon and Lake Chad	8
Aral Sea, Ganges-Brahmaputra-Meghna, Jordan, Kura-Araks, Mekong, Tarim, Tigris and Euphrates, and Volta	6

Case study: Some major international rivers

The Danube rises in the Black Forest Mountains in Germany and flows for 2,850 km to the Black Sea passing through Germany, Austria, Slovakia, Hungary, Croatia, Serbia, Bulgaria, Romania, Ukraine and several other countries. It provides drinking water for 10 million people and the International Commission for the Protection of the Danube River, comprising 13 member states and the EU, was set up in 1998 to promote and coordinate sustainable and equitable water management, including conservation, improvement and rational use of the water of the river, its tributaries and the groundwater resources.

The Ganges rises at Gaumakh in the southern Himalayas on the Indian side of the Tibetan border and flows for 2,510 km through China, India, Nepal and Bangladesh where it joins the Brahmaputra and Meghna rivers. The Ganges river basin is one of the most fertile and densely populated in the world and covers an area of 1,000,000 km². The river flows through 52 cities and about 48 towns. A UN Climate Report in 2007 suggested that the glaciers that feed the Ganges could disappear by 2030; the river's flow would then become seasonal, fed mainly by the summer monsoon rainfall.

The Nile flows for 6,700 km through ten countries, draining more than 3 million km², about one-tenth of the entire African landmass, and is formed by three major tributaries, the White Nile, the Blue Nile and the Atbara. The primary problem facing the Nile and the countries it serves — Burundi, Democratic Republic of Congo, Egypt, Ethiopia, Kenya, Rwanda, Sudan, Tanzania, Uganda and Eritrea — has to do with the scarcity and the over-use of the water. Before dams were built on the river, the discharge at Aswan varied widely throughout the year.

The Jordan is 320 km long and flows to the Sea of Galilee and then to the Dead Sea, which is about 400 m below sea level and has no outlet. It is formed from three tributaries: the Hasbani which flows from Lebanon, and the Banias and the Dan which both flow from Mount Hermon whose summit is on the border of Syria and Lebanon, while the southern slopes have been in Israeli control since 1967. Two more tributaries join from the east: the Yarmouk and the Jabbok. In 1964, Israel began operating a dam that diverts water from the Sea of Galilee and Jordan constructed a channel diverting water from the Yarmouk. Syria has also built reservoirs that catch the Yarmouk's waters. Now 70–90% of the water is used for human purposes and the flow is so reduced that the Dead Sea is shrinking.

The Colorado River is approximately 2,330 km long and drains 629,100 km² of land from the western slopes of the Rocky Mountains to the Gulf of California. Its flow was much higher before river management commenced; now virtually the entire flow of the river is captured, reducing the flow so much in its lower course in Mexico that it no longer consistently reaches the sea. A series of 29 dams, such as Hoover and Glen Canyon, have been built along the river and several canals divert water to cities in California and Arizona. Two-thirds of the water is used for the irrigation of more than 1.5 million hectares of farmland, and the remainder supplies urban areas, provides water to riparian vegetation, or is evaporated.

In 2000, the European Union (EU) Water Framework Directive (WFD) was adopted to protect and enhance the quality of European groundwater, rivers, lakes, estuaries and coasts. About 60% of the surface area of the EU lies in river basins that cross an international border, so each member state is responsible for the sections of the international river basins within their countries and are bound to coordinate their actions with fellow member states. The WFD extends the process of joint management within the 40 international river basins in Europe and sets up a legal framework to protect and restore clean water, to protect aquatic ecosystems, and to include public participation in planning and integrated economic management.

This European cooperation shows how nations can work together successfully to manage their water resources but there is a long history of conflict in other parts of the world, perhaps where water is more scarce. The water of the Nile and Jordan river basins continues to be contested and the Colorado has a long history of water treaties, compacts and agreements. Rights to and shares of water sources must be negotiated, but conflict is possible where demand exceeds supply or over-abstraction results in long-term degradation of water supplies.

Where climate change is causing rainfall to become depleted and unreliable, possibly encouraging desertification, considerable skills of diplomacy are required to ensure conflict is minimised. In extreme cases, some have predicted the very real possibility of 'water wars' occurring. Armed conflict was narrowly avoided between Syria and Iraq in 1970 over the waters of the Euphrates, but some attribute control of the Shatt al-Arab delta in the Persian Gulf as a cause of the Iraq–Iran war of 1980.

The countries sharing the basin of the Jordan River have very limited freshwater resources and access to the water has been a source of conflict. Israel's National Water Carrier system, a complex of canals, pipelines and tunnels diverting water from the river basin, was built in 1964 to carry water to the Israeli coastal plain and Negev Desert. In response, the Arab Summit of 1964 developed the Headwater Diversion Plan to divert the river water to Syria and Jordan.

Taking it further

Look at http://ec.europa.eu/environment/water/water-framework/index_en.html for more information on the EU WFD.

Taking it further

Search for the BBC World Water Crisis map and check out the water resource flashpoints.

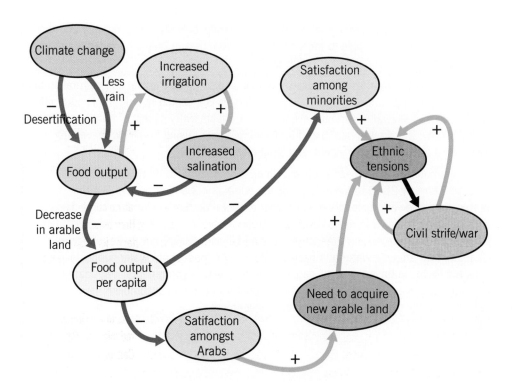

◀ **Figure 5.7:** This causal loop shows the impact of climate change on water and food needs and the potential for conflict between competing groups in northern Africa.

▶ **Figure 5.8:** A Berber camp in the High Atlas mountains of Morocco showing the corral for their animals to be kept safely during the night.

Despite the 1947 international convention banning the bombing of dams, Israel then destroyed the Khaled Ibn al Waid dam on the Yarmouk tributary in 1967. These incidents regarding water issues contributed to the outbreak of the Six-Day War in June 1967.

Those with political power may exploit their position at the expense of politically weaker communities. The Berber people, the largest group of which are the nomadic Tuaregs, are the descendants of the original inhabitants of northern Africa, but growing populations, resulting in over-grazing and desertification, are putting pressure on water resources and causing competition between them and their Arab neighbours. In the remote High Atlas mountains, water tables are falling as Arab cities in the lowlands pull in more water, and the land is becoming salinised. Consequently, both the Arab majority and the Berber minorities will struggle to meet their food demands and this will exacerbate ethnic tensions, so conflict may arise in the future.

Water is associated with every human activity but it also holds a social and cultural status distinct to each region, for example, the River Ganges is a sacred river in the Hindu faith and the focus of several ceremonial events. Water affects every aspect of human wellbeing and prosperity; it is vital to health and for growing crops, raising livestock, preventing disease and providing good hygiene and sanitation.

The total amount of water used each year in crop production could rise from 7,200 to 13,500 km^3 by 2050 to feed the predicted additional 3 billion people. But the combination of lower precipitation and higher evaporation due to climate change is reducing water volumes in rivers, lakes and groundwater in many regions. Also pollution is damaging ecosystems and the health, lives and livelihoods of those without access to adequate, safe drinking water and basic sanitation. An inadequate water supply is likely to contribute to continued poverty, geopolitical instability, environmental degradation and economic stagnation. Improved public health enables people to accomplish more so clean water is essential for social and economic development.

These examples show the challenges that arise from competing claims for scarce water resources and from developing aqueducts between areas of water surplus and deficit nationally and internationally. The pathways between water sources and consumers are complex and they show increasing levels of risk in regions of conflict, hence the importance of agreements and treaties between areas of surplus and deficit. Too often there are winners and losers in resource allocation, socially, economically and environmentally. The controversy surrounding the production of Coca-Cola in India shows the problems that occur when several players use the same water sources.

Taking it further

Find out more about the Coca-Cola controversy in India. Read 'Coca-Cola controversy' on your Student CD-ROM for some useful weblinks.

Case study: In India, do things go better with Coke?

Coca-Cola is the largest beverage company in the world and it used 283 billion litres of water in 2004. In India, for every four litres of freshwater abstracted, it produces one litre of product; the remaining water is used to clean bottles and machinery and is discarded as waste water. According to its website, India's Coca-Cola industry includes 27 company-owned and 17 franchisee-owned bottling plants. Usually the company sells concentrates and syrups to the bottling plants where they are converted into the finished product. It employs approximately 6,000 local people directly and creates employment for more than 125,000 people in supply-chain operations, including the manufacture of a range of products for the company and supply-chain operations. Coca-Cola invested more than US$1 billion in India between 1993 and 2003.

The Plachimada bottling plant in Kerala opened in 1998 and soon the wells began to dry up. The company was accused of putting thousands of farmers out of work by draining the water that feeds their wells and of poisoning the land with waste sludge that the company claims is fertiliser. It was also suggested that Coca-Cola was discharging its waste water to the fields and rivers around the plant, polluting both groundwater and soil. Studies have confirmed a significant depletion of the water table and that the water smells and tastes strange when extracted from greater depth, and high levels of toxic lead and cadmium have been found in the sludge as well as phosphorus, which is a fertiliser. Public health authorities have posted signs around wells and hand pumps advising people that the water is unfit for human consumption. Many residents have to rely on water supplies trucked in daily by the government, and coconut groves and vegetable crops had to be abandoned. Following protests, the local government revoked the company's licence in 2004 and ordered Coca-Cola to shut down its $25 million plant. Since then, however, those who worked at the plant have protested that it should be reopened.

The company denies that water shortages have anything to do with its use of up to 1 million litres of water a day from the underground aquifer, claiming that there is no scientific evidence to link the groundwater shortage to the company's operations. Some Indian leaders believe the issue may be less about science and more about the politics of anti-globalisation. On the other hand, the charity ActionAid says the crisis facing the once prosperous farming area is an example of the worst kind of inward investment by multinational companies in developing countries.

Summary

In this chapter you have learnt:

- that development, extraction and use of water sources can have social, economic and environmental implications.
- that water supply is increasingly a geopolitical issue, with competition for natural resources across international and interregional borders.
- that conflict can arise where demand exceeds supply and where different users use the same source of water.
- that the development of water transfers from regions of surplus to regions of scarcity has political and environmental implications.

MCQ

CHAPTER 6 What are the possible conflicts and solutions to increasing demands for water?

Key terms

BRICs
Privatisation
Transboundary aquifers

Learning objectives

After studying this chapter, you will be able to discuss these ideas and concepts and provide located examples of them:

• Increase in demand for water combined with diminished supply will lead to insecurity of supply in many regions; climate change is exacerbating this situation.

• Decision-makers involved in influencing the future of water resources may have conflicting aims and interests.

• There is a range of responses to current and projected demands for water, including diverting supplies, increasing storage, restoring lost supplies and water conservation.

• There are technological solutions to the problem of water shortage, but these often have environmental consequences.

The challenges ahead

Population growth, urbanisation, economic development, industrialisation and migration have increased water demand to unsustainable levels. Figure 6.1 shows the rising trends in water demand, driven by improving standards of living and economic growth in industry and agriculture. But future projections are based on uncertainties:

• Climate change is occurring but its exact impact cannot be predicted.
• Continued economic growth is not inevitable as the 'credit crunch' has shown.
• Population growth is slowing due to lower birth rates and higher death rates.
• Political and religious conflicts can create severe shocks demographically and economically.

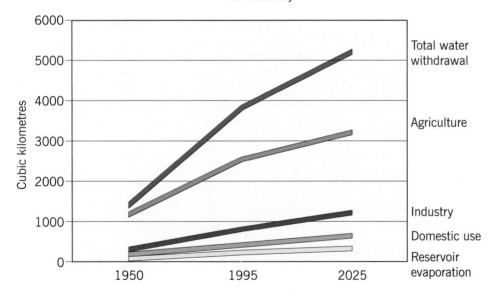

▲ **Figure 6.1:** Past and predicted water consumption by sector, 1950 to 2025.

The supply of water in agriculture in developing countries will need to increase in order to meet the MDG to 'Halve, between 1990 and 2015, the proportion of people who suffer from hunger'. To reduce hunger, agricultural output must increase and thus the water use. All the indicators suggest an increasingly insecure water future for many regions. By 2025 there could be 3.5 billion people living in water-stressed countries. By then it has been predicted that the USA will have lost its status as the world's most dominant nation as the rise of the BRICs (Brazil, Russia, India and China) is changing the balance of the global economy. The demand for water is growing rapidly in these nations, and in similar smaller developing countries, but each country faces its own unique challenges.

India, for example, will need to accommodate:
• continuing rapid population growth
• economic development raising living standards and expectations
• a reduction of input from melting Himalayan glaciers as climate change causes their retreat
• declining water tables as thirsty industrial processes abstract too much water from aquifers
• the extension of irrigation schemes for agricultural expansion to feed the growing population.

More than 21 million Indian farmers use private pumps to tap underground reservoirs to water their crops. This water took thousands of years to accumulate and is now rapidly running out as the rate of fall in the levels of these fossil aquifers is about 3 m a year. To combat the insecurity of water supply, rainwater storage capacity is being increased to catch the rainwater brought by the annual monsoon storms.

In 2007 the UK Meteorological Office provided advice to senior defence officials on likely flashpoints around the world where resource issues could be driven or exacerbated by climate change. Shortages of food and water may get worse as populations grow and weather patterns change so the impact of climate change could exacerbate inequalities in health systems, as well as access to adequate food, clean water and other resources. Rainfall patterns in Africa are moving away from the continent's interior to its coasts, leaving millions of people inland without enough water for consumption or food production. Long-term drought is causing migration and this is likely to increase. The areas most likely to suffer water shortages include western Asia, the Middle East, Central America, and the Mediterranean and Amazon basins.

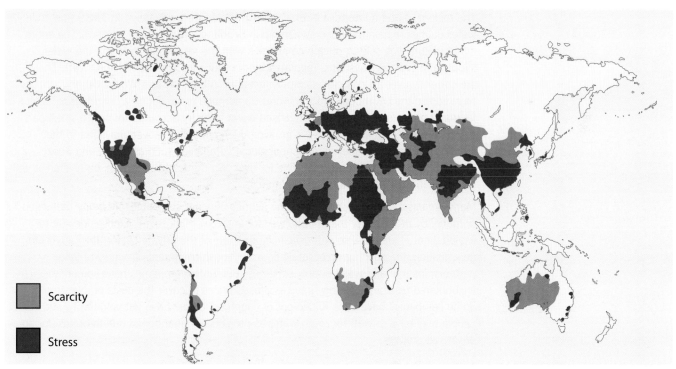

Scarcity

Stress

Millions of people live without access to adequate or clean water now with little hope that their situation will improve as global water shortages increase. Mathematical analysis that combines climate model outputs, water budgets and socio-economic data suggests that a large proportion of the world's population is already suffering from water stress and that rising water demands greatly outweigh climate change in determining the state of global water systems by 2025.

▲ **Figure 6.2:** The areas thought most likely to suffer water scarcity or stress in 2025.

Taking it further

For further information about the people involved in the supply of clean water go to your Student CD-ROM.

Taking it further

For further information on understanding political ideologies go to your Student CD-ROM.

Stakeholders and decision-makers

The potential for conflict is widespread where human activity disrupts water regimes, over-utilises resources and degrades water quality. Water wars are already a reality in many parts of the world and are likely to become more common in the future. Different players and decision-makers have key roles to play in securing future water supplies, but their aims may conflict. Developing management strategies to ensure supply will require the cooperation of these players as well as changes in the way in which water is valued and used.

The actions taken to supply water are influenced by the economic and political structure of a country. There is also a distinction to be made between top-down (from government or industry) and bottom-up or grassroots (from individuals and communities) actions. Sustainability may be developed from the top or the bottom but it is more likely to succeed with community involvement. The people and groups involved are the players or stakeholders and each has a different amount of power and authority in any decision-making situation.

There are many individuals, pressure groups and political movements, governments, businesses, charities and agencies involved in monitoring and managing water resources. Each puts a different value on these in economic, social and environmental terms and they meet at forums, conferences and conventions to discuss and plan the management of water at local, national and international levels. The success of their actions is variable and each case study needs to be assessed on its own terms.

Water privatisation

The regional water authorities in England and Wales were privatised in 1989 (the water utilities remain in public ownership in Scotland and Northern Ireland). The entire infrastructure was sold to private companies with the responsibility to run the water supply and sewerage systems, regulated by the Office for Water Service (Ofwat). There are currently over 20 companies supplying water in England and Wales. Other countries have copied the UK model and the World Bank made privatisation a condition of finance for water projects. Although the privatised water industry accounts for only a small part of global water utilities, business is growing. Mergers and takeovers have led to the creation of a small number of influential global companies such as Veolia and Suez, French companies that are responsible for over two-thirds of the private water market with contracts in Brazil and China, for example.

Many organisations actively criticise the actions of water companies for being motivated primarily by profit rather than public welfare and they think that it exposes people to exploitation. There are also enthusiastic supporters of the private sector; they advocate deregulation, the opening up of markets, and the establishment of public–private partnerships in major water supply schemes. But water companies have sometimes encountered resistance as they have increased prices to cover the costs of investment. Some companies have been forced out of countries, others have left voluntarily, and some people may have to wait for clean water as projects are abandoned due to opposition to privatised projects.

Integrated management

Managing water is an integral part of land use management, development and agricultural policy; it involves a careful balance between supplying personal needs, economic demands and the conservation of the natural environment. These demands need to be met within the framework of sustainable development and there needs to be integrated management:
- of resources: surface and groundwater, quantity and quality, upstream and downstream basins

- of resource development and water purification and treatment
- of supply: renewable natural resources, non-renewable resources, unconventional resources
- of resource uses (including the management of aquatic environments).

There are 240 transboundary aquifers worldwide but they are difficult resources to manage as they flow across the boundaries. The quantity of water available for one country may be significantly diminished by over-pumping in a neighbouring country or water quality may be affected by transboundary pollution. It is hard to define and enforce private property rights over groundwater. Assigning ownership to the land overlying aquifers does not solve the problem as any abstraction will affect the entire aquifer, not just the part that is owned. It is much easier to focus on the control and use of surface water. Management of water in Africa is complex: the collective ownership of water is recorded in oral tradition and not in written documents, handed down through generations, but national boundaries were largely determined during colonial rule, producing difficult political and cultural relations.

The international principles governing transboundary aquifers have developed from agreements that focused on surface water. There are three fundamental principles in determining and implementing states' rights and duties with respect to transboundary aquifers:
- the principle of equitable and reasonable utilisation of shared watercourses
- the duty not to cause injury to countries sharing the same rivers
- the duty to cooperate with other states sharing the same aquifer.

The first agreement on the regulation of international watercourses was in 1911 since when there have been many treaties, agreements and protocols.

The UN Convention on the Law of Non-Navigational Uses of International Watercourses is intended to prevent and resolve disputes between states. It was approved by the UN General Assembly in 1997 and passed by an overwhelming majority. However, it does not become legally binding until it is ratified by 35 countries and, so far, too few countries have signed the treaty. The Convention includes measures to protect, preserve and manage water and covers issues such as flood control, water quality, erosion, sedimentation, saltwater intrusion and living resources. The representatives of some countries felt there was a lack of balance between the rights and obligations of the upstream and downstream riparian states, but a basin state may not deny a reasonable supply of water to another state in the same basin by storing water for future use and must not pollute the water.

Increasing the supply of water

One of the greatest challenges of the 21st century is to supply sufficient clean water for all. New strategies are needed to manage water supplies and responses to the growing demand for water include diverting supplies, increasing storage, restoring lost supplies, and water conservation.

Diverting supplies

Inter-basin transfers are used to redistribute water from areas of water surplus to those experiencing a shortage. In the UK, a national water grid has been considered; this would allow water from well-stocked parts of the country, such as Northumberland, to be piped to areas where there are shortages, such as the South East. So far this plan has been ruled out because of the costs of the infrastructure and the energy needed to pump the water. Smaller interregional schemes have been set up such as the Kielder Project, drawing water from the Kielder Reservoir in Northumberland to the River Tees, and, in 1996, Yorkshire Water announced its decision to develop a £50 million water transfer scheme from the River Tees to the River Ouse in Yorkshire.

Type of interaction	Number of interactions
International Water Treaty	157
Military support	7
Non-military agreement	436
Verbal support	628
Neutral	96
Verbal hostility	414
Hostile acts	56
Military acts	37

▲ **Figure 6.3:** State-to-state water interactions in transboundary basins, 1946–1999.

Taking it further

For more information on the rules on the uses of the waters of international rivers read 'The Helsinki rules' on your Student CD-ROM.

Taking it further

Assess the strategies discussed below that are intended to increase the supply of water by considering their social, economic, political and environmental costs and benefits.

Taking it further

Find a map of the water supply infrastructure for the UK in your school atlas or online. What observations can you make about the distribution of aquifers, the location of high rainfall areas, and the inter regional transfers of water?

Taking it further

Read more about the Chinese water transfer scheme at www.water-technology.net/projects/south_north/.

Parts of Essex receive less than 500 mm of rainfall per year and, in a dry year, up to a third of its water needs are supplied by the Ely Ouse to Essex Transfer Scheme, which transfers water from the Great Ouse River in Norfolk via pipelines and pumping stations to the headwaters of Stour and Blackwater rivers. Another 20% of water for Essex is provided by raw water bulk transfer from the Lea Valley reservoirs to the Chigwell treatment works before supply to customers.

While there is growing interest globally in developing water transfer schemes to meet water demands, there is considerable concern that such projects may cause serious environmental and social impacts. Continuous use may cause long-term changes to local and regional hydrological conditions, possibly increasing flood risk, and change the natural character of the river ecosystem by damaging fish stocks, spreading disease and introducing alien species into river environments. Long-distance water transfer projects are under construction in the Maghreb, Libya, Egypt and Senegal despite the high energy costs of their operation. The south-to-north water diversion project in China is probably the most ambitious scheme. Planned for completion in 2050, it will transfer 44.8 billion m³ per year over a distance of nearly 2,500 km to the cities of the drier north. The scheme will link China's four main rivers, the Yangtze, Huang He (Yellow), Huai He and Hai He, and comprise three diversion routes south to north across the eastern, central and western parts of the country.

▲ **Figure 6.4:** The Chinese water transfer scheme.

Increasing storage capacity

At least 45,000 large dams (that is, 15 m or more high or with a volume of over 3 million m³) have been constructed to meet energy or water demand, about half principally to supply irrigation and nearly half of the world's rivers now have at least one large dam. Supporters of dams highlight the social and economic development benefits such as irrigation, electricity, flood control and water supply, but large dams have had negative social and environmental impacts: opponents refer to debt burden, cost overruns, the displacement and impoverishment of people, destruction of important ecosystems and fisheries, and the inequitable sharing of costs and benefits.

Globally, there are many dam projects at various stages of planning and development:
- The countries with the most large dams under construction are Turkey, China, Japan, Iraq, Iran, Greece, Romania and Spain, and countries in the Paraná basin in South America.
- The river basins with the largest dams under construction are the Yangtze with 38, the Tigris and Euphrates with 19 each, and the Danube with 11.

In North America and Europe most technically attractive sites have already been developed. Their value is now called into question as an appropriate response to water supply needs. More water evaporates from reservoirs than people use and, despite the potential for multipurpose use, there are ongoing maintenance costs, such as the need to dredge the sediment to maintain volume.

The World Commission on Dams, reporting in 2000, concluded that the outcome that any project achieves must be the sustainable improvement of human welfare. This means a 'significant advance of human development on a basis that is economically viable, socially equitable and environmentally sustainable'. A large dam should be built only if it achieves these aims better than other options.

Overall the Commission judged that large dams generally did not achieve their water supply and irrigation targets and have delivered poor economic returns, and it recommended better management systems to improve the efficiency of existing large dams.

Ethiopia, which is typical of many sub-Saharan African countries, has a storage capacity of 38 m³ per person; while Australia has almost 5,000 m³ per person, yet even this may be insufficient with the impacts of climate change. Whilst there will be a need for new large and medium-sized dams, the construction of small dams for single villages or farms may prove to be a more sustainable solution. The UK also needs more reservoirs to store water but they take years to build, even once permission has been granted. Thames Water hopes to create a reservoir near Abingdon, Oxfordshire, but the earliest it could be completed is 2020. It plans a twin-track approach to maintaining water supplies: reducing demand by tackling leakage and encouraging people to use less water; and finding new sources of water, including collecting and storing water when it is available.

Restoring lost supplies

Rapid population growth and economic development combined to increase water use several times over during the 20th century. Surface and groundwater stores were in some places substantially reduced and measures are now being taken to replenish some of these stores. The North London Artificial Recharge Scheme is the only one of its kind in the UK and one of the largest in the world. It stores treated water for use in times of shortage by pumping water into the chalk that lies beneath London. Water abstraction from this aquifer in the past had lowered the water table, creating space for water to be stored. Drought conditions in 2005 brought this store into use, enabling water to be abstracted from boreholes located in Enfield, Haringey, Walthamstow, Tottenham and Chingford.

Long Island, New York, contains a series of sand and gravel aquifers fed by precipitation, which takes from 25 to 1,000 years to percolate, and all of its water supply comes from these underground water reserves. Almost 4 million gallons each day are abstracted for the resident population; most homes are on a municipal water system but there are still many homes with their own wells. Development has lowered and contaminated the groundwater to the extent that it is limiting the region's growth, so the local authorities have instructed that any new development must build recharge basins, proportional to the size of the development, to collect runoff via sumps and storm water drainage. As about half of precipitation is lost to evapotranspiration, it makes sense to capture as much as possible from impermeable surfaces.

Water conservation

Leakage before and after water treatment can be minimised; around 22% of water does not meet the end user due to leakage in the UK and it is the responsibility of the water companies to repair the ageing water mains. When drought threatens water supplies, hosepipe and sprinkler bans are common. Water conservation includes reducing consumption, recycling, and technological and policy options that promote efficiency of water at the user end of the supply chain. Methods of reducing domestic consumption include:
- installing water meters in every home
- reducing the amount of water used in lavatory cisterns
- planting drought-resistant species in 'water-wise' gardens
- using grey water to flush the lavatory or water the garden.

In industry, water is used in many manufacturing processes and companies have installed more efficient systems to reduce their water costs. Almost all manufacturing uses water at some stage for washing, diluting, cooling, or incorporating water into a product.

Taking it further

Learn more about the World Commission on Dams at www.dams.org.

Taking it further

See www.geo.sunysb.edu/esp/Science_Walks/Campus_hydrology/hydrology.htm for more information about the water collection system on a college campus on Long Island.

Taking it further

In India, only 1.6% of arable land uses efficient irrigation systems, compared with 100% in Germany and Israel, 37% in South Africa and 21% in the USA.

Taking it further

For more information on the Jersey Water desalination plant take a look at www.jerseywater.je/pdffiles/fact_ sheets/raw_water_processing.pdf.

▲ **Figure 6.5:** The Ashkelon seawater reverse osmosis plant in Israel is the largest in the world, providing 15% of Israel's domestic needs. The complete installation holds 40,000 membrane elements and uses multistage RO.

In agriculture, the efficiency of irrigation systems varies. There are three broad types of crop irrigation: surface, sprinkler and micro. Surface irrigation through small channels or surface flooding are the least efficient due to wastage in runoff, a high level of evaporation and increased salinity. Sprinklers have high energy costs and require careful monitoring; those that throw water into the air are also prone to evaporation losses. Micro-irrigation techniques are the most efficient, using mini-sprinklers or drip-irrigation from tubes with many holes that can be laid on the surface, suspended from wires or buried beneath the soil surface. Modern control systems, using automation and remote control, for water supply and demands in irrigation networks also substantially reduce the volume of water used.

Other technological solutions

Technology has an important role to play in improving water supply and reducing water insecurity, despite the associated financial and environmental costs. The MDG aim to provide sufficient clean water for everyone presents complex challenges for governments, water managers and NGOs, but there are sustainable solutions. Developments to reduce losses through evaporation from natural bodies of water, such as the Jonglei Canal transferring White Nile water around the Sûdd swamps in Sudan, have increased water supply, but such schemes have environmental impacts. The treatment of waste water is also being improved for certain uses, as better purifying techniques are applied, and is especially useful for increasing the supply of urban water. More than half of seawater desalination capacity is in the Middle East and it provides 70% of Saudi Arabia's water. Desalination is the most expensive option for water supply due to its energy use. The unit in Jersey uses 6.8 kWh of electricity per cubic metre of freshwater produced (compared with 0.11 kWh to boil a litre of water).

In the 1970s, towing an iceberg from Antarctica to Arabia for drinking water was considered. It was estimated to be cheaper than desalination despite the length of journey and loss through melting. Others suggested that the iceberg would not survive crossing the Equator, even if wrapped in sailcloth and plastic to slow melting. In 2006, Thames Water considered bringing icebergs from Greenland or northern Scandinavia. The idea of towing flexible polypropylene bags filled with freshwater has also been proposed. Water could be transported from Kielder to Essex, for example, but the high costs of a connecting pipeline mean this option would be the last resort in severe drought.

In poorer and remoter regions, where access to technology is limited, traditional or intermediate technology may be more appropriate. Traditional techniques of water collection (catching rainwater and building small dams) can benefit from modern improvements to increase their efficiency. Methods of constructing wells depend on the underlying rock. Hand-dug wells in clays, sands and gravels need to be lined and old wells can be rehabilitated by improving the lining. Tube-wells work better in fine sands and silts as they are narrower and deeper, and boreholes into harder rock need power-driven drills and so are more expensive. This work may be done by charities supported by development banks and governments but the local community is also involved and trained in maintenance.

Ways to draw the water from wells include treadle-, rope-, horse- and wind-powered pumps; their production, marketing and maintenance at local level can also encourage private enterprises, providing new employment. These intermediate technology methods cost considerably less in set-up and running costs than diesel or electric pumps, they do not require specialist maintenance skills, and components can be sourced locally. Sunlight can be used to improve the quality of drinking water as ultraviolet light inactivates the harmful coliforms that cause diarrhoea. Transparent plastic or glass bottles filled with contaminated water are exposed to the sun for six hours a day, which is sufficient to destroy the micro-organisms. Clay water filters are used for removing suspended fine particles (known as turbidity) but they do not eliminate bacteria. Inexpensive new filters are being introduced that can reduce turbidity as well as 98–100% of the bacteria causing diarrhoea, cholera and other water-borne diseases.

Summary

In this chapter you have learnt:

- Increases in demand for water combined with diminishing supply will lead to insecurity of supply in many regions; climate change is exacerbating this situation.
- Decision-makers involved in influencing the future of water resources may have conflicting aims and interests.
- There is a range of responses to current and projected demands for water including diverting supplies, increasing storage, restoring lost supplies and water conservation.
- There are technological solutions to the problem of water shortage but these often have environmental consequences.

MCQ

Exam Practice – Section A

Water Conflicts

(a) Using Figure 2 and your own knowledge, explain why competition for groundwater sources is likely to lead to water conflicts. [10]

(b) Assess the extent to which plentiful supplies of water in some parts of the world can be used to make up for shortages elsewhere. [15]

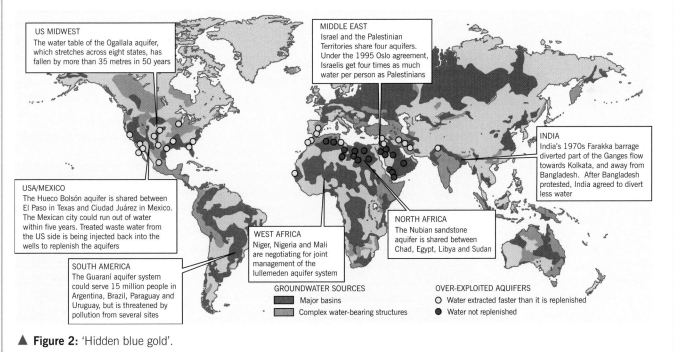

US MIDWEST
The water table of the Ogallala aquifer, which stretches across eight states, has fallen by more than 35 metres in 50 years

MIDDLE EAST
Israel and the Palestinian Territories share four aquifers. Under the 1995 Oslo agreement, Israelis get four times as much water per person as Palestinians

INDIA
India's 1970s Farakka barrage diverted part of the Ganges flow towards Kolkata, and away from Bangladesh. After Bangladesh protested, India agreed to divert less water

USA/MEXICO
The Hueco Bolsón aquifer is shared between El Paso in Texas and Ciudad Juárez in Mexico. The Mexican city could run out of water within five years. Treated waste water from the US side is being injected back into the wells to replenish the aquifers

SOUTH AMERICA
The Guaraní aquifer system could serve 15 million people in Argentina, Brazil, Paraguay and Uruguay, but is threatened by pollution from several sites

WEST AFRICA
Niger, Nigeria and Mali are negotiating for joint management of the Iullemeden aquifer system

NORTH AFRICA
The Nubian sandstone aquifer is shared between Chad, Egypt, Libya and Sudan

GROUNDWATER SOURCES
- ▨ Major basins
- ▨ Complex water-bearing structures

OVER-EXPLOITED AQUIFERS
- ○ Water extracted faster than it is replenished
- ● Water not replenished

▲ **Figure 2:** 'Hidden blue gold'.

CHAPTER 7 What is biodiversity and why is it important?

Key terms

Abiotic
Biodiversity
Biodiversity hotspot
Biosphere
Biotic
Ecosystem
Endemic
Net Primary Productivity
Nucleotides
Phyla
Terrestrial

Learning objectives

After studying this chapter, you will be able to discuss these ideas and concepts and provide located examples of them:
- Various definitions of biodiversity can be used.
- There is a range of factors that influence biodiversity with some being more important than others.
- Biodiversity is not evenly spread across the globe.
- Some megadiverse locations called biodiversity hotspots exist.
- Ecosystems have an ecological, cultural and economic value in terms of providing goods and services.

How can we define biodiversity?

The biosphere is the layer of the earth where there is life and it includes parts of the atmosphere and lithosphere. Here there is an amazing variety of life forms, only some of which have been recorded by humans. Today's buzzword often used to describe this variety is biodiversity. The term is a shortening of 'biological diversity', but what does it really mean? On a basic level it means the variety of life, but it is more involved than that. At the 1992 Convention on Biological Diversity in Rio de Janeiro the following definition was given:

'Biological diversity means the variability among living organisms from all sources... Terrestrial, marine and aquatic ecosystems and the ecological complexes of which they are a part: this includes diversity within species, between species and of ecosystems.'

The earth has a vast array of species, but we know there are many more yet to be discovered. Figure 7.1 summarises the number of species that have been recorded and how many it is thought still remain to be discovered.

Group	No. recorded	Estimated number (a working figure)	Recorded species as a % of estimated number	Accuracy of the estimate
Vertebrates	45,000	50,000	90	Good
Molluscs	70,000	200,000	35	Moderate
Crustaceans	40,000	150,000	26	Moderate
Insects	950,000	8,000,000	11	Moderate
Arachnids	75,000	750,000	10	Moderate
Nematodes	25,000	400,000	6.3	Poor
Plants	270,000	320,000	84	Good
Algae	40,000	400,000	10	Very poor
Protozoa	40,000	200,000	20	Very poor
Fungi	72,000	1500,000	4.8	Moderate
Bacteria	4,000	1000,000	0.5	Very poor
Viruses	4,000	400,000	1.0	Very poor
TOTAL	1,635,000			

▶ **Figure 7.1:** Table of species recorded.

The UK is in the temperate zone. Overall it has cool, moist winters and warm, moist summers. This has meant that it has a surprising range of biodiversity for a small island, but it may also reflect the fact that natural history recording has been carried out in this country for several centuries.

The table in Figure 7.1 is using the idea of the number of species to show biodiversity. However, biodiversity can also be investigated by looking at diversity within species and also between ecosystems. Figure 7.2 shows where these definitions overlap.

Key terms

Phyla — the major subdivisions of a Kingdom (e.g. Animals) such as insects and vertebrates.
Nucleotides — pivotal in development of life and are important in formation of DNA which provides information for the replication of cells.

Ecosystem diversity	Genetic diversity	Species diversity
Biomes Bioregions Landscapes Ecosystems Habitats Niches Populations	Populations Individuals Chromosomes Nucleotides	Kingdoms Phyla Families Genera Species Subspecies Populations Individuals
Looking at the diversity/ range of, e.g., niches	Looking at variety within species from molecular level up to population	Looking at the range and variety of species from kingdom down to individuals

◀ **Figure 7.2:** Types of biodiversity.

▼ **Figure 7.3:** Advantages and disadvantages of different types of diversity.

Definition	Advantages	Disadvantages
SPECIES DIVERSITY **This definition is linked to species richness — the number of species in a given area.**	• A good general measure of biodiversity. On a basic level areas can be compared. • Sometimes better if a range of indicator species is specified, ones that suggest a richer system if they are present. • Also better to use taxonomic diversity, e.g. If an island has 1 rodent, 2 bird and 1 lizard species then it is more biodiverse than an island with just 4 bird species on it.	• Take care when assessing area as larger areas tend to be more diverse. You need to compare like with like. • Many species as yet undiscovered are likely to be microscopic. Might skew a biodiversity index based on species numbers. • Species richness does not cover the distribution of the species or the interactions between species.
GENETIC DIVERSITY **This definition looks at the genetic variation within species. This can be in populations that have been separated geographically, but also amongst individuals within single populations. Variation in genetic make-up more easily allows populations to adapt to changing environments: 'adapt or die'.**	• Allows an accurate picture of the diversity within a population. • Helps explain how isolated groups of, e.g., birds have adapted to new environments.	• Difficult to assess without high-level biological skills as DNA has to be analysed.
ECOSYSTEM DIVERSITY **This looks at the variety of different ecosystems or habitats that occur within an area and takes into account biotic and abiotic components.**	• This definition involves the interaction of species with each other and with their environment. A more complex measure. • May be more useful when assessing areas to protect as has a wider focus than the other two definitions.	• Difficult to know where to place the boundaries for the area under investigation. Sand dunes may merge into sea meadow and then into Carr woodland. • Need a consistent set of criteria to demarcate an ecosystem. Then numbers and distribution of the ecosystems can be compared within a region.

Biodiversity is the sum of all three definitions. Although species richness is perhaps the most easily achievable measure, it tells only part of the story and the interactions between species, and between species and their environments, need to be taken into account for a true understanding. This makes defining biodiversity very difficult.

▲ **Figure 7.4:** A macaw, an example of a species that is dependent on the tropical rainforest.

What factors influence biodiversity?

Biodiversity is not evenly spread out across the earth, so why are some areas more diverse than others? Figure 7.5 summarises the main factors that impact on a location's biodiversity. The size of the area is important as generally more species can live and interact within a larger area. A growth in human population has an impact on biodiversity because we are in competition with other species for space and resources as human numbers increase; the biodiversity will decrease if there is a lack of management.

There are also certain human activities, such as hunting, that target specific species and can lead to their extinction if unregulated. As humans practise agriculture the multi-layered natural system is changed into a single-layered one, a monoculture, and thus reduces the biodiversity of an area. In more recent times industrial activity has led to the pollution of water courses and seas with impacts on the life forms that live within them, often reducing their numbers directly or their ability to breed. Some regions, particularly islands, have species that are found nowhere else as they are endemic to that location and this increases biodiversity.

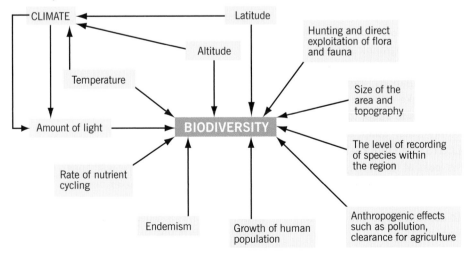

▶ **Figure 7.5:** Factors that influence the level of biodiversity.

However, the most important impact on the level of biodiversity is the location's climate. This can be regarded as a limiting factor, i.e. it determines the limits within which a plant or animal can exist. Overall there is an increase in the number and variety of organisms towards the Tropics (see Figure 7.6) and this is also true for marine ecosystems. For example, on the Great Barrier Reef of Australia there are 50 genera of reef corals at its northern end (the end nearest the Equator), whereas there are only 10 genera at the southern end.

Tropical country	Area (1,000 km²)	Number of mammal species	Temperate country	Area (1,000 km²)	Number of mammal species
Brazil	8,456	394	Canada	9,220	139
Democratic Republic of Congo	2,268	415	Argentina	2,737	258
Thailand	511	251	France	550	93
Philippines	298	166	UK	242	50
Rwanda	25	151	Belgium	30	58

◀ **Figure 7.6:** Number of mammal species in tropical and temperate countries of comparable size.

Nearer the Equator, i.e. at lower latitudes, the climate is warmer and usually more humid. These are ideal conditions for the fast breakdown of dead biotic and also abiotic material and subsequently rapid nutrient cycling. In mountainous regions biodiversity varies according to altitude. In the Tropics there can be tropical rainforest with high species richness at the foot of mountains, moving through several vegetation types until alpine tundra with its lower biodiversity is found near the peaks.

In some areas of the world biodiversity is low because the climate is too dry (deserts) and/or too cold (polar and tundra regions). Climatic extremes usually have low biodiversity because there are not enough food sources to support large populations and often only specialised organisms can survive. Plants form the base of all terrestrial (land-based) food chains and grow best in warm, moist conditions.

The rate at which they fix the Sun's energy (photosynthesise) is measured in grams per square metre per year (or tonnes per square kilometre per year) and is known as Gross Primary Productivity (GPP). Net Primary Productivity (NPP) is GPP less the energy lost via respiration. In Figure 7.7 you can see the wide variation in NPP for a range of ecosystems. Ecosystems like the tropical rainforests and estuaries have few limiting factors, so biodiversity is high.

Key terms

Biotic — the living components of an ecosystem such as plants.

Abiotic — the non-living components of an ecosystem, such as water and soil.

Ecosystem	Area (million km²)	Mean NPP g/m²/yr	World net primary productivity (billion tonnes per year)	Mean biomass (kg/m²)
Tropical rainforest	17.0	2200	37.4	45
Savannah	15.0	900	13.5	4
Tundra and alpine	8.0	140	1.1	0.6
Temperate grassland	9.0	600	5.4	1.6

◀ **Figure 7.7:** Table of Net Primary Productivity and plant biomass for different types of ecosystem.

In some countries biodiversity has undergone large reductions such as New Zealand.

Case study: The biodiversity of New Zealand

This case study looks at the factors that affected the biodiversity of New Zealand and what the results were.

80 million years ago New Zealand broke away from the ancient supercontinent of Gondwanaland. This isolation and the relatively late arrival of humans on its islands led to a high level of endemic species, which were found nowhere else in the world. The warm to cool moist climate supported dense forests on both islands and as no large mammals were on the islands when they broke away, its ecosystems were dominated by birds.

With no mammal predators, the birds grew to a large size, such as the over 2 metre tall Giant Moa. Even the parrots became large and with no predators some lost the ability to fly, such as the ground-dwelling and nocturnal Kakapo. The national bird of New Zealand, the Kiwi, is another species that lost the need to fly. Birds adapted to new environments and the only alpine parrot in the world, the Kia, lives in the Southern Alps. The forests ranged from tall Kauri forests on North Island to temperate rainforests on the west coast of South Island.

However, with the coming of humans with the migrations of the Maori from 1000AD rapid changes occurred. By the late 17th century the Moa was extinct and the dogs and rats the Maori brought with them hugely reduced the numbers of ground-dwelling birds. With the arrival of the Europeans a few hundred years later the changes were more severe. Huge areas of the Canterbury Plain, South Island, were cleared for sheep farming. Settlers brought plants they were familiar with to use as field boundaries such as gorse, but given the lack of pests or diseases it was subject to in New Zealand, it spread widely and out-competed natural vegetation.

Weasels and stoats were also introduced as pest control, but they reduced the numbers of the indigenous birds as they are notorious egg thieves and again had no real predators. New Zealand has a unique biodiversity that is now heavily affected by human activities, but it is working to preserve its indigenous species.

New Zealand has:

30,000	named indigenous land species (including 88 birds, 3,080 plants and 61 reptiles)
29	indigenous freshwater fish species
8,000	marine species recorded in New Zealand waters (including 41 mammals, 61 seabirds and 964 fish)

▶ **Figure 7.8:** A tree fern forest of New Zealand.

Taking it further

Find out more about New Zealand's biodiversity at www.biodiversity.govt.nz.

How is biodiversity distributed around the world?

We have already looked at what influences biodiversity and begun to explore the link between high NPP, a lack of limiting factors and species richness. Figure 7.9 shows the distribution of terrestrial biodiversity by country and also species richness of corals in the marine environment.

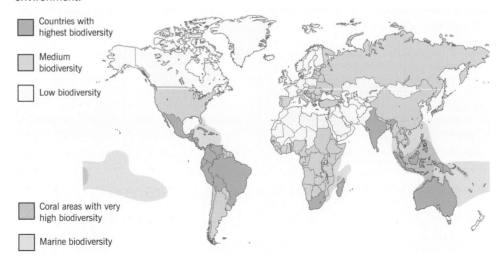

Countries with highest biodiversity

Medium biodiversity

Low biodiversity

Coral areas with very high biodiversity

Marine biodiversity

▶ **Figure 7.9:** Map of global biodiversity.

Clear patterns emerge with areas of tropical rainforest in South and Central America, Madagascar, Malaysia and Indonesia showing high species richness. India still has some rainforests left and, because of the country's size, it covers a wide range of different ecosystems providing a variety of natural habitats. Australia is a dry continent, but has some rainforest in the north. It also has a high number of endemic species, which adds to the importance of its biodiversity.

Generally animal biodiversity is greatest where there is the greatest diversity of plants as more food sources are provided and more niches for organisms to fill. Species diversity is least in areas at high latitude and in desert areas where there are more limiting factors. The former is because of lower levels of solar energy and lower temperatures, whereas the latter is due to a lack of moisture.

Coral reefs are sometimes referred to as the 'rainforests of the sea' and are very biodiverse. From the map (Figure 7.9) it can be seen that the corals with the greatest number of species are those in the Pacific Ocean and the eastern edge of the Indian Ocean around Indonesia, Malaysia and the Philippines.

Looking at Figure 7.10 it can be seen that the five countries with the highest diversity index are found around the Equator or the Tropics, whereas the countries with the lowest diversity index are either cold countries or ones with large areas of desert. The exception is the low biodiversity of Ireland, which is a temperate country with a cool, wet climate that supports mainly grassland vegetation with limited niches for organisms.

Most diverse countries	Index	Least diverse countries	Index
Indonesia	1.00	Iceland	0.113
Colombia	0.935	Qatar	0.189
Mexico	0.928	Kuwait	0.224
Brazil	0.877	Libya	0.240
Ecuador	0.873	Ireland	0.279

◄ **Figure 7.10:** Top and bottom five countries according to the Biodiversity Index. The diversity index was based on estimates of how many species of plants and animals were in a country and also how many were endemic. The maximum index is 1 and the least is 0.

Overall, the greatest biodiversity is found in areas of tropical rainforest with over half of the earth's species, even though they cover only about 7% of the planet's surface. They generally have the highest diversity of plants within them, which then support a wide range of insect, bird and mammal life forms.

Biodiversity hotspots

The map of biodiversity by country (Figure 7.9) tells us about overall species richness for a nation, but does not highlight particular areas where the biodiversity and endemism are exceptionally high yet under threat. Several bodies such as the World Conservation Monitoring Centre and Conservation International have tried to identify such areas which are known as 'biodiversity hotspots'. In 1999 25 terrestrial hotspots were identified, which covered the range of the earth's species.

Subsequently marine hotspots were identified, including coral reefs.

They are used as a tool to assess conservation priorities, i.e. to see where there is high biodiversity that is under threat. Conservation International has recently updated an analysis of the earth's biodiversity and has identified 34 hotspot areas, which are home to over 50% of the planet's plants and 77% of terrestrial vertebrates between them. The location of hotspots does not correlate exactly with the location of the greatest biodiversity shown on the biodiversity by countries map and they have a much wider locational spread. For example, France does not have a particularly high biodiversity, yet its southern shores are part of the Mediterranean Basin Hotspot. Biodiversity hotspots allow areas with very high biodiversity to be identified, as well as endemism that may not be within a region of high diversity.

Taking it further

Find out about world marine hotspots at www.starfish.ch/reef/hotspots.html.

Taking it further

Discover where the UK's five marine hotspots are located and why they are so important. Go to www.panda.org and search for the article 'UK marine hotspots marked for protection'.

However, the majority of hotspots are between the Tropics in the warmer areas of the world. Hotspot areas are important for the range of diversity they contain, often in quite small regions. If they are not protected, the survival of a large number of organisms is threatened. One such hotspot is the Atlantic Forest of Brazil, a newly industrialising country.

We do not know how many species exist on earth. This renders the mapping of biodiversity at best incomplete and at worst inaccurate. The mapping of such distributions is only a guideline to the more obvious areas of high biodiversity.

Case study: The Atlantic Forest, Brazil

This case study shows the reasons behind this region being designated a biodiversity hotspot.

The Atlantic Forest is situated in south-eastern Brazil, largely, but not entirely, along the coast. Only 8% of its original extent remains and it's under constant threat from urbanisation by Brazil's large cities of Rio de Janeiro and São Paulo. There is pressure from illegally built housing and also using the resources of the forest such as timber for fuel and for construction. Its present day area covers 99,944 km² and of this 50% is now protected. Its biodiversity is summarised in Figure 7.11. This biodiversity led to the forest being designated as a Brazilian National Heritage Site in 1988 and a UNESCO World Biosphere Reserve in 1992. In 1999 it was highlighted as a Biodiversity Hotspot. It's important due to the species it contains, but is also in danger from the threats it faces.

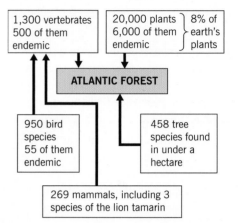

▲ **Figure 7.11:** Biodiversity of The Atlantic Forest, Brazil.

Examiners' tip

Do not use vague references to the value of an ecosystem, but give details, making it clear that the value is not just economic, but also ecological and cultural.

The value of ecosystems

When referring to the value of ecosystems and biodiversity, we are not just talking about financial value although that is a consideration. Figure 7.12 suggests some of the values that may be attached to biodiversity. Another way of looking at value is by dividing it into direct and indirect use values. Direct use values are the uses humans put biodiversity to in terms of consumption or production and include food, fuel, medicines, timber, resins, hunting and ecotourism. Indirect uses include the services that biodiversity provides such as soil formation, supporting the food chain on which we depend and also the role plants play in the hydrological cycle. Aesthetic uses could be regarded as indirect uses or even as non-uses.

The value of a global ecosystem – coral reefs

Coral reefs have a very high level of biodiversity. Vertical reefs rising from 25 m offer a range of habitats and niches for a dazzling array of organisms, with some reefs being more biodiverse than others. South-east Asia is home to over 30% of the world's coral reefs and has more than 700 species of coral out of an estimated world total of 1,000. Overall, the coral reefs that are in or border the Pacific Ocean have the greatest biodiversity. They are thought to be generally older than those in the Atlantic Ocean.

Coral reefs are found in shallow seas (no deeper than 25 m) with an average annual temperature above 18°C. Corals are adversely affected if there is too much sediment flowing off the land, perhaps due to deforestation, as it smothers and can kill them. Where rivers flow off the land into the sea, there are no corals as they can only survive in saline (salt) water, but they also require a certain amount of wave action to oxygenate the water. Corals are animals, but they have a symbiotic (mutually beneficial) relationship with algae known as zooxanthellae, for which the corals act as host. The algae photosynthesise, therefore needing high light levels, and produce 95% of the nutrition for the coral.

Taking it further

To complete a fieldwork activity on biodiversity see 'Assessing species richness' on your Student CD-ROM.

ECOLOGICAL VALUE	ECONOMIC VALUE	CULTURAL/AESTHETIC VALUE
• A stable environment is more likely as more organisms interact with each other and their environment. Loss of biodiversity makes ecosystems less stable and more vulnerable. • Plants' ability to photosynthesise (to fix the Sun's energy) provides the base for food chains. Reduction of biodiversity reduces this ability. • Ecosystems, particularly large forests, act as carbon sinks. Absorb carbon dioxide and release oxygen. • Plant communities are essential components in the hydrological cycle. Transpiration recycles water back into the atmosphere. Also act as interceptors and aid infiltration of rainfall. Can reduce flood impact. • Wastes are broken down within ecosystems by bacteria as part of the nutrient cycling processes.	• Healthy forests as a source of fuelwood. • Healthy marine ecosystems mean food supply via fish/crustaceans. • Food supply. 90% of calories from the human diet come from 30 plants. • Maintaining a genetic pool means we can access ecosystems for new medicines/foodstuffs. 25% of all drugs are from plants (or are chemically modified versions originally from plants). • Only just beginning to understand how species can offer help for future, e.g. horseshoe crab, peptides in its blood look as if will aid resistance to HIV in humans. Rosy periwinkle was source for successful drug for childhood leukaemia. • Only 1% of rainforest plants have been tested for medicinal use so far. • Pollinators, such as bees, are needed to help maintain, e.g., fruit orchards. • Resins, rubber and timber products can be extracted from healthy forests. • A healthy ecosystem can help reduce financial impact of floods. • Provides a gene pool that we may need to access in the future.	• Recreational use. Many want access to natural ecosystems for walking, outdoor activities. Adds to quality of life. • Education and scientific research, expanding our understanding of the natural world. • Supporting the lives of local peoples and helping maintain traditional cultures which are usually much more closely linked to nature. • Ethically we should be able to pass on to our grandchildren the same resources that we have had access to without damaging the earth – the idea of sustainability.

▲ **Figure 7.12:** The importance of biodiversity.

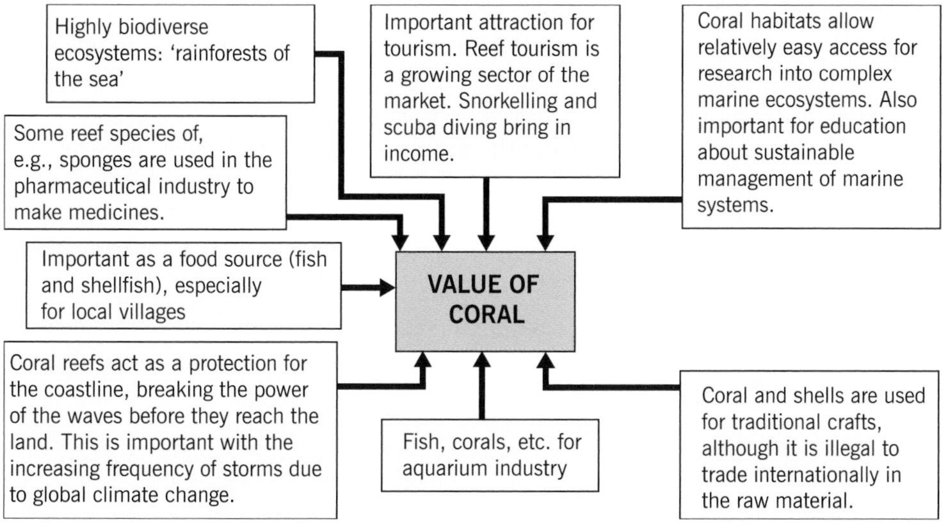

Highly biodiverse ecosystems: 'rainforests of the sea'

Some reef species of, e.g., sponges are used in the pharmaceutical industry to make medicines.

Important as a food source (fish and shellfish), especially for local villages

Coral reefs act as a protection for the coastline, breaking the power of the waves before they reach the land. This is important with the increasing frequency of storms due to global climate change.

Important attraction for tourism. Reef tourism is a growing sector of the market. Snorkelling and scuba diving bring in income.

VALUE OF CORAL

Fish, corals, etc. for aquarium industry

Coral habitats allow relatively easy access for research into complex marine ecosystems. Also important for education about sustainable management of marine systems.

Coral and shells are used for traditional crafts, although it is illegal to trade internationally in the raw material.

▲ **Figure 7.13:** Biodiversity around a coral reef.

◀ **Figure 7.14:** The value of coral reefs.

Summary

In this chapter you have learnt:

• that there is more than one way to define biodiversity and they all have different merits.
• that several factors, some quite complex, affect the level of biodiversity of an area.
• that the varied factors that affect biodiversity have led to an uneven distribution of biodiversity across the planet.
   • that some locations called biodiversity hotspots have a very high number of species within them and many are endangered.
   • that there are many reasons to value biodiversity on earth as our wellbeing depends on it.

MCQ

Taking it further

Find out more about the value of coral reefs at the following website, which has links to take you further: http://news.mongabay.com/2006/0124-reefs.html.

CHAPTER 8 What are the threats facing the world's biodiversity?

Key terms

Abiotic
Alien species
Anthropogenic
Ecoregions
Keystone species
Megadiverse
Pristine areas

Synoptic link

To find out more about the impacts of global warming in the Arctic, look at pages 46-7 of Edexcel AS Geography.

Learning objectives

After studying this chapter, you will be able to discuss these ideas and concepts and provide located examples of them:
• There are patterns in the areas where biodiversity is most under threat.
• There is a range of threats to maintaining biodiversity.
• Ecosystem processes can be disturbed by these threats to the detriment of their biodiversity.
• There are links between economic development and ecosystem destruction.

Which are the areas of biodiversity most under threat?

Although there is a degree of correlation between the areas with highest biodiversity and those areas where there is the most threat, there are other areas where, although the level of biodiversity may not be great, the threats against them are major and may result in extinctions. Tundra areas, which are not highly biodiverse, are under severe threat from global warming and species, such as the polar bear, are facing extinction.

By definition, biodiversity hotspots are all under threat to a certain degree, having lost at least 70% of their original vegetation cover. The majority of these areas are located within the Tropics. Data on threatened species show there are distinct clusters of critically endangered mammals and birds in Indonesia, Brazil, Central America, Vietnam and Tanzania. These are areas of high biodiversity and are under multiple threats. Areas of lower biodiversity, such as the boreal forests situated in the northern hemisphere's high latitudes, tend to have lower threat levels. These regions are not in demand for agriculture due to their unsuitable climates and logging extraction has not had a huge impact on the reduction of biodiversity.

The 34 biodiversity hotspots now identified used to cover nearly 16% of the globe; now they cover only 2.3%. The table below shows some of the ways in which the level of threat to biodiversity can be measured.

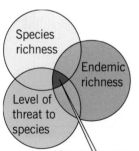

Biodiversity hotspot where biodiversity and the threat to its existence are both high

▲ **Figure 8.1:** Venn diagram showing the elements that form a hotspot.

▶ **Figure 8.2:** Methods of measuring the threat to biodiversity.

Name of assessment	Method
IUCN Red List of Endangered Species www.iucnredlist.org/	Constantly being updated and classifies organisms as critically endangered, endangered or vulnerable and are the species most likely to become extinct.
Living Planet Index http://www.panda.org/news_facts/publications/living_planet_report/living_planet_index/index.cfm	Tracks populations of animal groups such as amphibians, vertebrates, etc. globally and compared over time. Index first calculated in 1970.
World Resources Institute – Earthtrends http://earthtrends.wri.org	Looking at trends in animal populations, highlighting threats.
Millennium Assessment www.millenniumassessment.org/documents/document.354.aspx.pdf	Originally an assessment of the state of the world's biodiversity at the start of the 21st century. Ongoing research.

Case study: The Mediterranean Basin Biodiversity Hotspot

This hotspot region is a densely populated area supporting a large tourism industry.

It has 11,700 endemic plant species, 11 endemic threatened mammals and 9 endemic threatened birds. It also has a human population density of 111 per km^2. Its original extent was over 2 million km^2, but now only 98,000 km^2 of the original vegetation cover remain, less than 5%. Originally forests of oaks and conifers dominated, but human activity, particularly the use of fire to clear for agriculture, has led to most of the vegetation being a fire- and drought-resistant mixture of shrubs called maquis, which supports less biodiversity, but is itself now under threat from coastal development.

Taking it further

Access the IUCN website and have a look at the Red List species in the UK: www.iucnredlist.org.

What is the range of threats facing the globe's biodiversity?

Newspaper articles and television programmes highlight the problems of global biodiversity and the threats it is facing, which are largely linked to anthropogenic reasons.

Key term

Anthropogenic — caused by human activities.

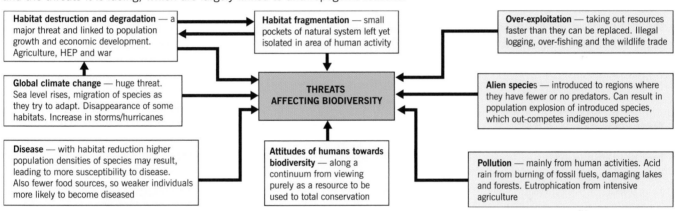

▲ **Figure 8.3:** Threats affecting biodiversity.

Figure 8.3 summarises the main causes of biodiversity reduction, although several of them can be linked together, e.g. human attitudes towards biodiversity will affect the other threats. One of the greatest threats to biodiversity is global climate change. (See the AS book chapters on climate change.) It is clear that most glaciers are retreating and ice sheets are melting due to the overall rise in global temperatures, resulting in a rise in sea level. Low-lying countries such as Tuvalu and its ecosystems, where the islands rise to a maximum height of 4 m, are under threat of inundation. The islands are coral atolls and it is likely they will be completely under water within 50 years. In mountainous regions ecosystems such as alpine tundra and cloud forest will retreat to higher altitudes where the temperatures will be cooler, but eventually they will die out as the inhospitable peaks are reached and they can go no further: a sort of eco-squeeze.

In the UK a generally warmer climate with drier summers and wetter winters has led to the migration northwards of some species. The UK is home to over 50% of the world's bluebell population, but it is now not growing as successfully in the south of England due to the increase in temperature. It is being replaced by the more vigorous Spanish bluebell, an alien species. With continued rises in temperatures our woodland communities may reduce in complexity.

At the present time, there are nearly 7 billion people on earth. Food is needed for the entire population and there are increasing pressures on the environment as more people strive to achieve the standard of living presently enjoyed by most Western countries. Huge demands are being put on the world's forests, destroying habitats in such locations as the Amazon rainforest. Most tropical rainforests are located in developing countries which have a low GDP. As their populations grow these nations need to earn money from trade.

Key term

Megadiverse — an area that has extremely high species richness.

Taking it further

Find out some of the pressures experienced by tropical forests on the Mongabay website: www.mongabay.com.

Case study: Palm oil production in Borneo – national level of threat linked to global demand

This case study looks at the reasons behind forest destruction in Borneo.

The island of Borneo is divided between Indonesia, Malaysia and the small state of Brunei. The vegetation over much of the island is tropical rainforest and supports a wide biodiversity.

Much of the lowland rainforest in the Malaysian sections has been cleared to make way for palm oil plantations as palm oil is one of the country's major exports. It is used in lipsticks, soap, cooking and foodstuffs such as margarine. Together Malaysia and Indonesia produce 86% of global palm oil, responding to global demand. The trade brings in much needed foreign exchange and provides thousands of jobs. However, to set up the monoculture of oil palms, the area is first clear-felled with any commercial timber being extracted and what is left is burnt.

▲ **Figure 8.4:** An increasingly rare sight – an orang-utan mother and young.

The increasingly rare orang-utan is a native species of the lowland forests that are being cleared and its survival is seriously under threat as its habitat is being destroyed. Many of the remaining pockets of forest are fragmented, therefore orang-utans do not have enough territory in which to survive. If the predicted doubling of palm oil production by 2020 occurs, it follows that the outlook is not good for the forests of Borneo or for the orang-utan.

Taking it further

There are several campaigns requesting consumers to be more aware of what is in their cosmetics and foodstuffs and to avoid products containing palm oil. Access the Friends of the Earth website and use the search engine to find out about their campaign to save the orang-utan: www.foe.co.uk.

Taking it further

To look at the implications if resource extraction continues without sustainable management read 'The Grand Banks, Newfoundland' on your Student CD-ROM.

The over-exploitation of resources occurs all around the globe as humans continue to take without allowing time for reproduction and renewal. This is true of the extraction of tropical hardwoods, such as mahogany and teak, where there are no more areas remaining of trees with a large diameter. As certain species are completely wiped out, loggers turn to other trees in an unsustainable production system, which impacts severely on habitat and biodiversity. With an increasing number of people living along coasts there is more pressure on fish stocks for food. These pressures impact on ecosystems in developed countries, too.

Other threats such as pollution are linked to population growth and industrial development. With the spread of intensive agricultural practices using chemical fertilisers there is the risk of problems such as eutrophication, thereby reducing biodiversity.

Acid rain may be produced due to the burning of fossil fuels. In Sweden this has led to some lakes becoming lifeless as their plankton are killed off by acidity, resulting in the demise of the fish that depended on them. This is a transnational problem as the pollution crosses borders. Other localised threats include the introduction of alien species to a new environment. What may occur in these circumstances is a massive population explosion as the organism finds itself suited to the climatic conditions and it does not have many, if any, predators.

The biggest threat of all to biodiversity is the human attitude. Although leadership is required on the global and international level, individual governments need to be aware of the level to which we all depend on the goods and services that biodiverse ecosystems provide. It is no good preserving a species or protecting an area unless the local population supports it. This will not occur unless locals fully understand the reasoning behind it and have been given an alternative way of generating an income.

How threats can affect ecosystem processes

Natural systems operate a dynamic equilibrium – a moving, changing balance. Weather events or disasters can alter the balance, but the systems gradually adjust either to new conditions or revert to the previous situation. With the coming of humans and their domination of so much of the natural world this balance has been drastically altered and, in many cases, so quickly that ecosystems have not been able to adapt.

Energy flow

Nearly all life on earth is dependent on solar energy, but only plants can use this directly to convert it to carbohydrates through photosynthesis. This food is then consumed by other organisms and the solar energy is passed along the food chain.

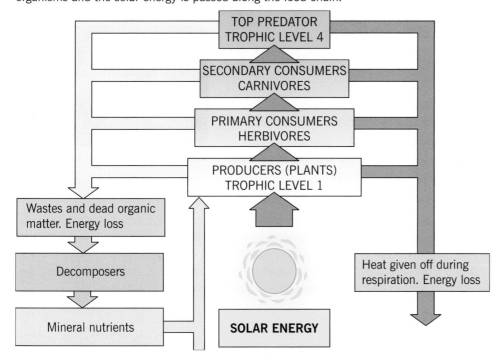

Figure 8.5: This shows a simple food chain and its components and how waste materials become part of the nutrient cycle. The movement of energy through a food chain is linear, whereas nutrients form a cycle.

Human action on one level of the food chain has an impact on the others that are dependent on it.

Case study: The giant kelp forest ecosystem off the Californian coast

This case study shows how one human action can completely upset an ecosystem's equilibrium.

Giant kelp is a type of seaweed and it forms underwater forests supporting a wide range of species off the coast of California, as well as acting as a breeding ground and nursery for many fish. One of the most voracious herbivores of this seaweed is the sea urchin and, left unchecked, it would destroy their food source and this important habitat. However, one of this system's top predators is the sea otter, which is responsible for keeping the sea urchins at reasonable levels.

During the 19th and early 20th centuries the sea otter was hunted almost to extinction along the west coast of the USA. This was followed by a population explosion of sea urchins, which almost totally destroyed the kelp forests along the coast of California. The whole kelp ecosystem collapsed. Hunting of otters stopped in 1911, but recovery has been very slow along the Pacific coast of North America south of Alaska. Otters were reintroduced to the Californian coast off Monterey and with their return the giant kelp also began to recover and the ecosystem regained its equilibrium. When a species such as the otter has such a pivotal role within an ecosystem, it is known as a keystone species.

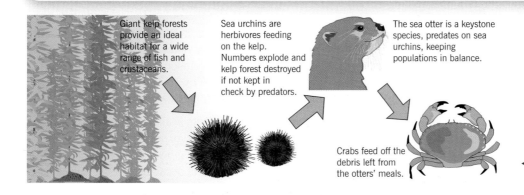

Giant kelp forests provide an ideal habitat for a wide range of fish and crustaceans.

Sea urchins are herbivores feeding on the kelp. Numbers explode and kelp forest destroyed if not kept in check by predators.

The sea otter is a keystone species, predates on sea urchins, keeping populations in balance.

Crabs feed off the debris left from the otters' meals.

Figure 8.6: Food chain in the kelp forests, California.

67

Alien species are those that have been introduced to a region, sometimes by accident and sometimes deliberately. Often they have no real predator in their new environment and can therefore multiply and cause problems for the indigenous ecosystem, reducing its biodiversity. Although the introduction of an alien species is on a local level, the threat can expand to a national or international scale.

Case study: A Chinese stowaway, the case of the mitten crab

This case study outlines some of the problems for the local ecosystem of the accidental introduction of an alien species.

The mitten crab, a Chinese crab the size of a dinner plate, travelled to the UK in ballast water and escaped into rivers and coastal ports when the water was released. It lives mainly in rivers and burrows into banks, destabilising them and affecting riparian communities by preying on protected UK species. They can migrate across land and have few predators in the UK, which explains why their numbers are increasing rapidly in rivers such as the Thames, Tyne and Humber.

▲ **Figure 8.7:** A mitten crab.

Taking it further

To learn more about how an alien species can cause damage to an indigenous ecosystem, read 'Cane toads in Australia' on your Student CD-ROM.

Taking it further

Explore the range of alien species on the website for the Convention on Biological Species: www.cbd.int/invasive.

Sometimes an alien species is introduced deliberately, perhaps because it is attractive in a large garden such as the Japanese knotweed, a plant that now grows widely in the UK and is difficult to eradicate. It has no insect predators in this country and, once established in a location, it out-shades and out-competes all the indigenous plants. Animals are sometimes deliberately introduced to a new location such as the cane toad in Australia.

Nutrient cycling

We have seen that nutrient cycling occurs alongside the flow of energy through an ecosystem. Without the feedback of minerals from decomposed organic material, plants would not have the nutrients they need for continued healthy growth.

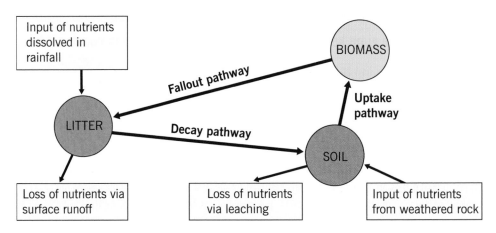

▶ **Figure 8.8:** Gersmehl's model of the cycling of nutrients within an ecosystem.

In the model the circles represent stores where the nutrients stay for varying amounts of time with the arrows representing the flows between them. The type of climate dictates the speed of the nutrient cycling with the moist, hot climates of the Tropics leading to fast nutrient cycling with much slower rates in the cold regions. In tropical rainforest most of the nutrients are stored in the biomass as they spend very little time in the litter or soil stores. This means that when humans remove the vegetation from a tropical area by logging they are not only destroying habitat, but they have made it much harder for the original species of vegetation to return as most of the nutrients have been taken away.

Sometimes human activity increases the amount of nutrients available to an ecosystem through runoff from farmland containing nitrate fertilisers and/or sewage runoff with high levels of phosphates. This extra nutrient load encourages the growth of algal blooms in water courses and lakes. When the algae die, the bacteria of decay use up the oxygen in the water and the fish and other organisms die.

This process is called eutrophication and is occurring in many areas where there is intensive agriculture or where there is a heavy sewage overload within rivers. Examples include parts of the Norfolk Broads in the UK and Chesapeake Bay on the east coast of the USA.

Development and destruction

During the 20th century and into the 21st many countries shifted from having economies based on primary industries, especially agriculture, to mixed economies including manufacturing and service industries. This has put incredible pressure on their ecosystems as natural resources were extracted. Even in countries at an earlier stage of industrial development, population growth has meant using whatever resources they have in order to support the economy and provide for their citizens.

Guyana in South America has pristine rainforest, but that does not provide money for its people, which the country needs in order to develop the economy. There is pressure to destroy its forests by logging unless alternatives can be found. The Guyanese government has approached the UK and other countries to provide income for its country if it protects these pristine forests.

In some cases it is population growth that has caused the degradation or destruction of a habitat. In 1997–98 much of South-east Asia was covered in dense smog from thousands of fires burning across much of Sarawak, Borneo and other islands. Although some of these fires had been started by logging companies trying to clear land illegally, the majority were started by individual subsistence farmers clearing land in order to grow crops for their families. Large-scale outbreaks of these fires now almost always occur annually. Huge damage is caused when these fires get out of control. In 2006 it was estimated that up to 1,000 critically endangered orang-utans were killed in fires.

Rapid development in China has led to air pollution such as acid rain, which has an impact on forests. There is also an expansion of agricultural land, partly due to population growth, but also because farmers want to improve their standards of living, farming more land so there is a surplus to sell. China's huge population means that some areas are being destroyed as farming and urbanisation expand, but the Chinese are already trying to mitigate some of the damage. In 2007, with help from international bodies, China set up its first National Park in the south-west of the country in one of the most biodiverse regions of the world and is involving local communities in its management.

A country with a stable economy and education has the freedom to choose to support biodiversity without compromising its people's ability to be fed and housed. If a developing country, such as Costa Rica or Guyana, is to be able to support its natural environment, it needs to be helped to have choices and to change the perceived needs of its citizens by offering alternatives to over-use of its natural ecosystems.

Taking it further

To explore the impacts on biodiversity of excessive nutrient overload on a body of water, read 'Chesapeake Bay, a localised threat' on your Student CD-ROM'.

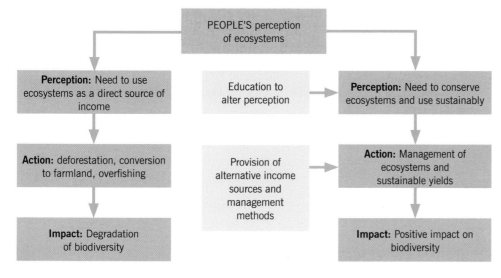

◀ **Figure 8.9:** Changing perception.

As more natural systems are coming under pressure from development and/or population growth, the World Wide Fund for Nature (WWF), amongst others, has developed the concept of the ecoregion. This is a broader concept than the hotspots approach and covers the full range of the earth's habitats so that conservation is more comprehensive. Each of the 238 ecoregions covers a large area, within which are a characteristic group of species for that habitat type. Some ecoregions have suffered from heavy human use and are degraded landscapes that need to be studied and conserved to ensure their future survival; others are in pristine condition.

There is pressure for development even in pristine ecoregions, often as a result of demand for resources from more developed nations. Conservation often occurs only because a resource is no longer needed or an economic replacement has been found.

Case study: Protecting the giant panda – the Guanyinshan Nature Reserve, Shaanxi Province, China

This case study looks at how protection of a habitat can lead to long-term support for an endangered species.

China does not have a long history of nature conservation, but biodiversity was supported within parkland, temple grounds and hunting areas. Since the 1980s China has passed many conservation laws and the greatly depleted bamboo forests of western China, on which the giant panda depends for food, are being protected. Unfortunately, population pressures and economic development have led to the fragmentation of much of the remaining forest, resulting in isolated populations of pandas with declining breeding rates. In the Qinling Mountains, within the Guanyinshan Nature Reserve, a large area of bamboo forest was bisected by a main road, separating two populations of pandas.

The road has been replaced by a tunnel and where the road once ran there is newly planted bamboo to rejoin the two populations, resulting in one of the largest continuous areas of bamboo in China. The country is developing economically and this is causing environmental degradation in some regions, but on the plus side there is more money available to invest in conservation. The giant panda is being heavily protected, with its remaining habitat conserved, thus allowing other species that share its forests to benefit.

It would seem that development of a country inevitably leads to at least some destruction of habitat. However, once a country has developed, with a stable economy and an educated populace, there are more choices available. Sustainable choices mean supporting the planet's biodiversity by means of conservation and limiting our demands.

Summary

In this chapter you have learnt:

- that the most threatened areas are often the most biodiverse.
- that there is a wide range of threats to biodiversity stemming from human activity.
- that ecosystem processes such as nutrient cycling and energy transfer can be severely altered by human activity.
- that there are links between economic development and the degradation of ecosystems, but they are complex.

MCQ

CHAPTER 9 To what extent can the threats to biodiversity be managed?

Learning objectives

After studying this chapter, you will be able to discuss these ideas and concepts and provide located examples of them:
- The use of the concept of maximum sustainable yield in planning resource extraction from an ecosystem.
- The roles that different groups and individuals play in managing biodiversity.
- The conflicts that can arise from different roles within management.
- There is a range of strategies and policies for managing biodiversity and each has advantages and disadvantages.
- The tension between economic development and conservation of biodiversity will cause problems in the future unless difficult choices are made.

Key terms

Carrying capacity
Ecological footprint
Global orchestration
Maximum sustainable yield

Assessing safe levels of resource use/extraction

Within ecosystems carrying capacity indicates the maximum number of individuals the system can support. If the carrying capacity is exceeded then the numbers of a population will fall due to a lack of food resources or perhaps stress caused by overcrowding. A balance is achieved over time. Humans harvest natural populations of trees, fish and animals and there has always been the tendency in our species to use what we can and then to move on to the next when that stock is depleted, thereby not allowing populations to recover.

This is unsustainable use of natural resources. As the human population has grown rapidly, we have become more aware that by over-harvesting we are preventing the resource being used for many years to come. This was shown by the over-fishing of the Grand Banks off Newfoundland where stocks of Atlantic cod still have not recovered.

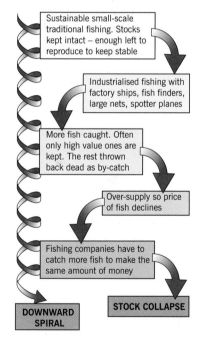

▲ **Figure 9.1:** Showing how the extraction of a natural resource can lead to the collapse and perhaps, ultimately, to the extinction of a species.

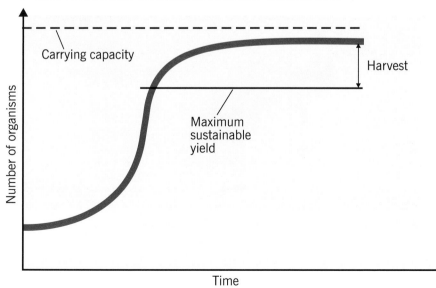

▲ **Figure 9.2:** Model of an ecosystem where the population of an organism shows the typical S-curve.

Figure 9.2 shows a model of an ecosystem where the population of an organism exhibits the typical S-curve, plateauing out as the carrying capacity of the environment is reached. Within the S-curve a point is reached at which the rate of increase begins to decline. If the organism were to be harvested below this point then the population would decline. Above it, the population should remain stable if that amount were harvested. Maximum sustainable yield (MSY) is the harvesting of an amount of a resource that can be replaced through reproduction so that the biomass or number of organisms is maintained from year to year. It is a concept that is now used in the conservation of fish stocks and other animals. The gains and losses within the stock of a species can be represented by:

End stock = stock a year ago + [Growth (G) + Recruits (R)] − [Mortality (M) + Fishing (F)]

(Recruits refers to new fish being born.) If the maximum sustainable yield is achieved then the end stock will equal the stock a year ago. However, if the mortality and the amount harvested are greater than the birth and growth of the stock, there will be an overall decline in the population.

The problem with MSY is that it is often applied after a species has been harvested for several years. Quotas based on this MSY assume that the present stock is the original level, which it is not. Other problems are that for many species, such as whales, it is difficult to assess the numbers that exist and it may result in wildly inaccurate calculations of the MSY. Quotas, when set, apply only to those fishing enterprises or hunters that operate legally. It is thought that nearly 50% of the world's fishing goes unrecorded and this again affects any calculations. MSY does not take into account a poor breeding year and can therefore result in over-fishing or extraction of a species in one year, which will have an impact in subsequent years. People have different perspectives on levels of resource extraction.

Examiners' tip

When researching/revising try to choose case studies that can be used for a variety of questions. The Galapagos Islands case study can be used for: how biodiversity is assessed; biodiversity hotspots (because of their endemism); threats from alien species, human activities; the problems of conflict between conservationists, tourists, businesses and the migrants from Ecuador's mainland; examples of management on a local and national scale (see Taking it further activity page 77).

Case study: Kangaroos in Australia

This case study looks at different views of sustainable yield within the rangelands of Australia.

The red kangaroo, an indigenous species of Australia, grazes the same semi-arid lands that farmers use for extensive sheep rearing. It is regarded as a pest by the farmer because of the competition with sheep for vegetation. They would prefer much lower densities of kangaroos across these lands. However, sheep farming is barely sustainable in these locations because of the long-term drought that Australia is experiencing at present. It is thought that it will decline rapidly over the next decade.

Conservationists would like to see fewer kangaroos killed (some would like a complete ban on all hunting), but there are towns that are dependent on this resource. Kangaroo hides and meat are harvested and currently this is thought

▲ **Figure 9.3:** Kangaroos with sheep ranching in evidence.

to be at MSY level, about 10–20% of the red kangaroo population in any year. If more were culled, above the MSY, to appease the farmers, there would be fewer to harvest in the future and the leather and meat industries would suffer. In the long term it is felt that the kangaroo is a better 'crop' than sheep if harvested at MSY as it is uniquely adapted to the drought-prone climate of the Australian interior.

MSY can be useful as a guideline, but all factors such as the level of illegal fishing/hunting have to be included in a calculation or there is a danger of over-estimating the stock and under-estimating the extraction. It is not a failsafe method for planning the use of an ecosystem.

Roles in managing biodiversity

Loss of biodiversity is driven by factors on local, national and international scales, therefore responses in order to combat this loss also need to be across the board. However, without the actions of individuals, non-governmental organisations (NGOs), governments and international bodies, biodiversity would be at a lower level than today.

Money, expertise and time have been provided through various stakeholders to help mitigate the negative impacts on the planet's ecosystems of human population increase and economic growth. The IUCN's Red List shows that whereas many species have become increasingly endangered, others such as the humpback whale have made a considerable recovery and have been brought back from the brink of extinction. Figure 9.4 summarises some of the players in the management of biodiversity. Operating on a global level, such as organisations linked to the United Nations, down to the individual, the actions that are taken have an impact on biodiversity.

Individuals

All organisations are made up of individuals, so in one sense they have the greatest impact on decisions and actions. Here we are thinking about an individual's decision perhaps to decide to reduce their ecological footprint in order to contribute less to global warming and the threat that poses for biodiversity. Alternatively, it may be an individual subsistence farmer who illegally clears another patch of rainforest in order to grow food for his family, further stressing a fragile ecosystem.

Communities

Made up of individuals, a community, particularly an indigenous community, often has a clear sense of its surrounding environment and will wish to conserve it for their use. There are increasing conflicts with outside players such as TNCs (transnational companies), which wish to avail themselves of local resources, in some cases the genes of plants for use in the pharmaceutical industry. Ownership of these plant genes is in dispute at present.

NGOs

These bodies are independent of the government and often support a particular species or group of species, such as Project Seahorse, but also include the campaigning groups such as Greenpeace, World Wide Fund for Nature (WWF) or Friends of the Earth. Being independent they can disagree with government legislation and organise specific campaigns and publicity to highlight what they see as threats to biodiversity. The National Trust in the UK is an NGO and protects large stretches of our coastline and also iconic areas such as the Lake District. Like National Parks, the National Trust wants people to have access to the land, but aims to support people and biodiversity through balanced management.

Global

Global players include the work of the United Nations through UNESCO and UNEP. Having a world remit helps important areas of biodiversity to gain recognition and be designated as ecologically important. The UN Biosphere Reserves set standards in biodiversity conservation, which then can act as models for other protective designations.

The number of players involved in managing biodiversity is complex and there are often competing and overlapping roles, which can lead to conflicts.

PLAYER	TYPE	ROLE	DESCRIPTION
Farmer	Individual	Manage environment for food production. Biodiversity management as part of this.	Aims to get surplus harvests. Traditionally farming was balanced with the ecosystem. In developed countries now trying to include support for biodiversity.
Individual	Individual	Make choices that will affect biodiversity	Decisions will depend on cultural background, education level and how economically secure the individual is.
RSPB (Royal Society for the Protection of Birds)	NGO	Campaigning body in UK. Runs 200 reserves. www.rspb.org.uk	Largest environmental organisation in Europe with >1 million members. Birds used as indicators of health of ecosystems.
Badger Trust	NGO	Specifically to conserve the British badger population. www.badger.org.uk	The conservation and wellbeing of badgers. Helps run Badger Groups in most counties. Badgers are under threat from culling because of alleged link between them and TB in cattle.
Project Seahorse	NGO	Conservation and sustainable use of the world's coastal marine ecosystems. www.projectseahorse.com	Seahorses are the focus for finding solutions to problems in the marine environment. Scientific research is carried out and management along with partner organisations.
DEFRA (Department of the Environment, Food and Rural Affairs)	National government	Develop a well-managed countryside along with conservation of wildlife. www.defra.gov.uk	DEFRA plays several roles, but is mainly linked with agriculture. Scientific research is carried out and it links with local authorities with the BAPs (Biodiversity Action Plans).
Local government (UK)	Government	Manage local reserves and monitor local wildlife.	BAPs are helping to focus this role.
Natural England	National government	Conserve landscape and wildlife, but also allow access to visitors. www.naturalengland.org.uk	Designates and manages the 222 National Nature Reserves (NNRs) plus the SSSIs (Sites of Special Scientific Interest) and the 36 AONBS (Areas of Outstanding Natural Beauty).
Transnational companies	International	Develop industries in a range of global locations in order to access markets and keep costs down. Profit is their main motive.	In accessing developing country locations infrastructure is built that can directly impact on biodiversity. Extraction of resources such as minerals or timber again impact on biodiversity. Collecting wild organisms for pharmaceutical research can impact locally on ecosystems. Their decisions, made in HQ in other countries, impact directly on biodiversity elsewhere.
UNESCO (United Nations Scientific and Cultural Organisation)	Global	Set standards and urge agreements through research and exchange of ideas.	Runs the Biosphere Reserves, which are under national jurisdiction, but comply with agreed standards and share ideas and expertise.
WRI (World Resources Institute)	Global NGO	A think tank providing objective information. www.wri.org/about	Provides data, maps and tolls to aid conservation. Works in partnership with other organisations on small and large scale.
UNEP (United Nations Environment Programme)	Global	Information source. Research. www.unep.org	Provides range of online sources of information. Online magazine *Our Planet*. Encourages partnership working.
WWF (World Wide Fund for Nature)	Global NGO	Work with governments and other partners to manage threatened areas.	Works in many countries of the world to help conserve ecosystems and species. Also runs campaigns.

▲ **Figure 9.4:** Players and their roles.

Case study: Heather moorland and the red grouse

This case study looks at how different players who care about the countryside can conflict over the way in which it is protected and managed.

The red grouse is a bird of the upland regions of the UK and is a major game bird, which means it is bred in some areas to be shot for sport. Over the second half of the 20th century much of the UK's moorland was lost to being ploughed up and 'improved'. This meant being planted with grass seed to provide rough grazing for sheep. Other areas were planted with conifer plantations as a crop.

However, 75% of the world's remaining moorland is in the UK. Paradoxically it has been grouse shooting that has helped to preserve some of our moorland areas in the traditional manner. Grouse need a mosaic of heather at different stages of growth – young heather shoots for food and older stands to provide nesting and cover. This is achieved by systematically allowing grazing or by setting fire to the heather in rotation to provide patches at different ages. This traditional management also supports other species such as the merlin, hen harrier and the skylark.

The Moorland Association (an NGO) represents the owners and managers of grouse moors and believes that it is conserving the countryside and providing jobs and income to rural communities. Grouse shoots require accommodation for the participants, restaurants, beaters, other helpers on the shoot and gamekeepers. In some areas the RSPB (an NGO) believes that the burning has been carried out too extensively and has changed the habitat. There have also been problems with the illegal killing of birds of prey that will prey on the young grouse.

PLAYER	Moorland Association	Farmers	Gamekeepers	Natural England	RSPB
Moorland Association	✗	◆	✗	●	●
Farmers	◆	✗	◆	◆	●
Gamekeepers	✗	◆	✗	●	●
Natural England	●	◆	●	✗	✗
RSPB	●	●	●	✗	✗

KEY ✗ = No conflict ◆ = Low conflict ● = High conflict ▲ **Figure 9.5:** Conflict matrix for the heather moorland.

This table shows the conflicts that can arise in such a situation between the various players. The gamekeepers regard the red grouse as the most important element and although they manage the ecosystem to support the grouse and other associated birds, they may also protect them by killing birds of prey. Farmers may wish to remove the heather and use their land for rough grazing to improve their income. It is difficult to reconcile all the players unless they work together cooperatively and all parties can see advantages of any planned actions.

This has occurred on some grouse moors in Teesdale with a reduction in the levels of heather burning and compliance with the law prohibiting the killing of hawks and owls. This has increased species biodiversity, whilst having little impact on grouse numbers; an example of a more sustainable approach involving all players.

Taking it further

To look at a case study showing how bringing people together to discuss a framework can help to overcome conflicts, read 'Clayoquot Sound, Canada' on your Student CD-ROM.

Taking it further

Read about conservation in the UK on your Student CD-ROM.

Sometimes bringing people together to discuss a framework that would protect an area, and yet allow sustainable extraction, can help to overcome conflicts. This was the case in the Clayoquot Sound, Canada.

It is difficult with so many players representing varied interests to avoid conflict, but cooperation can happen, especially if there is a global-level framework helping to drive the dialogue forward.

How best can biodiversity be managed?

During the 20th century it was gradually realised that biodiversity needed to be protected and that the landscapes that supported this also needed to be conserved. It was not enough to house endangered species in zoos if they were never going to be able to live in the wild again due to total loss of habitat. Views towards conservation vary from the ecocentric view that we are part of the biodiversity of life and should only use resources sustainably to the other extreme of a technocentric view where the planet's biodiversity and resources are there to be used and exploited.

Taking it further

Conservation at a local level can be very successful if the views of the local people are taken into account. Read 'The Community Baboon Sanctuary' on your Student CD-ROM.

The majority view is found somewhere between the two extremes. The more recent strategies for the management of landscapes and biodiversity incorporate community involvement and the sustainable use of resources where this does not permanently harm endangered species. Figure 9.6 summarises some of the strategies and policies that are used to conserve biodiversity from global to local scales.

Biosphere reserves are designated by UNESCO and are planned to bring together a wide range of players who are involved in the biodiversity of a region. They operate on a number of levels. Locally they involve local people and the landscape they know in order better to serve the community, while at the same time ensuring the continuity of the biodiversity on which they depend.

▼ **Figure 9.6:** Advantages and disadvantages of a range of strategies and policies.

STRATEGY OR POLICY	ADVANTAGES	DISADVANTAGES
World Biosphere Reserve	Internationally recognised. Work cooperatively. Part of global network. Access to centrally held data to help in decision-making. Usually a core, which is a heavily protected area with buffer zones around it.	Some countries do not have finances to fully monitor or manage. Pressure from development may be difficult to control.
CITES Convention on International Trade in Endangered Species	International agreement, so when it works, it encourages cooperation. Has protected many hundreds of species and slowed down much live animal trade as well as animal furs and body parts (for traditional medicines) and rare plants.	Cultural perspectives may be different, e.g. use of bush meat (e.g. monkeys, including endangered species) to supplement poor diets in some parts of Africa. Can lead to higher prices and so more income for some rare species. Temptation to target certain species.
Special Protection Areas (SPAs)	Europe wide. Protects rare and migratory birds and their habitat.	Difficult to police. Problems in, e.g., Italy as raptors migrate from Africa.
Special Areas of Conservation (SACs)	Europe wide. Particularly rare or threatened habitats preserved such as the Caledonian Forest of Scotland.	Often in more remote areas so difficult to police. Local community is not always involved and can lead to conflicts.
National Parks	Set up nationally and have high profile. Allow access to spectacular landscapes and aim to preserve biodiversity of species, but also cultural diversity.	Tension between resource use/extraction and conservation. Over-use of some areas such as Dovedale in Peak District.
Marine Protected Areas (MPAs)	Restore balance within oceans. Protect areas where fish breed and allow no-catch zones so that fish stocks can recover. Allow restoration of coral reefs or eel grass meadows by reducing use.	Difficult to police. Can initially impact on local small-scale fishing (but will benefit in the long term).
Debt for nature swaps	Enable developing countries to exchange foreign debt for protecting an endangered resource such as tropical rainforest. Country keeps control of land, but has the finance to support it sustainably.	Often done at government level with very little consultation with people who might be affected by decision.
Gene banks	Most famous is on island of Spitzbergen, Svalbard in the Arctic Ocean, Global Seed Vault. Has duplicates of all seeds in other collections around the world. It backs up other gene banks such as Kew in London. Ensures a species is preserved even if only in seed form.	If habitat is destroyed then the plant will be able to be grown only in artificial conditions. A failsafe strategy, which is hoped will never be used. Not yet collected seeds of all the plants in the world.
In situ conservation	Protects a species where it normally lives, e.g. the panda reserves in China. Protects habitat and species. Also protects the species with which it interacts. Larger area is best or several smaller ones with links between them.	May still be threatened, e.g. poachers of tigers in nature reserves in India. Population of species may be too small to preserve and gene pool may be limited, which would affect survival rate.
Ex situ conservation (includes gene banks)	Removes endangered species and breeds/conserves in captivity such as zoos. Allows them to survive even if extinct in the wild. Can be re-introduced into natural habitat later.	Expensive and can only look after relatively few of any one species. Zoo environment can cause severe stress to some species. May not breed successfully.
Community conservation	Involves local people. Helps them realise the value of their indigenous wildlife. Can provide sustainable income while conserving wildlife.	Income may take time to enter economy until project is up and fully running. May not be part of traditional culture.

Taking it further

To read a case study that looks at how the zoning policy has helped to alleviate some of the threats to biodiversity on the islands, read 'The Galapagos Islands' on your Student CD-ROM.

▲ **Figure 9.7:** The Rodrigues Island fruit bat.

Taking it further

Find out about the conservation work of Chester Zoo by reading 'The Rodrigues Island fruit bat' on your Student CD-ROM. You can access its website at www.chesterzoo.org.

Taking it further

Access the Wildlife Trusts' website at www.wildlifetrusts.org and look for the link to "Living Landscapes", which looks at the threat of climate change and how we can help to restore our degraded ecosystems.

On a national level the reserves stand as models to inspire further conservation and internationally there is the World Network of Biosphere Reserves, which helps and supports the reserves. The biosphere designation of the Galapagos Islands has helped to implement a zoning strategy that goes some way to solving the problems the area faces.

The Galapagos Islands show how in situ conservation can work, protecting both the rare species and the environment on which they depend. However, sometimes it is necessary to take drastic action and protect a species by removing it from its habitat. This is called ex situ conservation.

Conservation on a local level can be very successful if the views of local people are taken into account. Involving local people allows for futurity, that the enterprise can go on into the future without harming the environment.

What does the future hold for earth's biodiversity?

There is great uncertainty as regards how many species there are on earth. Although it is common knowledge that species are being lost, we are unsure at what rate or what the impacts are likely to be in the future. The Rivet Theory proposes that all the species on earth are like the rivets holding together an aeroplane. Initially, as the plane loses rivets it still holds together and functions. However, there comes a point at which so many rivets have been lost that the plane (the ecosystem) falls apart and crashes. How near are we to that scenario? This is a particular problem with keystone species such as the sea otter (see Chapter 8) and bees, whose demise causes a far greater impact than would at first seem likely as so many components of an ecosystem are dependent on their existence.

A major problem with conserving biodiversity is poverty. The majority of earth's most biodiverse ecosystems are located in developing countries where increasing populations are struggling to make a living and there is great pressure on all natural resources there. The majority of hotspots are also located within developing countries (see Chapter 7), but this does mean that if money is invested in these regions there will be a higher return in terms of biodiversity protected per dollar. Globalisation of trade and industry (see AS book Unit 1 Topic 2 Going global) brings added pressure as TNCs operating in developing countries put extra stress on their resources and systems.

Biodiversity loss is undervalued with publicity seeming to be given to only the larger and more appealing fauna such as whales and pandas. Generally people are unaware of the ranges of goods and services that ecosystems provide us with, therefore the threat of biodiversity loss or damage is not included in most of the prices we pay for goods. In the future it may be that people such as farmers and landowners are paid to maintain some of these ecosystems' services. On tropical coasts the important role of mangroves in protecting the coastline has now been realised, especially from hazards such as hurricanes and tsunami. Many coastlines have been cleared of mangrove forests for development or to set up shrimp farming. Many of the people involved are poor and would need an alternative income source to relinquish their business, although coastal societies as a whole would benefit, as would the ecosystem and biodiversity. The problem is that restoration is often the most expensive option when trying to conserve biodiversity and most restoration projects have occurred within the developed world.

One of the greatest threats to biodiversity is global climate change. Organisms are already altering their location or their habits due to climate change. Due to our dependency on biodiversity for our wellbeing, humans will need to learn how to help them survive these changes.

In the early 21st century the Millennium Ecosystem Assessment (MA) investigated the state of the world's ecosystems and found that we were damaging them at a faster rate than had been thought and that biodiversity loss can lead to the total collapse of ecosystems (see Chapter 8 and the kelp forests.)

Case study: Changing back – water meadows in the UK

This case study looks at how our greater understanding of ecosystem services means we can choose to pay to rectify past mistakes and make sustainable choices.

During the 20th century UK farmers were encouraged to drain and plough fields adjacent to rivers, which had been seasonal grazing land for centuries, known as water meadows. In the short term they were able to make more income by growing arable crops, but the water falling on the fields drained off much faster into the rivers, raising the water levels and often causing flooding further downstream in towns and villages. Returning these fields to being fully integrated with the floodplain means they can act as a sponge, slowing up delivery of water to the river and reducing the risk of flooding. As well as supporting a wide range of biodiversity, the reinstatement of water meadows reduces flooding further downstream so there is less financial loss and insurance risks are reduced. Farmers should be able to receive payments for this service.

It also stated that poverty drives economic degradation as the poor have limited choices and have to find a way in which to survive. When looking at the success of protectionist strategies, the MA discovered that they did not work on their own and that only by including local communities and allowing their 'ownership' of biodiversity could they be truly successful.

The poor have to be given access to the biodiversity or given alternatives, thus making the protection sustainable. The MA came up with four future scenarios that assumed continued biodiversity loss over the next 50 years, but suggested that the different approaches would have different results for human and ecosystem wellbeing.

We are gradually building up our knowledge of the species with which we share this planet, but earth's biodiversity can still surprise us. During the past decade over 1,000 new species have been found in the Greater Mekong region of South-east Asia alone. One species, the Laotian rat, was thought to have been extinct for 11 million years. The future may hold even more surprises.

It is virtually impossible to prevent extinctions if we do not know how many species there are to start with. Biodiversity is under threat from all angles as human populations increase along with the extraction of resources and we are losing species before we even know they exist. However, at the same time, we are much more aware, globally and locally, of our impacts on species and habitats. We have access to more data than ever before and we are beginning to use this knowledge to raise awareness of our impacts and to plan sustainable management in order to take all of us into the future.

▲ **Figure 9.8:** A traditional water meadow, flooded.

Taking it further

To look at a case study about how humans can help organisms adapt to climate change, read 'Climate change and green corridors' on your Student CD-ROM.

1. Global Orchestration - In this scenario all trade barriers and subsidies are removed to allow free trade. Economic growth is high and the standard of living of the poorer countries improves. The assumption is made that as wealth increases there will be the money and the will to deal with environmental problems but may be too late. High biodiversity loss in this scenario.

2. Order From Strength - Protection of national boundaries is paramount. Rich countries will close their borders to protect own standard of living. There will be security worries. Problems of ecosystem degradation in poorer countries and they will struggle to survive. Ecosystem collapse, however, does not recognise borders and biodiversity loss will be great in this scenario.

3. Adapting Mosaic - Will manage ecosystems locally and regionally. Local control of ecosystems so more sustainable. Lower biodiversity loss than 1 and 2. People working co-operatively to try and develop economically but also maintain ecosystems. As this occurs wealth increases steadily but some ecosystem damage as try to discover best way to develop sustainable use.

4. Techno Garden - Using technology to help provide ecosystem services. Excellent connectivity at global level and ideas shared. Develop strategies to gain multiple services from the same ecosystem without permanent harm. Could have problems with over reliance on technology and ecosystsems suffering. Wealth increases for poorer countries as knowledge and technology is shared.

◄ **Figure 9.9:** The MA Four.

Summary

In this chapter you have learnt:

• that maximum sustainable yield is a useful tool, but cannot be relied on as being accurate.

• that there are many different players within biodiversity management who may all have a different perspective.

• that conflicts can arise due to their different perceptions even though the players all care for the ecosystem.

• that there is a wide range of strategies from global to local and they all have something to offer the conservation of biodiversity.

• that the future for the maintenance of biodiversity is fraught with difficulties, but there is hope in new initiatives.

MCQ

Taking it further

Use the following website and put 'First Contact in the Greater Mekong' into the search field. Explore the range of new species that have been found in this region. Why do you think it has taken this long to discover them and what threats do you think they will face? www.panda.org/about_wwf.

Exam Practice – Section A

Biodiversity Under Threat

(a) Explain the distribution of the world's terrestrial and marine hotspots in Figure 3. [10]

(b) Evaluate the relative advantages and disadvantages of the 'hotspot' approach to biodiversity management (compared with other strategies). [15]

▲ **Figure 3:** The world's terrestrial and marine hotspots.

Terrestrial

Marine

CHAPTER 10 Who are the superpowers and how does their power develop over time?

Learning objectives

After studying this chapter, you will be able to discuss these ideas and concepts and provide located examples of them:
- The concept of a superpower has developed to include economic, cultural, military and geographical influence.
- The geography of power and international influence can be seen through geographical patterns of military reach, trade and cultural dominance.
- Patterns of power change over time.
- There are differences in the emerging powers versus the existing superpowers in terms of regional and global influence.
- World systems analysis and dependency theory help explain these differences.

Key term

Superpower — a nation or group of nations that has a leading position in international politics.

Synoptic link

Look at the Crossing the border article on pages 78–9 of Edexcel AS Geography.

Power – both economic and political – is unevenly distributed. Some countries have a disproportionate influence over regional and global decision-making, whereas others have little influence. The geography of power changes over time. Some nations gain power and influence, while others lose it. Equally, the nature of power has changed, from direct to more subtle indirect control, through trade, culture, flows of capital and resources.

Who are the superpowers and how does their power develop over time?

The concept of a superpower has developed to include economic, cultural, military and geographical influence, for example, the development of the USA and the former USSR, and more recently the growth of China, India and Brazil.

Superpowers are able to influence policy on a worldwide scale, and often in different regions at the same time. The term was first used in 1944 by T.R. Fox, in his book *The Superpowers: The United States, Britain and the Soviet Union – Their Responsibility for Peace*. These three nations fought on the same side in the Second World War, but afterwards became involved in a battle for economic, political and military power. At the end of the war, the British Empire covered about 25% of the world's land area and had 25% of its population. However, its power was in decline, whereas the USA and USSR were emerging as the new superpowers.

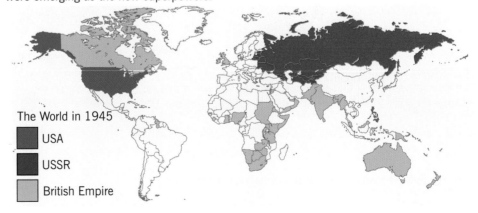

The World in 1945
- USA
- USSR
- British Empire

▶ **Figure 10.1:** 1945 map of world superpowers.

The British Empire became the Commonwealth of Nations and former colonies became independent of Britain. The USA did not suffer as much damage on its territory as European or Asian countries. By the end of the war it had developed into a very strong military and industrial country, as well as a major creditor for countries weakened in the war. Post-war US policy was to contain the spread of Soviet influence.

After the war, competition between the USA and USSR led to the development of the Cold War. Both countries sought to increase their dominance on the world scene. By the 1980s their respective powers had greatly increased.

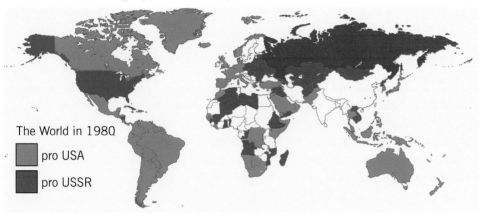

The World in 1980

pro USA

pro USSR

▲ **Figure 10.2:** 1980 map of superpower influence.

There were several differences between the USA and the USSR. Politically, the USSR promoted communism and the economy was state-controlled. In contrast, the USA was managed as a democracy and had a free market (capitalist) approach to the economy. Both countries were keen to extend their influence and support other countries. The USSR developed strong links with eastern Europe and developing countries. The USA, on the other hand, had firm relations with western Europe, the Commonwealth, Latin America and key Asian countries. The USA also supported a number of right-wing dictatorships in their attempt to reduce Soviet influence and the spread of left-wing tendencies.

The two nations had shared characteristics in terms of population, land and resources. While the USSR was the world's largest country, with a land area of over 22 million km^2, the USA was the world's third largest with over 9 million km^2. The USSR was the world's third largest in terms of population size (over 285 million at the time of its break-up), whereas almost 250 million people resided in the USA. Both had many valuable economic resources; in particular the USSR had oil and gas, whereas the USA contained valuable minerals, metals, forests and a modern agricultural and industrial system. At the time, the USA had the world's greatest economy, while the economy of the USSR was the second largest. To complete the superpower checklist, the USSR had the world's largest land-based army and the world's largest stockpile of nuclear weapons. In contrast, the USA had the world's largest and most powerful navy and one of the two most powerful air forces in the world.

Culturally both the USA and USSR affected large areas of the world. Conflict between the two superpowers was not limited to military threats – the Cold War also affected the worlds of chess and basketball, and the respective countries and their allies did not attend the Olympic Games held in Moscow in 1980 and Los Angeles in 1984.

Synoptic link

Refresh your memory about Commonwealth countries by looking at page 82 of Edexcel AS Geography.

Key terms

Cold War — the name given to the period of heightened tensions and competition between the USA and USSR and their allies between 1945 and the early 1990s.

Communism — a form of political development that envisages equality among people and a classless society. It's a type of revolutionary socialism based on the common ownership of the means of production and a shared economy. Each person should work according to his/her capacity and gain according to his/her capacity.

Democracy — a form of political development in which the government is elected by the people in free elections.

Capitalism — an economic system for the generation of goods and services based on private enterprise. Most of the resources/means of production are owned by a relatively small number of individuals or companies. Workers convert their labour for wages.

After the collapse of communism and the break-up of the USSR in 1991, the USA was left as the world's only superpower. However, since 2001 and the terrorist attacks on the USA, US military involvement in Iraq and Afghanistan has not achieved its desired ends. Some critics argue that the USA is losing its superpower status. Economically, following the 2008 financial crisis, the USA has lost economic strength (as have many countries that had been propped up by US money) and other nations are in the ascendancy. China in particular has experienced massive economic growth, as well as having a very large military. Whether it fulfils all of the criteria of a superpower is debatable. The European Union, a group of 27 countries, has also been described as a superpower. Internal differences between member countries reduce the cohesion of the EU as a superpower.

Case study: How does Europe differ from the USA as a superpower?

The European Union (EU) has a population of about 493 million people, so it is one of the world's largest economic superpowers. In addition, most of the population is wealthy in global terms. In just 50 years, Europeans have made the likelihood of war between member countries remote. The EU has brought a number of its countries out of dictatorship into democratic governments. Surrounding the EU there are about 1.5 billion people who rely on the EU as their main trading partner and source of foreign investment and aid. Nevertheless, within the EU there are 27 different national governments, each with its own agenda. Despite differences, the EU attempts to incorporate and change countries into stable political and economic systems, such as in the case of Poland and currently Serbia.

Key term

Rising superpowers — countries, or groups of countries, experiencing an increase in economic, military, cultural and geographical influence, currently Brazil, Russia, India and China.

Taking it further

To find out about the concerns regarding potential superpowers in the early 20th century read 'Managing superpowers in the early 20th century' on your Student CD-ROM.

Taking it further

Use the Student CD-ROM to find out more about the characteristics of superpowers.

Examiners' tip

Stay up to date — save the BBC News website as one of your website favourites and keep up to date with news about your chosen superpowers.

Rising superpowers

The economic rise of the BRICs (Brazil, Russia, India and China) and the oil-rich OPEC states brings economic benefits to many. Equally there may be economic costs to the existing superpowers and environmental and resource implications. In an increasingly globalised and interdependent world, it is likely that tensions will develop as power shifts.

The geography of power and international influence

The USA: the evolution of a superpower

After the Second World War, the USA had a greatly enhanced status and power. The Great Depression of the 1930s had been replaced by an economy stimulated by wartime production. Unlike Europe, the USA did not suffer from wrecked infrastructure. US involvement in the Second World War – the large-scale air and land campaigns in Europe and the 'island-hopping' war against Japan in the Pacific – set a precedent for the global projection of US military strength.

It was not just economic and military strength. The USA encouraged the establishment of international institutions and international law. The United Nations headquarters were located in New York, and the World Bank and International Monetary Fund were based in Washington. Although these were, and continue to be, international organisations, US institutions had greater access to them than if they had been located elsewhere.

The growth of US military influence worldwide grew out of a number of doctrines. These included:

- the Monroe Doctrine of 1823 (which declared that European colonial intervention in the western hemisphere would be resisted by force)
- the Truman Doctrine of 1947 (which committed the USA to support free peoples threatened by communist takeover)
- the Nixon Doctrine of 1969 (under which arms shipments rather than US troops would be supplied to allies in the fight against communism)
- the Reagan Doctrine of the 1980s (which provided US arms and training to groups seeking to overthrow Soviet-backed rulers).

The USA has by far the world's largest and most technologically advanced fleet of warplanes, ships, tanks and artillery systems. These give it dominance over air, sea and land. Control of space and information are key aspects of US military strategy for the 21st century. There are many interlocking strands in the USA's global military presence. These include overseas bases, ships and aircraft that allow the USA to apply force to any part of the globe, the supply of weapons and military training to a wide range of countries, and a network of listening posts which gather and disseminate vital information.

The US defence industry employs over 2 million people, with local manufacturing plants or research and development facilities in most US states. Approximately 1 in 6 households in the USA has someone employed in the military industrial complex. Annual spending on defence exceeds $100 billion a year. Federal funding for military research is $40 billion a year, twice what is spent on health, energy and environment combined. The institutions and organisations which have developed over 50 years of intensive military spending have created vested interests with huge political clout.

For example, most US warplanes, bombs and missiles are made by a small group of very large contractors, including in particular Lockheed Martin, Boeing, Raytheon, TRW and Textron. In 1998–9, Lockheed Martin employed 130,000 people in the USA and overseas and had over 900 facilities in 45 US states. Internationally, the company had business locations in 56 nations and territories. In the early 1990s, when defence spending dropped in the wake of the Soviet collapse, the US government urged defence contractors to merge with each other in order to consolidate their strength and maintain America's defence capabilities. The outcome was a rapid series of mergers, which gave rise to a handful of giant groups.

Selling arms and military services worldwide

Moreover, the USA accounts for half of all international arms sales. Much US military equipment destined for export is manufactured abroad under licence. For example, Turkey has made F-16s since the mid-1980s. The USA cooperates closely with certain allies, including the UK and Israel, on high-tech projects such as missile defence.

Apart from the huge ongoing requirement for production of new aircraft, tanks, ships and weapons systems, there is a vast procurement programme for spare parts, fuel, munitions and the myriad other supplies which sustain the US military machine. Huge amounts are spent on developing new weapons. Although the USA is widely acknowledged to have the world's most advanced combat aircraft, it is busy making the next generation of fighter planes.

Space, the final frontier – superpowers and space missions

It is no surprise that the countries that have developed space technology are the superpowers. They have the finance and the technology. For a country to be considered as a superpower, it needs to have a space programme. The following list shows how space programmes vary between the original superpowers and the emerging superpowers.

Key term

Military industrial complex — the part of the economy that provides goods and services for the military, such as aircraft, warheads, missiles, clothing, catering, etc.

Synoptic link

Refresh your memory about multinational companies by looking at page 75 of Edexcel AS Geography.

USA: NASA put Neil Armstrong on the moon in 1969. Plans include a return manned trip to the moon by 2020.

China: Completed its first manned space flight in 2003 and launched a lunar satellite in October 2007. In 2008 Zhai Zhigang became the first Chinese to walk in space. Ambitious plans include the creation of its own space station.

Russia: First to launch a satellite in 1957, and four years later launched the first human into space.

Europe: European Space Agency's Ariane rocket programme became a world leader in commercial space launches in the 1990s. Plans a mission to search for signs of life on Mars in 2016.

Japan: First ever space development minister appointed in 2008.

Patterns of power change over time

We have seen how the British Empire covered about 25% of the world's land area and had 25% of its population in the past. However, the cost of fighting two world wars and the damage to the British economy and infrastructure meant that it could not afford to run its colonies. Moreover, many of the people in the colonies wanted independence from Britain. The post-war period therefore marked the decline of the former British Empire and the independence of the former colonies.

The collapse of the USSR as a superpower was later and different. In 1979 Russia invaded Afghanistan in an attempt to prop up the communist government there. Russian troops were later withdrawn from Afghanistan in 1985. During this period the USA had developed the neutron bomb, cruise missiles and a 'Star Wars' defence system with space satellites. Russia could not afford the arms race and its economy was backward. The Russian president Gorbachev started Strategic Arms Reduction Talks. Free elections in Poland led to Solidarity, originally a banned trade union, gaining power, and this was followed closely by the fall of the Berlin Wall in November 1989.

Taking it further

To learn about India's space mission read 'India's space mission – or another military industrial complex?' on your Student CD-ROM.

Case study: Economic transformation of China

Since 1978, the standard of living of most people in China has tripled. Market reforms have been introduced gradually, avoiding the 'big bang' approach. Following the death of the Chinese leader, Chairman Mao, in 1976, a more moderate faction led by Deng Xiaoping gained control of the government. One of Deng's first acts was to inject an element of free enterprise into agriculture, allowing peasant families to keep for themselves anything they produced over the state quota. This responsibility system resulted in an almost immediate leap in food production. A similar approach was later applied to the industrial sector.

In 1992 Deng gave official blessing to business entrepreneurship throughout China. When Deng died in 1997, Jiang Zemin became the leader. Under his leadership, China saw major improvements in its diplomatic standing and economic strength, although there were growing disparities between urban and rural living standards.

China's economic miracle has had an enormous impact on ordinary people. Village and township enterprises have sprung up all over the country. The Yangtze valley has become integrated into the Asia-Pacific trade bloc. Developments in the Pearl River Delta Region have built upon Hong Kong's success to create a dynamic business region in southern China. Economic growth in China has had a major impact on trade among the superpowers and the geographic regions of the world (see Figure 10.3). The EU is the dominant trading region, followed by Asia and then North America.

Taking it further

To find out how the imports and exports of traditional and emerging superpowers have changed between 1948 and 2007 read 'World merchandise imports and exports' on your Student CD-ROM.

Synoptic link

Revisit China by looking at pages 93, 124–5 and 149 of Edexcel AS Geography.

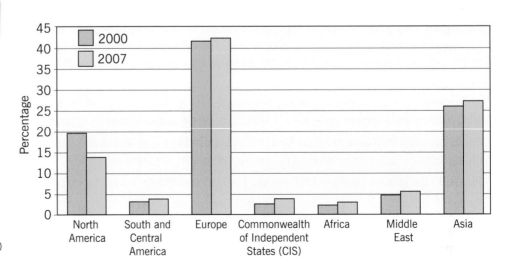

► **Figure 10.3:** Regional shares in world merchandise exports, 2000 and 2007.

The Asian financial crisis saw the collapse of many Asian banks and the value of their stocks and shares in the late 1990s. Many countries were forced to restructure their economies and reduce their levels of debt.

Despite the Asian financial crisis in 1997–8, China's GDP has continued to grow by 8% a year.

China's demand for the raw materials of this economic boom had a major impact on world markets in oil, iron ore, metals, petrochemicals and machinery. One of the largest of China's many infrastructure projects was the Three Gorges Dam, the world's largest hydro-electric plant. More giant projects are planned, including the diversion of river water from the south to the water-hungry north. Despite rapid change, the structure of the Chinese economy still has the character of a poor developing country, with almost half the workforce employed in the primary sector. Industry accounts for 22% of jobs, but 51% of output, with manufacturing 35%. This reflects the fact that China has become the world's leading manufacturing centre, although much of the value-added output is from foreign-owned plants in China's special development zones.

Rank	Country	Spending $US bn
1	USA	535.9
2	China	121.9
3	Russia	70.0
4	UK	55.4
11	India	22.4
13	Brazil	16.2

◀ **Figure 10.4:** Defence spending in 2006.

Rank	Economy	GDP $US bn
1	USA	13,164
4	China	2,645
5	UK	2,377
10	Brazil	1,067
11	Russia	987
12	India	912

◀ **Figure 10.5:** Size of the economy in 2006.

Theories relating to superpowers

Dependency theory

According to dependency theory, countries become more dependent upon more powerful, frequently colonial powers, as a result of interaction and 'development'. As the more powerful country exploits the resources of its weaker colony, the colony becomes dependent upon the stronger power. Goods flow from the colony to support consumers in the overseas country.

Andre Frank (1971) described the effect of capitalist development on many countries as 'the development of underdevelopment'. The problem of poor countries is not that they lack the resources, technical know-how, modern institutions or cultural developments that lead to development, but that they are being exploited by capitalist countries.

Dependency theory has a very different approach from most models of development.

- It incorporates politics and economics in its explanation.
- It takes into account the historical processes of how underdevelopment came about, that is how capitalist development began in one part of the world and then expanded into other areas.
- It sees development as a revolutionary break, a clash of interests between ruling classes and the working classes.

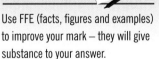

Examiners' tip

Use FFE (facts, figures and examples) to improve your mark – they will give substance to your answer.

Key term

Dependency theory — countries become more dependent over time as more powerful, frequently colonial powers push them into a state of underdevelopment.

Synoptic link

Revisit the following pages in the Edexcel AS Geography textbook: Developed world 31–2, 58; Developing world 29–30, 81, 241–3; Development pathways 54, 59–60; Economic group of nations 80–2; Economies in transition 54, 58, 62. Also take a look at Unit 3 Topic 5 Bridging the Development Gap in this book.

Key term

World systems analysis — treats the whole world as a single unit and divides the countries into a core, largely MEDCs; the periphery, which can be identified with LEDCs; and the semi-periphery, where social change and class struggles are taking place.

- It believes that modernisation does not necessarily mean Westernisation and that underdeveloped countries must set goals of their own, which are appropriate to their own resources, needs and values.

However, it is a largely economic theory (from a Western perspective) seeing the outcome as a form of economic determinism.

World systems theory

World systems analysis is identified with Immanuel Wallerstein (1974) and is a way of looking at economic, social and political development. It treats the whole world as a single unit. Any analysis of development must be seen as part of the overall capitalist world economy, not on a country by country approach. Wallerstein argued that an approach that looked at individual countries in isolation was too simplistic and suffered from developmentalism. The developmentalism school assumed that:

- each country was economically and politically free (autonomous)
- all countries follow the same route to development.

Developmentalism suggested that what happened in North America and Europe was best and would automatically happen elsewhere, which is not necessarily the case.

According to Wallerstein, the capitalist world system has three main characteristics:

- a global market
- many countries, which allow political and economic competition
- three tiers of countries.

The tiers are defined as core, largely MEDCs, the periphery, which can be identified with LEDCs, and the semi-periphery. The semi-periphery refers to countries where there are class struggles and social change, such as Latin America in the 1980s and eastern Europe in the late 1980s and early 1990s. It also includes the NICs where large-scale economic growth has occurred. Some of these NICs, notably China, India and Brazil, may be superpowers in the future.

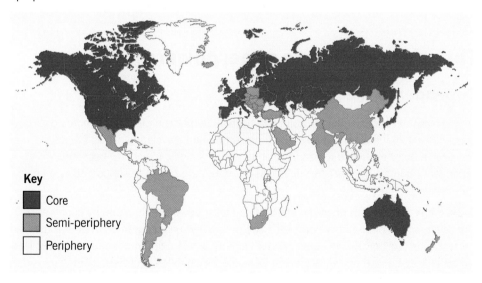

Figure 10.6: Global core, semi-periphery and periphery.

Wallerstein argued that capitalist development led to cycles of growth and stagnation. One of these cycles is a long-term economic cycle known as a Kondratieff cycle. This identifies cycles of depression at roughly 50- to 60-year intervals. The last two were in the 1920–30s and the late 1980s. Stagnation is important for the restructuring of the world system and allows the semi-periphery to become involved in the development process. Indeed, the recent financial crises may see some mini-superpowers emerging, notably the oil-rich Gulf States, with their vast financial resources.

According to the world systems approach, capitalism includes feudalism and socialism. They are extreme variations on the division of labour. As the world develops and changes, there will either be a swing towards a more socialist system or there will be a transition towards a more unequal (feudal) system.

Case study: Comparing China and India – impressive growth, important differences

China and India, together containing one-third of the world's population, have experienced tremendous economic growth since 1990. Their successes in advancing average wellbeing imply major improvements for a large section of humanity. Though both countries have achieved rapid, sustained economic growth, their rates of progress have been very different. China has enjoyed the fastest sustained economic advance in human history, averaging real per capita growth of 8% a year over the past decade. Its per capita income is now $5,400 in PPP (Purchasing Power Parity) terms. Meanwhile, real per capita income in India grew at an average rate of 4.4%, reaching $2,600 in 2007.

China's exceptional growth is partly explained by its market-based reforms that started in 1978, well before India's reforms in 1991. These reforms have enabled China to integrate with the global economy at a phenomenal pace. Today it is the largest recipient of foreign direct investment (FDI) among LEDCs. FDI in India has also increased significantly, though at much lower levels.

Strong export growth has contributed to the economic performance of India and China, with a growing dominance of manufactured exports. Again, China has had much more success in this area. Its exports reached $320 billion in 2001, compared with $35 billion for India. Manufactured exports accounted for 53% of China's total exports in 1981 and 90% in 2001; in India that share rose from 60% to 77%. China has had particular success in moving from labour-intensive to technology-intensive exports; telecommunications equipment and computers now account for one-quarter of its exports.

Social investments are required for sustained economic growth. In China public spending on education is 2.3% of the GDP, while that on health is 2.1% of the GDP. India, in contrast, has traditionally had lower spending levels. Human development indicators for India remain much lower than for China.

It would be misleading to talk solely in terms of national averages for two countries so large in population and area. In China the highest economic growth has occurred in the coastal provinces, while the geographically isolated north-western provinces have experienced much lower growth. India also harbours stark regional variations. In 1992–7, the per capita economic growth ranged from -0.2% in Bihar to 7.8% in Gujarat.

Summary

In this chapter, you have learnt:
- that the concept of a superpower has developed to include economic, cultural, military and geographical influence.
- that the geography of power and international influence can be seen through geographical patterns of military reach, trade and cultural dominance.
- that patterns of power change over time.
- that there are differences in the emerging powers versus the existing superpowers in terms of regional and global influence.
- that world systems analysis and dependency theory help explain these differences and partly explain why there are potentially emerging superpowers.

Key terms

Kondratieff cycles — a long-term (approx. 50-year) fluctuation in the world economic system. Also known as long waves. Each cycle heralds the rise of new technologies, major infrastructural investments, changes in the international location of industry and technological change.

Feudal — a pre-capitalist mode of production in which land was held by rich landlords and peasants worked the land for the lord, but received protection from him.

Socialism — a movement to establish a classless society by substituting public ownership for private ownership of the means of production, distribution and exchange.

Purchasing Power Parity — the value of gross national income related to local prices.

Examiners' tip

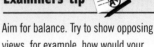

Aim for balance. Try to show opposing views, for example, how would your views differ if you were/were not living in a superpower?

Taking it further

To find out data for the literacy and infant mortality rate (IMR) for China and India, read 'Literacy and infant mortality rate for China and India' on your Student CD-ROM.

CHAPTER 11 What impacts and influences do superpowers have?

Key terms

Aid
Debt
Neocolonialism
United Nations

Learning objectives

After studying this chapter, you will be able to discuss these ideas and concepts and provide located examples of them:

- Power can be maintained directly or indirectly.
- Superpower rule has changed from colonial rule to indirect neocolonial rule through trade, aid and debt.
- Superpowers play a key role in international decision-making, policy and action through direct and indirect processes.
- Control of trade in terms of generating wealth, power and global influence is important.
- Superpower influence extends to the idea of a developing 'global culture' of ideas and norms, which has led to a backlash among some groups.

The geographic outcome of the Great Depression and two world wars was to shift the centre of the political power from Europe to the USA. In the period following the Second World War, the USA was also the dominant economic force globally. The need for secure trading partners became a major issue during the post-war era. Rather than ensuring a continuous supply of raw materials through imperialist expansion (there were no 'new lands' to discover and conquer), the new political order emphasised long-term access to resources and market access for the sale of goods. More recently access to cheap labour for the manufacture of goods to be sold in the global marketplace has been an important development.

The USA was eager to make allies with potential new trading partners, so it supported the independence of colonies, particularly through its leading role in the United Nations. Nevertheless the USA was reluctant for decolonisation to take place too rapidly as it was wary of the advance of communism. The US government argued that too rapid a decolonisation of South-east Asia would weaken the major colonial powers (France and Britain) and would allow communist spread into much of Asia.

Key terms

Aid — any help that is given, for example, financial, personnel, loans, equipment and skills.
Debt — the money owed by one country to another.

The shift from political imperialism to economic imperialism

As the level of direct political control by the colonial powers over their colonies decreased, the level of economic control increased. This economic imperialism (or neocolonialism) resulted from three interrelated factors:

- the economic dependence of most colonies on a very narrow base of primary commodities
- the economic dominance of multinational companies in the market
- the impact of foreign aid and foreign debt.

Dependence on primary products

The result of colonialism was that the economies of most colonies were directed towards supplying the rich countries with much of their resources.

Companies controlled by the rich nations operated in the colonies to supply raw materials. These companies did little to develop economic growth or large-scale infrastructural developments in the colonies. The profits of the export trade remained with the rich nation, and only a small amount was reinvested in the colony, so its industrial growth was limited. Consequently the economies of the colonies/poor countries were built on a very narrow base of products, usually primary products such as sugar, tea, coffee, rubber or copper. For example, Mauritius received up to 90% of its revenue from sugar and Zambia received 90% of its income from copper. This made these countries very vulnerable to changes in the world price and demand for their goods. Even as late as 1998 a number of LEDCs depended on a single primary product (see Figure 11.1).

'Perpetual' single commodity exporters	
Comoros	Spices 100
Dominica	Fruits 85
Gambia	Oilseeds 67
St Kitts-Nevis	Sugar 94
St Lucia	Fruits 85
St Vincent and the Grenadines	Fruits 52

'Transitory' single commodity exporters	
Benin	Cotton 83
Burundi	Coffee 97
Central African Republic	Cotton 76
Colombia	Coffee 51
Côte d'Ivoire	Cocoa 53
El Salvador	Coffee 55
Ethiopia	Coffee 75
Ghana	Cocoa 67
Honduras	Coffee 55
Mali	Cotton 94
Paraguay	Oilseeds 51
Togo	Cotton 66
Turkmenistan	Cotton 87
Uganda	Coffee 63

▲ **Figure 11.1:** Countries with more than 50% of agricultural export earnings from one commodity in 1998.

The rise of multinational companies

In many instances multinational companies began to dominate the economic scene, especially in terms of the primary products. Multinationals operate to produce a profit, which is distributed among the company shareholders. Due to their size and wealth, some multinational companies are able to dominate the worldwide market price for both the purchase and sale of primary commodities. By controlling the labour market and the commodities market, multinationals also influence the country's political decision-makers. In some cases these companies exert indirect influence on government policies. There are many examples, however, in which the multinationals have intervened directly in the politics of these nations.

Synoptic link

Look at pages 222–3 and 80 of Edexcel AS Geography to find out more about employment and international trade.

Foreign aid and foreign debt

Since the end of the Second World War, many rich nations, especially the USA, have been giving aid to peripheral countries. Aid has been provided in many forms, including untied cash grants, loans that must be used for a particular purpose, donations of capital equipment, technicians, teachers, health workers and advisers. Much of this aid has served to tie the peripheral nations even more closely to the economies of the core nations. For example:

- International aid organisations such as the World Bank and the International Monetary Fund distribute aid funds from the perspective of Western nations and do little other than create greater trading ties with the core.
- Aid funds have been allocated on the condition that particular goods and services will be purchased only from the donor nations. Sometimes these items are more expensive than those which can be purchased from non-donor nations.

Foreign debt levels

In the late 1970s interest rates around the globe reached levels over 20%. Due to high interest rates many nations and companies cut back on their spending, and the world economy entered a slump. Many peripheral nations faced very high debt repayments at a time when their national income from exports was falling. The result was a sharp fall in the standard of living in many countries. In 1988 it was estimated that total debt from the periphery to the core amounted to $US 1,000 billion.

Case study: Mexico's foreign debt

In Mexico in 1981 wages were halved and the price of basic foodstuffs rose. In 1982 Mexico announced that it could no longer afford to pay its debts, which amounted to about $US 100 billion (primarily to the USA). By this time many of the banks that had provided funds to Mexico had lent so much that they had to continue lending in order to enable Mexico to continue repaying its debts. In 1995 the US government guaranteed to underwrite Mexico's foreign debt.

Examiners' tip

Plan your answer. Make sure you have an introduction and a conclusion as well as the main body of the answer.

Taking it further

Use the Student CD-ROM to find out how Mauritius has managed to break away from its dependency.

Key term

United Nations — the global association of governments enabling cooperation in terms of international law, security, economic development and social equity.

International decision-making

The United Nations (UN)

The United Nations is probably the most influential and best-known international alliance in the world. It was established in 1945 and included 192 member nations by 2008. 26 countries signed the founding Charter of the UN, which aims to 'save succeeding generations from the scourge of war, which twice in our lifetime has brought untold sorrow to mankind, and to reaffirm faith in fundamental human rights, in the dignity of the human person, in the equal rights of men and women and of nations large and small'.

The UN provides a forum where member nations can express opinions and grievances, suggest actions to resolve tensions and disputes or ask for or offer assistance to other nations.

The UN General Assembly

The General Assembly is the core of the UN. All members appoint an ambassador to represent their country at the assembly. These ambassadors discuss international issues and try to resolve disputes by political means. At the assembly each member nation has one vote. In this way differences in the wealth, power and prestige of nations are overcome. Decisions are reached by a simple majority vote. Matters discussed by the assembly include international peace talks, strategies for settlement of national or international conflict, disarmament, preserving human rights and international political cooperation. Although the decisions of the assembly have no legally binding force, they carry the weight of world opinion on major national and international issues. Each year the General Assembly elects a new president and 21 vice-presidents. To make sure that all the world's geographic areas get equal representation the presidency rotates each year between five regions: western Europe, eastern Europe, Latin America, Asia and Africa.

The Security Council

Under the United Nations Charter the UN Security Council has primary responsibility for maintaining international peace and security. The council has five permanent members (the USA, Russia, China, France and the UK) and 10 other members who are each elected for a two-year period. Whereas all other UN organisations can only make recommendations to governments to take action of some kind, the Security Council has authority to direct member nations to take action. The Security Council can employ a number of measures to control conflict, including:

- requiring member nations to place economic sanctions, such as trade restrictions or embargoes, on aggressor nations
- insisting that nations are brought before the International Court of Justice
- limited military intervention, such as the direct involvement of UN peacekeeping forces.

The UN forces comprise military personnel drawn from the armed forces of member nations.

NATO

The North Atlantic Treaty Organisation was founded in 1949 to counter the rise of communist power in what was then the USSR. The Warsaw Pact was NATO's communist counterpart. These two international alliances represented the division in East–West political relations between about 1950 and 1990. The NATO alliance comprised the USA, Canada, Norway, the UK, Denmark, West Germany, the Netherlands, Luxembourg, Belgium, France, Spain, Portugal, Italy, Greece, Turkey and Iceland. The Warsaw Pact nations included the former USSR, East Germany, Poland, Czechoslovakia, Hungary, Romania and Bulgaria.

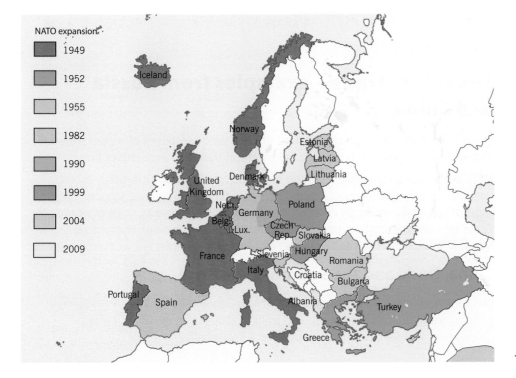

◀ **Figure 11.2:** Map of NATO.

Synoptic link

Take a look at pages 36–7 and 57–62 of Edexcel AS Geography to find out about the UN Framework Convention on Climate Change.

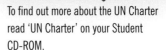

Taking it further

To find out more about the UN Charter read 'UN Charter' on your Student CD-ROM.

Originally NATO was an economic alliance between western Europe and the USA to assist the redevelopment of West Germany after the Second World War. It became a main means for the western European nations to contain the spread of communism by tying the military might of the USA to the affairs of Europe. However, the USSR viewed the rearming of West Germany and the establishment of NATO military bases in western Europe as a threat to its own safety. The Warsaw Pact alliance was created to counter NATO's growth. By the end of the 1960s both alliances had strong but roughly equal military forces to oppose one another, which ensured peace of a kind.

Since the collapse of communism the member nations of the former Warsaw Pact have been seeking to join NATO. They view NATO as a means by which they can gain access to Western democracy and Western economic markets. Belonging to NATO will help to protect them from possible conflict with Russia, which is still a powerful nation with nuclear capabilities.

The G7/8 is a group of the world's wealthiest and most powerful countries. G7 include Japan, the USA, France, Italy, the UK, Germany and Canada. G8 countries are the G7 plus Russia. The G10 is a collection of, in fact 11 countries. These are the wealthiest members of the International Monetary Fund and include Belgium, Canada, France, Germany, Italy, Japan, Netherlands, Sweden, Switzerland, the UK and the USA.

Synoptic link

Find out more about the G8 on page 82 of Edexcel AS Geography. Also look at pages 80–7 to find out about political groups of nations and their power.

Case study: International organisations and Iraq

Iraq has been a member of the UN since 1945. In the conflict in Iraq, the UN Security Council refused to endorse US–UK military invasion. However, following the bombing of the United Nations headquarters in Baghdad in August 2003, the UN pulled out of Iraq. In 2004 the UN sent a mission to Iraq to help build a new government. Critics have argued that the US has limited the role of the UN in Iraq on purpose, but at the same time has used the UN to legitimise its actions there. By 2006 there were troops from over 20 non-US military forces operating in Iraq. Most were European, but there were also troops from El Salvador, Australia, South Korea and Mongolia.

NATO had no role in the campaign in Iraq, but took action to protect Turkey from potential spill-over impacts from the Iraq War. Since 2004 NATO's role in Iraq has been in training, equipping and giving technical assistance, but not involvement in combat.

Among the G7/8 countries there was some opposition to the war – France, Germany and Russia were all against the war. China was also against the war. In 2003 the G7 countries agreed a multilateral deal to reconstruct Iraq's economy; at that time Iraq had external debts of $190 billion.

The actions of the international community have therefore been varied and at times contradictory, but it became a conflict in which there was a great deal of international involvement.

Examiners' tip

Evaluate. This requires you to give a measure of the relative importance of factors or features.

The role of trade – examples from Russia and China

International trade has been an important factor in the development of superpowers and there is a strong relationship between the volume of trade and standards of living.

MEDCs and LEDCs have different export and import patterns. MEDCs mostly export machinery, transport equipment, chemicals, agricultural products, and services. Their range of imports is similar. By contrast, LEDCs have a much smaller range of exports. These are mostly agricultural products and raw materials. The range of imports is similar to that of MEDCs, but is likely to be cheaper and less sophisticated.

China, trade and the scramble for Africa

China's African Policy was released in 2006. This was an official Chinese government paper aimed at promoting economic and political cooperation as well as energy development without interfering in each other's internal affairs.

China took advantage of the fact that Africa did not seem to have been a diplomatic and economic priority with the USA, Europe and Japan.

Chinese interest in Africa dates from the mid-1990s and has been based on international trade and on securing considerable quantities of a wide array of raw materials to feed its industrial development.

Trade between Africa and China increased from $3 billion in 1995 to over $32 billion in 2005. The latter figure amounts to 10% of Africa's total trade, but only 2.3% of China's. Economists predict that trade between the two will double by 2010. One-third of China's energy imports now come from Africa. Angola is China's largest supplier of oil, ahead of Saudi Arabia.

Synoptic link

Take a look at pages 45–6, 227–9 and 233–4 of Edexcel AS Geography to find out more about Africa.

Case study: Neocolonialism or South–South development?

China's strongest critics see it as the new imperial power in Africa and its major involvement in Africa as an example of neocolonialism. They are particularly critical of China's dealings with repressive regimes. Chinese support for countries such as Zimbabwe and Sudan is seen in the West as legitimising brutal dictatorships which seem to admire China's unique development model – considerable economic growth governed by a one-party totalitarian state with control over all aspects of economic activity.

China's most controversial energy relationship is with the Sudan. While most other major countries sought to impose United Nations sanctions on Sudan because of the government's 'support' for the genocide in Darfur, China strongly opposed Security Council actions. China has invested $3 billion in Sudan's oil and gas industry. There are claims that 4,000 Chinese troops are guarding Sudanese oil pipelines. Sudan now supplies 7% of China's oil imports.

China and foreign TNCs

Major mining transnational corporations (TNCs) are becoming increasingly concerned that China is freezing them out of many African countries as China is negotiating more and more comprehensive agreements with African countries. The international mining companies are finding it difficult to compete with the huge incentives China is offering, such as building roads and railways in return for mineral rights. China spent more than $10 billion on infrastructure projects in Africa in 2006 according to the World Bank.

Technology transfer is another important aspect of economic development. For example, China is helping Nigeria to launch a second space satellite. With Chinese assistance Sudan has recently built three weapons factories near the capital city, Khartoum.

Key term

Neocolonialism — used to describe the ways in which rich countries dominate the economy of poorer countries. It is a form of economic imperialism rather than political control.

Russia and natural gas

Russia vies with the USA as the world's number one gas producer. Both countries account for about one-fifth of global production. Production in Russia has increased from 555.4 billion m^3 in 1995 to 598 billion m^3 in 2005.

Russian gas is piped to a large number of countries by means of an extensive pipeline network. The pipeline networks for both oil and gas are owned by the state. Gas supplies by Gazprom (a state company with a monopoly on Russian gas exports and therefore having considerable power) account for approximately 23% of gas consumption in the EU. The largest buyer of Russian gas in absolute terms is Germany, followed by the Ukraine and Italy. At present Russia does not export gas to eastern Asian countries or to the USA.

Disputes over the price and supply of gas raised EU fears about its increasing reliance on energy supplies from Russia. Currently, Europe relies on Gazprom for about one-quarter of its gas. Critics argue that Russia has a habit of manipulating gas and oil supplies for political purposes. The disputes illustrated that Europe's energy sources needed to be more diverse. The EU is therefore looking to build interconnecting pipelines and power lines and to diversify supplies.

Taking it further

Look into the case study 'The Chambishi Copper Mine, Zambia' on your Student CD-ROM.

Taking it further

Use the Student CD-ROM to assess the costs and benefits of Chinese investment.

▶ **Figure 11.3:** Map of Russian natural gas fields and pipelines to Europe.

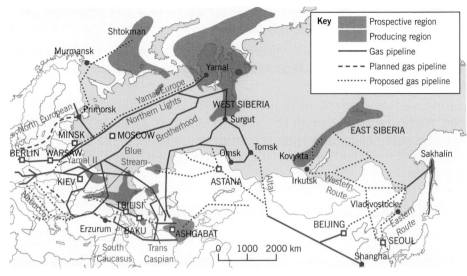

Synoptic link

Take a look at pages 68–9 of Edexcel AS Geography to learn more about fossil fuels. Also look at Topic 1 Energy Security in this book.

Taking it further

To find out about recent disputes between Russia and neighbouring countries over the price and supply of gas and oil read 'Disputes between Russia and neighbouring countries' on your Student CD-ROM.

According to the *Financial Times* (13 November 2006), 'NATO advisers have warned the military alliance that it needs to guard against any attempt by Russia to set up an "Opec for gas" that would strengthen Moscow's leverage over Europe.' The study warned that Russia could seek to construct a gas cartel including the countries of central Asia, Algeria, Qatar, Libya and perhaps Iran.

Increasing links with China

In 2006 Russia said it would build two natural gas pipelines to China and become one of the country's biggest gas suppliers within the next decade. Some analysts believe that this would not be possible without disrupting supplies to Europe.

Russia's importance as an international energy supplier has increased significantly over the last decade and it will become even more critical in the future. This may even return Russia to superpower status. This importance will give the country greater economic and political power. There is growing concern about how this power will be used as the energy security of many parts of Europe could be threatened.

Global culture of ideas and norms

McDonald's restaurants

On an average day over 30 million customers are served at 20,000 McDonald's restaurants in more than 100 countries around the world. The world map shows that the first restaurants were located in the USA and Canada, and then spread to Europe, Australia and Japan during the early 1970s.

Synoptic link

Take a look at pages 80 and 83–6 of Edexcel AS Geography to learn more about McDonald's. Also look at Option 4 The World of Cultural Diversity in this book.

▶ **Figure 11.4:** McDonald's around the world.

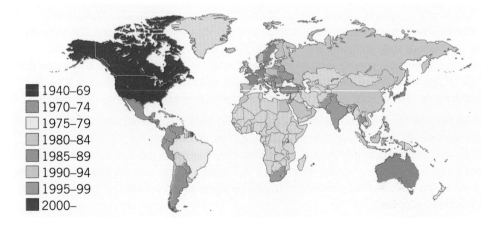

■ 1940–69
■ 1970–74
□ 1975–79
□ 1980–84
■ 1985–89
□ 1990–94
□ 1995–99
■ 2000–

By the end of the 1970s McDonald's was consolidating its position in Europe, New Zealand and South America. The 1980s saw expansion in South America, Mexico, Europe and South-east Asia. China, Russia and parts of the Arab world were reached in the 1990s.

Over half these restaurants are in the USA, but the UK has over 600 outlets, Brazil over 250, China nearly 200 and Thailand nearly 50. They are famous due to their uniformity and the same service style the world over. And yet, McDonald's may not be the force for cultural homogenisation that this suggests. McDonald's has been localised, indigenised and incorporated into traditional cultural forms and practices. Exactly how this has happened varies. In Beijing, McDonald's has lost its American role as a place of fast and cheap food. Instead, it has become a middle-class consumption place, somewhere for a special family outing, somewhere 'customers linger <...> for hours, relaxing, chatting, reading, enjoying the music'. McDonald's here is seen as American, but in Beijing American stands for something stylish, exotic and foreign! In Japan, while there is a similar leisurely use of McDonald's, it is not a place of exotic social prestige, but a youth hangout; McDonald's restaurants in Hong Kong are filled with people of all ages, few of whom are seeking an American cultural experience.

McDonald's has been at the centre of anti-capitalism, animal rights and environmental rights protests. Protesters argue that the company is merely a profit-making organisation, which values money above all else. McDonald's has been the focus for anti-capitalism protests partly on account of its high profile, its logo and the high-profile legal cases it has taken against protesters.

McDonald's has donated over $180 million to McDonald's Children Charities and claims to donate more money than any other commercial enterprise in the USA, over $50 million annually. Critics argue that McDonald's produces over 1 million tonnes of packaging, which is used just for a few minutes.

Coca-Cola

Founded in 1886 by pharmacist John Styth Pemberton in Atlanta, Georgia, the Coca-Cola Company is the world's leading manufacturer, marketer and distributor of non-alcoholic beverage concentrates and syrups used to produce nearly 400 brands. The Coca-Cola Company continues to be based in Atlanta and employs 49,000 people worldwide.

Coca-Cola is one of the most recognised trademarks in the world. The word Coca-Cola itself is thought to be the second most widely understood word in the world after 'OK'!

Nowadays, Coca-Cola is located in more than 200 countries, where the drinks are produced by local people with local resources. Coca-Cola produces brands that embrace distinct tastes and local preferences.

Taking it further

Find out if two neighbouring countries with a McDonald's restaurant have ever gone to war with each other? What might the reasons be — are these are wealthy consumer countries? Most battles are now fought by long-distance aggressors or peacekeepers? Are most of these civil wars?

Taking it further

Compare the global distribution of Starbucks and McDonald's. Visit http://www.princeton.edu/~ina/infographics/starbucks.html for the global distribution of Starbucks outlets and McDonald's restaurants.

Summary

In this chapter, you have learnt:

• that power can be used directly or indirectly.

• that superpower rule has changed from colonial rule to indirect neocolonial rule through trade, aid and debt.

• that superpowers play a key role in international decision-making.

• that control of trade is important for generating wealth, power and global influence.

• that superpower influence extends to the idea of a developing 'global culture', which has led to a backlash among some groups.

CHAPTER 12 What are the implications of the continued rise of the superpowers?

Key terms

Acid rain
Bipolar structure
Cartel
Weapons of mass destruction

Learning objectives

After studying this chapter, you will be able to discuss these ideas and concepts and provide located examples of them:

- The rise of the BRICs and continued growth in superpowers has resource implications in terms of energy, water and land.
- A balance needs to be achieved between the economic benefits and the environmental costs.
- Shifting power has implications for older core regions.
- Shifting power and the rise of emerging powers has implications for most of the world.
- Shifting power may cause increased tensions between one global culture and another.

The rise of the BRICs, resource implications and environmental costs

The rise of the BRICs is related to a number of geographic factors. Firstly, they are all large countries. In terms of physical size, Russia, China, Brazil and India rank first, third, fifth and seventh respectively. In terms of population, China, India, Brazil and Russia rank first, second, fifth and eighth. In addition, some of these countries have many resources – Russia in particular has oil and gas; Brazil has gold, diamonds, iron ore and rainforest; and India and China have vast quantities of coal. Nevertheless, China does not have a vast supply of resources given its population size and area.

► **Figure 12.1:** Emerging superpowers.

Source: http://en.wikipedia.org

China and Africa

Some commentators claim that China is a new version of a colonial power, an emerging superpower. Others, however, suggest that China's presence in Africa is an ideal opportunity for African nations to develop. The most common complaint centres on foreign policy. In its efforts to gain reliable supplies of raw materials, critics argue that China is ravaging the resources of poor countries, supporting dictatorships and subverting the attempts of the West to bring wealth and democracy. Others point to the benefits that China's commodity binge brings to poor countries. There has never been such a rapid development of the economies of African and Latin American countries. It is probable that this increase will remove more people from poverty than the aid schemes of the West.

Current Chinese foreign policy dates from the 1960s. Today there are over 800,000 Chinese running businesses in Africa. Over 800 businesses are involved in manufacturing and infrastructural developments such as the construction of railways, hospitals, ports and other facilities, at competitive prices, using relatively cheap labour.

China appears to have come up with a development model that has produced real results in terms of poverty alleviation and national control of resources. This makes China more appealing to most African countries than Western counterparts. Moreover, Chinese interest in the continent is increasing.

At the China–Africa forum in 2006, China promised to:
- double its aid to Africa by 2009
- put in place a $5 billion loan and credit programme
- increase the two-way trade with Africa to over $100 billion by 2010
- set up anti-malarial clinics across the continent
- establish five trade and investment centres to train 15,000 professionals in various fields
- cancel debt.

Nevertheless, China's main interest in Africa is economic. China needs Africa for its own economic development and its political strength. Although it has plenty of land (9.5 billion km^2), it has only 7% of the world's arable land and freshwater, 3% of its forests and 2% of its oil. China accounts for about 20% of the world's population, yet it consumes over half of the world's pork, half of its cement, a third of its steel and over a quarter of its aluminium. It is spending 35 times more on imports of soy beans and crude oil than in 1999.

Not only is China attracting criticism for its foreign policy, environmental issues are becoming more serious. Steelmaking, for example, uses 16% of China's power, compared with 10% of all the country's households combined. By far the most common fuel for power generation is coal. As a result, more steel mills and chemical plants mean more acid rain and smog, not to mention global warming.

Key term

Acid rain — the increased acidity of rainfall and dry deposition as a result of human activity.

In 2003 more than 250 Chinese cities were affected by acid rain, which triggered economic losses of $13.3 billion for the year, equal to approximately 3% of the country's gross domestic product. In south-western China, acid rain pollution proved extremely serious. Apart from Chongqing, the average pH value of the central districts was less than 5.0 and the acid rain frequency was 70%. In southern China, the acid rain problem was mainly distributed in the Pearl River Delta and central and eastern areas of Guangxi.

The two main causes of acid rain in China are the burning of coal for industrial development and the increase in the number of cars on the roads. In 2006 China produced 1,212 million tonnes of oil equivalent (mtoe) of coal, compared with 595 mtoe in the USA and 209 mtoe in India. Russia produced 144 mtoe. In addition, the burning of fossil fuels in homes contributes to the problem. The presence of large quantities of chimneys in the vicinity of ground level emits pollutants very close to the earth. In contrast, industrial chimneys are higher up and likely to send pollutants further up in the atmosphere where they are more easily dispersed.

▶ **Figure 12.2:** Air pollution in Beijing.

Beijing has been described as the 'air pollution capital of the world'. Indeed, China has 16 of the world's 20 most polluted cities. Poor air quality in China is blamed for over 400,000 premature deaths every year. High levels of nitrogen dioxide cause major respiratory problems. Up to one-third of China's urban population is exposed to dangerous levels of pollution. Acid rain now falls on about 33% of the country and up to 70% of China's rivers and lakes contain so many toxins that they are unfit for drinking.

Case study: Beijing – past and future

At the Beijing 2008 Olympic Games, US cyclists caused a stir when they got off their plane wearing face masks. The city authorities had attempted to improve air quality for the games by closing factories, removing cars from the roads and halting major building programmes. On a more long-term basis, Beijing's Capital Iron & Steel Group's new plant at Caofeidian, 220 km east of Beijing, will replace the old iron and steel plant at Shougang. This huge plant, which employed 65,000 workers, produced 12.5 million tonnes of steel each year. The new plant will be capable of producing 9.7 million tonnes of steel, 9.1 million tonnes of rolled steel and nearly 9 million tonnes of iron. China also plans to close down inefficient steel mills and iron foundries by 2010. The new plant will be more environmentally friendly than the old plant – up to 99.5% of solid waste and 97.5% of waste water will be recycled. In addition, less dust and sulphur dioxide will be emitted compared with the Shougang plant.

The implications of shifting power

The US National Intelligence Council produces a global trends review every four years. In 2004 it predicted there would be continued US dominance globally as most major powers had stopped trying to catch up with the US economy. In 2008, however, in its report 'Global trends 2025: A Transformed World', it suggested that China, India and Brazil would grow at the expense of the USA and EU. It predicts a world that will be increasingly fragmented, with conflicts over scarce resources, limited effective action by international organisations and the proliferation of nuclear weapons, especially in the Middle East, and even nuclear war. It suggested that the trend of wealth moving from the West to the East would continue, especially after the global financial crisis of 2008.

This is an emerging multipolar world in which the USA will be less dominant. It suggests a rocky time ahead with many potential crises, such as shortages of fuel, food and water and climate change, possibly triggering international flashpoints. Even countries that have been friendly up until now (such as EU countries and the USA) have been at loggerheads over how to deal with climate change, trade and market access.

Decline of the USSR and the rebirth of Russia

Throughout much of the post-Second World War period until 1990, the world had two superpowers and there were two opposing world views, one from the USA and one from the USSR. However, this has been replaced by a new world order. The decline of this bipolar structure has altered global geopolitics.

The former USSR declined as a superpower and was unable to sustain a global military presence. Many former Soviet states became independent such as the Ukraine, Lithuania and Latvia. Nevertheless, this has not always been a peaceful process. In 1995 the Chechens demanded independence and this resistance was crushed by Moscow. In 2008 the Russian army invaded Georgia. Within two months it had pulled all its troops back to the two disputed territories of Abkhazia and South Ossetia (see Figure 12.3). Many European Union leaders were swift to praise Russia. This was probably due to the fact that Russia is important to the EU.

Synoptic link

To find out more about the Olympic Games, look at pages 259 and 278–9 of Edexcel AS Geography.

Taking it further

Visit www.worldwatch.org/node/4496 for an update on acid rain in China.

Taking it further

Visit the National Intelligence Council's website and find out what it is predicting for the world in 2020.

Synoptic link

For further information on newly industrialising countries, see pages 82 and 93 of Edexcel AS Geography.

Key term

Bipolar structure — a pattern where there are two opposing forces; in this case, the USA and USSR as superpowers.

Russia supplies 25% of the EU's gas and it is the largest producer of natural gas. The EU currently uses 480 billion cubic metres (bcm) of gas per year and this is predicted to rise to 600 bcm by 2020. Russia could provide most of that need. The West also needs to be able to maintain talks with Russia about many things, notably efforts to prevent Iran from acquiring nuclear weapons.

Synoptic link

See Topic 1 Energy Security in this book.

Taking it further

Use the Student's CD-ROM to discover why Georgia and the Caucasus are important to the West.

◀ **Figure 12.3:** Map of Georgia and the disputed territories.

Nuclear issues

The dismantling of Soviet nuclear weapons and the subsequent black market trade in plutonium is an alarming consequence of the collapse of the USSR. Also of concern is the 'brain drain' of nuclear scientists to non-nuclear states and possibly terrorist organisations. Countries that belong to the 'nuclear club', which is to say those with nuclear weapons, include the USA, Russia, China, the UK, France, India, Pakistan, Israel and North Korea. Pakistan developed its programme to counter the threat from India. In addition, it is widely believed that Iran and Syria are developing nuclear capabilities. The NIC report of 2008 suggested that Iran is close to acquiring nuclear capability and states that once this occurs, a nuclear arms race may be triggered in the Middle East.

New alliances and economic superpowers

The USA has emerged as the world's supreme military power. However, as the 1991 Gulf War showed, the USA needs United Nations approval. Gathering such support involves establishing new and unusual alliances such as between the USA and Islamic states. Its alliance with Pakistan in the fight against al-Qaeda and the Taliban in Afghanistan is a good example of this. Despite the dominant military position of the USA, its economic power is being challenged by China and the European Union. The new world order that has emerged is not free from political and economic tensions and conflicts.

Uneven distribution of wealth

The growing disparity between the rich and poor countries of the world is a major cause of political tension. Inequalities have increased over time. In 2007 the average income of the five richest countries was nearly 70 times greater than the world's five poorest countries. In 1800 it was just three times greater. Huge foreign debts and worsening economic prospects for many countries highlight the unfair global distribution of wealth.

Trade wars

There are several trade wars around the world, in industries as diverse as bananas, beef, steel and cars. To prevent such frictions, 134 countries agreed on trading rules and joined the World Trade Organisation (WTO) to mediate disputes.

Case study: The beef trade war

The EU and the USA came to blows over beef. In 1988 the EU banned the import of hormone-treated beef. The EU claimed that beef from cattle reared using growth hormones is unsafe. While the Americans say there is no health risk, the EU maintains that some of the hormones may cause cancer. Hormones are widely used in US agriculture, with more than 90% of American cattle producers feeding them to their cattle to make them grow faster and bigger.

The United States claimed this was protectionism and the World Trade Organisation (WTO) approved an American request to impose sanctions on the European Union in response to its ban on hormone-treated beef. The US wanted to impose 100% duties against $202 million worth of imports from the EU (the amount of trade it claims to have lost due to the ban).

International policing

Another emerging area of conflict is the massive cost of international policing. The USA has borne the burden of military expenditure among Western powers, but there are strong internal pressures for the costs to be shared with other countries. If the USA does become involved it will be with UN sanction and as part of a UN team. If the USA is reluctant to act as global police officer, new tensions and conflicts will have to be dealt with by the UN.

International terrorism and the threat of nuclear weapons and WMD

The role of international terrorism changed with the 9/11 attacks on the USA in 2001. Non-conventional weapons were used as al-Qaeda terrorists hijacked and flew aircraft into the World Trade Center and the Pentagon, killing around 3,000 people.

Nuclear weapons continue to create political tension as regional arms races develop to counter the increased capabilities of neighbouring countries. India, Pakistan, Iran, Iraq and North Korea have been identified as countries in which nuclear tensions might spark a war. This identification led to the Iraq War. However, no weapons of mass destruction were ever found and the war in Iraq continues to this day. A major concern is the illegal trade of nuclear weapons to 'rogue states' and terrorist groups.

Shifting power and emerging power

Economic dominance has been a feature of the second half of the 20th century. Multinational corporations have a major influence on global commodity prices and most multinational corporations are based in superpowers, such as the USA and EU. Many rich countries direct a high percentage of their foreign aid to peripheral countries and this binds these nations to the core. Increasingly, however, some peripheral nations are gaining economic independence by two main means: nationalisation and cartels.

Some periphery nations have nationalised foreign-owned companies. This means that the state takes control of the company or its land holdings. In most cases the government purchases the business from the company shareholders. In some circumstances the government simply claims the company and any property as its own. In contrast, some countries have formed cartels.

Key terms

Weapons of mass destruction (WMD) — weapons that can kill a large number of people. They include nuclear, biological, chemical and radiological weapons.

Cartel — an organisation of people who supply the same product and join together to control its overall supply. The members of a cartel can force up the price of their good either by restricting its supply on the world market or by agreeing on a particular supply price and refusing to sell the good for less. The Organisation of Petroleum Exporting Countries (OPEC) is an example of a cartel. By agreeing to restrict supply, the members of OPEC were able to force up the world price of oil during the 1970s, thereby increasing revenue to their countries.

Case study: OPEC – an oil cartel

The Organisation of Petroleum Exporting Countries (OPEC) was established in 1960 to counter oil price cuts by American and European oil companies. Founder nations included Iran, Iraq, Kuwait, Saudi Arabia and Venezuela. Qatar, Indonesia and Libya joined in 1962 and the United Arab Emirates, Algeria, Nigeria, Ecuador, Gabon and Angola joined later. Gabon and Indonesia left OPEC in 1994 and 2008 respectively.

In 1979 the OPEC countries produced 65% of world petroleum, but only 36% by 2007. As early as 2003, concerns that OPEC members had

▲ **Figure 12.4:** Members of OPEC.

little excess pumping capacity sparked speculation that their influence on crude oil prices would begin to slip. However, revenues from oil have allowed member countries to invest in and diversify their economies, and to generate wealth over the last 40 years or so.

From a Western perspective, the development of OPEC and the control of oil had important implications. As OPEC controlled the price of oil and much of the production in the 1970s and 80s, Middle Eastern countries had increased economic and political power. It also increased the dependency of all the regions on the Middle East. Arguably this might provide an incentive for old industrialised countries to increase energy conservation or develop alternative forms of energy.

The importance of oil meant that countries needed to maintain favourable relationships with OPEC countries and that the Middle East would be involved in economic cooperation and development with industrialised countries. It also means that there needs to be political stability in the Middle East and a reassessment coal and nuclear power as energy options.

Demographic changes may also favour some North African and Middle Eastern countries. The world's population is forecast to grow by approximately 1.5 billion to 8 billion in 2025. Almost all of this growth will be in Africa, Asia and South America. Increasing population size may lead to increasing political clout, but it could also lead to rising unemployment, inequalities and violence.

Continued dependency or new opportunities?

The growth of new economic powers has implications for the majority of the world. The growth of China, for example, can be seen to be both positive and negative depending on the perspective one takes. It is a positive thing for investors from rich countries. MEDC countries have been keen to invest in China as it enables them to push their products or services, but it also gains them an important foothold in an emerging market. This is likely to be as true for energy and water companies as it is for manufacturing and financial companies. Likewise, consumers may benefit from the cheap products that are mass-produced in China and exported to MEDCs, thereby undercutting the prices of home producers. While shoppers enjoy cheap prices, many workers may be losing their jobs as a result. Many US manufacturers are worried that the rise of India and China will lead to a decline in the US economy. India and China pay lower wages and produce goods more competitively on the world market. Even the shift of US industry to low-wage locations such as along the Mexico–US border, the 'maquiladora industries', has alarmed industrialists in the USA.

Taking it further

Use the Student CD-ROM for a link to find out who are emerging as the Middle Eastern superpowers and how the USA and UK have helped them indirectly. See 'Middle Eastern superpowers'.

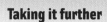

Taking it further

To find out about the state of the world's oil reserves, visit the OPEC home page at www.opec.org.

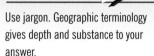

Examiners' tip

Use jargon. Geographic terminology gives depth and substance to your answer.

It is not only rich countries that are worried. China has developed an extensive trading network with many African nations. China is able to undercut local producers and is also using up resources which could have benefited the host nation. Many Western countries are worried that Chinese influence in the region is stronger than EU or US influence. Not only will the EU and USA lose out economically, they may also lose out ideologically.

Shifting power bases may also have environmental implications. Most developed areas have done so at the expense of the natural environment. Any large-scale development in China, India or Brazil, for example, will require large quantities of natural resources. China is resource-poor, hence the reason for Chinese efforts to secure resources from African nations and North Korea. Increased trade means more transport emissions. Although these might not be quantified as part of China's emissions in annual statistics, the emissions still occur. It is no surprise that environmental problems such as acidification and poor air quality are increasing in emerging powers, just as acidification is decreasing in northern Europe.

Cultural tensions

Case study: After 9/11 – the case against the USA

While most of the world condemned the terrorist attacks, there were scenes of rejoicing in Palestinian refugee camps in Lebanon. However, the Palestinian leader Yasser Arafat announced his country's genuine sorrow and unreserved condemnation of the attack.

Some of the world's people believe that the USA got what it deserved in the attacks. They consider the US government to be hypocritical and claim that the USA had ignored certain international agreements such as a world criminal court, the abolition of land mines, and the Kyoto agreement (the USA is the world's largest producer of greenhouse gases). In addition, the USA had refused to pay its dues to the UN and had cut its aid to the world's poorest nations. While it had been eager to prosecute African and Balkan war criminals, it had refused to allow its own citizens to submit to an international court. The USA had supported regimes in parts of Africa, Asia and Latin America when it suited their purpose. For example, it supported Kuwait, attacked Libya and Iraq, and continued to impose economic sanctions against Iraq. The USA has been criticised over its Middle East policy. The USA appears to have been lenient with Israel and not done as much to push the Palestinian cause.

New political unions

The USA lost no time rewarding its new allies in the war against terrorism. It lifted economic sanctions on Pakistan and India, rescheduled $379 million of Pakistan's bilateral debt, offered to expand Indonesia's special trade preferences and passed a long-delayed free-trade agreement with Jordan. Egypt's official foreign debt was cut in half in 1991, partly as a reward for its help in the Gulf War.

In a particularly striking shift in long-term thinking, Russia said it wanted closer ties with, and perhaps even membership of, the EU and NATO. Egypt said it would unhappily support the American-led coalition. When Iraq invaded Kuwait in 1990, Egypt gave prompt and full support to an American-led alliance, decisively tipping the Arab world against Saddam Hussein. Egypt's government was not about to let down a superpower that provides $2 billion a year in military and economic aid.

Saudi Arabia cut off ties with the Taliban, accusing it of recruiting and training impressionable Saudis to take part in international terrorism. Nevertheless, Bin Laden's religious views and his opposition to American forces in Saudi Arabia appealed to some Saudi dissidents.

Changed unions

The USA began to put pressure on Israel. Some of the ideas included:

• that Jerusalem should become the shared capital of the Israeli and Palestinian states

- a viable Palestinian state, based on one continuous tract of land, and not economically dependent upon Israel
- the preservation of the national state of each country – Israel as Jewish and Palestine as Arab (Muslim)
- the end of expansion of Jewish settlement on the West Bank
- that the USA still remains committed to Israel's security.

Changing patterns

In 2004 the NIC asserted that globalisation was irreversible, energy supplies were plentiful and the USA would remain the world's only superpower; climate change barely got a mention. However, in just four years there is an emerging multipolar world. Energy supplies are not guaranteed and climate change is recognised even in the USA. Global cooperation is required to tackle the financial, energy, security, economic and environmental problems of the future. In an increasingly multipolar world it might not prove easy to reach an agreement.

Synoptic link

To find out more about climate change, look at pages 13–14, 23–5, 36–43 and 54–70 of Edexcel AS Geography. Also look at Topic 2 Water Conflicts and Topic 6 The Technological Fix? in this book.

Taking it further

See the feature called 'Is globalisation doomed?' on the Student CD-ROM.

Summary

In this chapter, you have learnt:
- that there are changes occurring in the world order – away from a sole superpower to a multipower world.
- that the rise of the BRICs and continued growth in superpowers have resource implications in terms of energy, water and land. The example of China's activities in Africa illustrates this well.
- that a balance needs to be achieved between the economic benefits and the environmental costs.
- that shifting power has implications for older core regions.
- that shifting power and the rise of emerging powers have implications for the majority of the world.
- that shifting power may cause increased tensions between one global culture and another.

Exam Practice – Section A

Superpower Geographies

2000	2025	2050
1 USA	USA	1 = China
2 Europe	China	USA
3 China	Europe	3 = India
4 India	India	Russia
5 Japan	Japan	5 = Europe
6 Russia	Russia	6 = Brazil
7 Brazil	Brazil	Japan

By 2025 the international system will be a global multipolar one. That is a dramatic shift away from the time after the fall of the Berlin Wall and the dissolution of the Soviet Union when there was only one superpower.

'By 2050 there will be shift of power to Asia as the new Superpowers emerge'.

(a) Explain why the world power rankings in Figure 4 shown are likely to change between 2000 and 2050. [10]

(b) Evaluate the factors which lead to superpower status. [15]

◄ **Figure 4:** World power rankings based on economy.

CHAPTER 13 What is the nature of the development gap? How has it arisen?

Key terms

Dependency theory
Development
Development gap
Foreign direct investment
Free trade
GDI
GDP at purchasing power Parity
GEM
Modernisation theory
Newly Industrialised Countries
Non-governmental organisations
The terms of trade
Trade deficit
Transnational corporation
World system theory

Key terms

Development — the use of resources to improve the quality of life in a country.
Development gap — the difference in income and the quality of life in general between the richest and poorest countries in the world.
GDP at Purchasing Power Parity (PPP$) — the GDP of a country converted into US dollars on the basis of how the value of the currency compares with that of other countries.

Learning objectives

After studying this chapter, you will be able to discuss these ideas and concepts and provide located examples of them:

• The measurement of the development gap.
• The theories that can be used to explain the development gap.
• The major organisations which have an impact on global development.
• The impact of trade and investment on the development gap.

Measuring the global development gap

What is development?

Development, or improvement in the quality of life, is a wide-ranging concept. It includes wealth, but it also includes other important aspects of our lives. For example, many people would consider good health to be more important than wealth. People who live in countries that are not democracies where freedom of speech cannot be taken for granted often envy those who do live in democratic countries.

GDP: the traditional measure of development

The most common indicator of a country's wealth is the Gross Domestic Product (GDP). The Gross Domestic Product is the total value of goods and services produced by a country in a year. To take account of the different populations of countries the Gross Domestic Product Per Capita is often used. Here, the total GDP of a country is divided by the total population. However, 'raw' GDP data does not take into account the way in which the cost of living can vary between countries.

Top 15 countries		Bottom 15 countries	
Qatar	80,900	Rwanda	900
Luxembourg	80,500	Togo	800
Malta	53,400	Mozambique	800
Norway	53,000	Malawi	800
Brunei	51,000	Ethiopia	800
Singapore	47,700	Eritrea	800
Cyprus	46,900	Sierra Leone	700
USA	45,800	Niger	700
Ireland	43,100	Central African Republic	700
Switzerland	41,100	Somalia	600
Kuwait	39,300	Guinea-Bissau	500
Iceland	38,800	Liberia	400
Andorra	38,800	Burundi	400
Netherlands	38,500	Democratic Rep. of Congo	300
Canada	38,400	Zimbabwe	200

Source: Central Intelligence Agency

▶ **Figure 13.1:** Top 15 and bottom 15 countries in GDP (PPP) per capita 2007.

Organisations such as the United Nations now publish GDP data at Purchasing Power Parity (PPP). This takes account of differences in the cost of living between countries. Figure 13.1 shows the top and bottom 15 countries in GDP per capita (PPP). The development gap between the world's wealthiest and poorest countries is huge. However, a major limitation of both types of GDP data is that these are 'average' figures for a country, which tell us nothing about:

- the way in which wealth is distributed within a country
- how government invests the money at its disposal. For example, Cuba has a low GDP per capita but high standards of health and education because these have been government priorities for a long time.

Broader measures of development

The way that the quality of life has been measured has changed over time. In the 1980s the Physical Quality of Life Index (PQLI) was devised. The PQLI was the average of three development factors: literacy, life expectancy and infant mortality. However, in 1990 the Human Development Index (HDI) was devised as a better measure. It contains three variables:

- Life expectancy
- Educational attainment (adult literacy and combined primary, secondary and tertiary enrolment)
- GDP per capita (PPP$).

The actual figures for each of these three measures are converted into an index which has a maximum value of 1.0 in each case. The three index values are then combined and averaged to give an overall human development index value. This also has a maximum value of 1.0. Every year the United Nations publishes the Human Development Report which uses the Human Development Index (HDI) to rank all the countries of the world in their level of development. In 1995 the UN introduced two gender indicators, the Gender-Related Development Index (GDI) and the Gender Empowerment Measure (GEM).

Every measure of development has merits and limitations. No single measure can provide a complete picture of the differences in development between countries. This is why the United Nations combines three measures of different aspects of the quality of life to arrive at a figure of human development for each country. Although the development gap can be measured in a variety of ways it is generally taken to be increasing.

Level of human development	Human Development Index value	Number of countries 2005
High	0.800 and over	70
Medium	0.500 – 0.799	85
Low	Below 0.500	22

◀ **Figure 13.2:** High, medium and low human development worldwide.

Examiners' tip

Remember that data can be shown in both absolute and relative form. Absolute data, such as the total GDP for different countries, gives the total figures involved. Relative data, such as per cent, per thousand or per capita, means dividing the absolute figures by the total population or by another number.

Key terms

GDI — a measurement of the overall achievement of both men and women in the three dimensions of the human development index: life expectancy, educational attainment and real income, adjusted for gender inequalities.

GEM — focuses on three variables which reflect women's participation in political decision-making, access to professional opportunities and earnings power respectively.

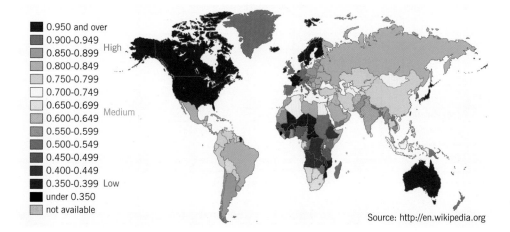

0.950 and over
0.900-0.949
0.850-0.899   High
0.800-0.849
0.750-0.799
0.700-0.749
0.650-0.699
0.600-0.649   Medium
0.550-0.599
0.500-0.549
0.450-0.499
0.400-0.449
0.350-0.399 Low
under 0.350
not available

Source: http://en.wikipedia.org

◀ **Figure 13.3:** Human Development Index values.

Synoptic link

Look at pages 80-1 of Edexcel AS Geography, which consider the main groupings of nations and global disparities. This section of the book explains the Gini coefficient which measures income distribution within countries.

Taking it further

Look at the Millennium Goals Report 2008 (www.un.org/millenniumgoals) to assess progress on the millennium goals.

Key term

Modernisation theory — a deterministic approach based on the economic history of a number of developed countries. Distinct economic and social changes are required for a country to move from one stage to another.

Figure 13.2 shows the human development index values for high, medium and low human development while Figure 13.3 shows the variation in human development in 2005.

The Millennium Development Goals (MDG)

The Millennium Development Goals established in 2000 by international agreement are probably the most significant major attempt to defeat poverty ever undertaken. The UN set out eight development goals to reduce global poverty substantially by 2015. They are viewed as basic human rights – the rights of every person on earth to health, education, shelter and security. Measurement of progress is based on 1990 figures. By 2015, all 191 United Nations member states have pledged to meet these goals. The eight Millennium Development Goals (MDGs) are as follows:

1. Eradicate extreme poverty and hunger.
2. Achieve universal primary education.
3. Promote gender equality and empower women.
4. Reduce child mortality.
5. Improve maternal health.
6. Combat HIV/AIDS, malaria and other diseases.
7. Ensure environmental sustainability.
8. Develop a global partnership for development.

Theories used to explain the development gap

Modernisation theory: the stages of development

In 1960, the American economist W.W. Rostow recognised five stages of economic development (Figure 13.4). The richest countries were in the final stage, having passed through all or most of the previous stages. Countries at all five stages could be recognised in the modern world. Rostow concluded that the development gap happened because countries were at different stages of the model. The model was based on the economic history of over a dozen European countries. Like all models, it is a simplification of reality.

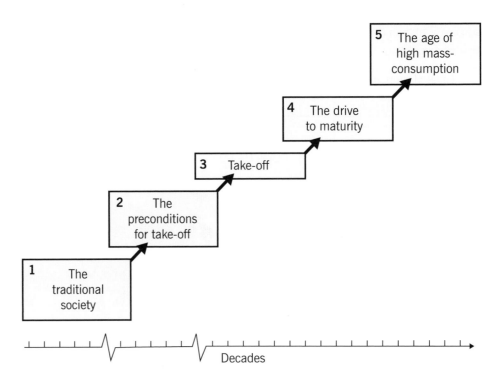

▶ **Figure 13.4:** The Rostow model.

The crucial part of Rostow's model is the 'take-off' stage: the decade or two when economy and society are transformed in such a way that thereafter a steady rate of growth can be sustained. Take-off is launched by an initial stimulus and characterised by:

- a rise in the rate of productive investment to over 10% of national income
- the development of one or more substantial manufacturing centres with a high rate of growth
- the emergence of administrative systems which encourage development.

In reality, take-off has proved very difficult to achieve in many countries.

Rostow argued that capitalism was fundamental to economic development. In his view, a communist system of government stifled enterprise. Modernisation theory held sway in the 1950s and early 1960s when there was general optimism about narrowing the development gap. However, as the painfully slow progress became more and more obvious, criticism of modernisation theory grew.

Dependency theory

The apparent failure of the capitalist Rostow model resulted for a while in the ascendancy of Marxist and neo-Marxist ideas on the development gap. Andre Gunder Frank, a Chicago-trained economist, popularised many of these ideas in 1966 with his 'development of underdevelopment theory'. This is generally referred to as dependency theory. Frank used an historical approach to argue the following:

- Poverty in the developing world arose through the spread of capitalism. Many countries had been prosperous before the arrival of European colonists.
- The process of absorption into the capitalist system sowed the seeds of underdevelopment.
- The development of the rich world was achieved by exploiting the raw materials of the developing world.
- Developing countries became even more dependent on the rich countries by farming export crops where once local food crops prevailed.
- The stronger the links to the developed world the worse the level of development.

Frank used a simple model (Figure 13.5) to explain how the 'metropolis' (the developed world) exploited the 'periphery' (the developing world). The model shows a chain of exploitation which begins with small towns in the periphery expropriating surplus from the surrounding rural areas. This process of exploitation works its way up the urban hierarchy in the periphery until, finally, the largest settlements are exploited by cities in the 'metropolis'. The intensity of poverty increases with the number of stages down the chain of exploitation.

Frank and others believed that socialist systems of government provide a better basis than capitalism for a fairer society; both between countries and within countries.

World system (core/periphery) theory

New approaches are often stimulated by the shortcomings of previous theorising. World system theory was popularised in the mid-1970s by Immanuel Wallerstein. It asserts that a capitalist world economy has existed since the 16th century. Before this, global interdependence did not exist.

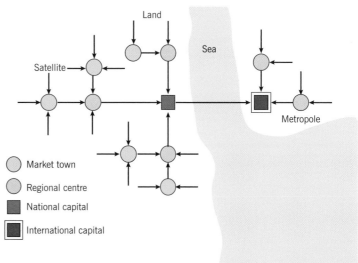

▲ **Figure 13.5:** The Frank model.

Market town

Regional centre

National capital

International capital

Key term

World system theory — this is based on the history of the capitalist world economy. Countries fall into three economic levels, and can move from one level to another if their contribution to the world economy changes.

From the 16th century, a growing number of previously more or less isolated societies were brought into the capitalist system. A small number of core countries transformed a much larger external area into a periphery. A semi-periphery developed between the core and periphery. Within the world system a division of labour operated. The core countries were manufacturers and the peripheral countries were agricultural, and other raw material, producers. The terms of trade were heavily skewed in favour of the core. The process of underdevelopment started with the incorporation of an external area into the world system.

The semi-periphery forms the most dynamic part of the system. The rising semi-peripheries of the present, the newly industrialised countries (NICs), are competing to varying degrees for core status. Thus, the world system approach has a degree of optimism lacking in dependency theory, recognising that some countries can escape from the state of underdevelopment.

The role of debt

Experts from a variety of different disciplines blame the rules of the global economic system for excluding many countries from its potential benefits. Many single out debt as the major problem for the world's poorer nations. An ever increasing proportion of new debt is used to service interest payments on old debts. Supporters of globalisation argue that economic growth through trade is the only answer. However, critics say that more economically developed countries (MEDCs) should do more to help the poor countries, through debt relief and by opening their markets to exports from less economically developed countries (LEDCs).

The total external debt of the very poorest countries (the 'low-income countries') was $375 billion in 2006. During 2006, these countries paid over $34 billion to the rich world to service their debts. These payments averaged $94 million a day. When a country has to use a high proportion of its income to service debt this takes money away from what could have been spent on education, health, housing, transport and other social and economic priorities. It is often ironic that much of the money originally borrowed was wasted on inappropriate projects and hived off in corruption so that there has been little lasting benefit to many of the indebted countries.

Taking it further

Look at the Jubilee Debt Campaign website (www.jubileedebtcampaign.org.uk) to see what the charities involved want governments to do with regard to the debt of poor countries.

The main global organisations affecting development

A range of global players and organisations have differing roles and contrasting perspectives in relation to the development gap. The actions of some organisations may arguably exacerbate the development gap.

The International Monetary Fund

The International Monetary Fund (IMF) and the World Bank are both United Nations agencies. While the IMF focuses primarily on the international financial transactions of a country, the World Bank deals mainly with internal investment projects.

A country running short of foreign currency reserves that it needed to maintain its currency exchange rate can turn to the IMF for help. IMF funds come from the contributions or 'quotas' of its member countries. IMF funding works as follows:

- Countries usually apply for funding from the IMF when they are unable to obtain funding from other sources.
- IMF money is designed to prevent the disruption to the international financial system that would occur through a country failing to meet its commitments to other nations.
- Along with funding, the IMF can also renegotiate the terms of debt on behalf of nations in financial difficulties.
- To prevent the situation reoccurring the IMF will usually impose conditions, in the form of a 'stabilisation programme', on its financial assistance.

- It is the nature of these conditions that has caused so much controversy about the way in which the IMF operates. Critics say that stabilisation programmes often hinder rather than enhance development.

The World Bank

The International Bank for Reconstruction and Development, commonly known as the World Bank, borrows between $20 billion and $30 billion a year in a variety of currencies. This money has provided financing for more than 4,000 development projects in 130 countries, through $300 billion in lending as follows:

- For most recipient countries, lending is at market rates of interest.
- In 1960 a branch of the World Bank was formed, known as the International Development Association (IDA).
- The IDA lends only to nations with a very low per capita income. For such countries loans are interest-free and allow long repayment periods.

The World Bank has many critics. They argue that the conditions attached to World Bank loans have:

- crippled economic growth in recipient countries
- hindered development
- promoted dependency
- increased poverty.

The World Trade Organisation (WTO)

Unlike its predecessor, the loosely organised GATT (General Agreement on Tariffs and Trade), the WTO was set up in 1995 as a permanent organisation with far greater powers to arbitrate trade disputes. Today average tariffs are only a tenth of what they were when GATT came into force (1947) and world trade has been increasing at a much faster rate than GDP.

The WTO exists to promote free trade. Most countries in the world are members and most of those who are not want to join. The fundamental issue is: does free trade benefit all those concerned or is it a subtle way in which the rich nations exploit their poorer counterparts? Most critics of free trade accept that free trade does generate wealth but they deny that all countries benefit from it.

Transnational corporations (TNCs)

Transnational corporations are the driving force behind economic globalisation. They are capitalist enterprises that engage in foreign direct investment. As the rules regulating the movement of goods and investment have been relaxed, TNCs have extended their global reach. The growth of foreign direct investment has expanded and the sources and destinations of this investment have consequently become more and more diverse. There are now few parts of the world where the direct or indirect influence of TNCs is not important. In some countries and regions, their influence on the economy is huge.

TNCs have a substantial influence on the global economy in general and on the countries in which they choose to locate in particular. They play a major role in world trade in terms of what and where they buy and sell. A considerable proportion of world trade is intra-firm, taking place within TNCs.

Governments

Along with TNCs, national governments are the major players in the global economy. National governments exert their influence through national policies and membership of major international organisations. Tackling the development gap is high on the agenda of some countries but does not appear to be a major issue with others.

Synoptic link

Look at pages 26-7 of Edexcel AS Geography. These examine the role of the World Bank in trying to reduce the losses occurring in countries as a result of natural disasters.

Examiners' tip

Candidates frequently mix up the roles of the International Monetary Fund and the World Bank. It is important to be clear about the distinction between the two organisations.

Key terms

Free trade — a hypothetical situation whereby producers have free and unhindered access to markets everywhere.

Transnational corporation — 'a firm which has the power to coordinate and control operations in more than one country, even if it does not own them'. (Peter Dicken)

Foreign direct investment — overseas investments in physical capital by transnational corporations.

1. The system helps promote peace
2. Disputes are handled constructively
3. Rules make life easier for all
4. Freer trade cuts the cost of living
5. It provides more choice of products and qualities
6. Trade raises incomes
7. Trade stimulates economic growth
8. The basic principles make life more efficient
9. Governments are shielded from lobbying
10. The system encourages good government

▲ **Figure 13.6:** The WTO view of the world trading system.

Key term

Non-governmental organisations — national or international private organisations, which are distinct from governmental or intergovernmental agencies.

Non-governmental organisations (NGOs)

NGOs such as Oxfam, CARE, CAFOD and WaterAid seek to improve economic and social development in poor countries. These organisations often combine their operations when major human catastrophes occur (e.g. floods, droughts, earthquakes) or when they want to exert maximum pressure on international opinion. Increasingly, relief and development NGOs receive large grants from governments' international assistance programmes.

The role of NGOs in development has increased because:
- they have developed considerable expertise over a number of decades in many different countries
- they have a more successful track record than other attempts at promoting development; development is generally targeted very carefully and the impact of projects is carefully monitored
- they concentrate on small- and medium-scale projects that benefit the poor rather than the better off in LEDCs
- they work with local people to sustain development in the long term
- they are seen to be independent of vested interests.

The role of trade and investment in development

The relationship between investment and trade

Synoptic link

Look at pages 75 and 82 of Edexcel AS Geography. These sections of the book examine the pivotal role of TNCs in the process of globalisation.

Trade and investment play a key role in the development gap and global wealth distributions. Investment in a country is the key to it increasing its trade. Some developing countries have increased their trade substantially. These countries have attracted the bulk of foreign direct investment. Such low-income 'globalisers' as China, Brazil, India and Mexico have increased their trade-to-GDP ratios significantly.

Key term

Newly Industrialised Countries — countries that have undergone rapid and successful industrialisation since the 1960s.

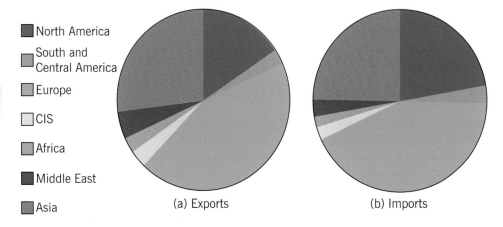

North America
South and Central America
Europe
CIS
Africa
Middle East
Asia

(a) Exports   (b) Imports

▲ **Figure 13.7**: World merchandise trade.

FDI and the emergence of NICs

The emergence of newly industrialised countries has been a key element in the process of globalisation. In Asia four generations of NIC can be recognised in terms of the timing of their industrial development and their current economic characteristics. All these countries have benefited from a high level of foreign direct investment. Within this region, only Japan is at a higher economic level than the NICs (Figure 13.8). Figure 13.9 shows the inflow of foreign direct investment for a number of world regions from 1970.

Examiners' tip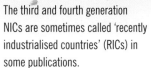

The third and fourth generation NICs are sometimes called 'recently industrialised countries' (RICs) in some publications.

Level of development	Countries	GNP per capita 2005
1	Japan: an MEDC	$38,984
2	First generation NICs e.g. Taiwan	$16,764
3	Second generation NICs e.g. Malaysia	$4,963
4	Third generation NICs e.g. China	$1,735
5	Fourth generation NICs e.g. Vietnam	$623
6	Least developed countries e.g. Mongolia	$380

Taking it further

Look at the World Trade Organisation website (www.wto.org) to find out what is currently happening with world trade negotiations.

◀ **Figure 13.8:** GNP per capita 2005.

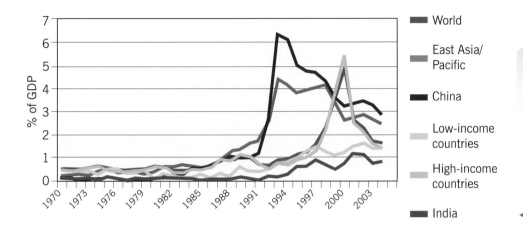

Legend:
- World
- East Asia/ Pacific
- China
- Low-income countries
- High-income countries
- India

Synoptic link

Look at page 89 of Edexcel AS Geography. Figure 2 provides useful information about the main trading countries in the world.

◀ **Figure 13.9:** FDI by world region.

Those left out of the investment and trade cycle

However, on the other side of the coin are the 2 billion people who live in countries that have become less rather than more globalised (in an economic sense) as trade has fallen in relation to national income. This group includes most African countries. In these 'non-globalising' countries income per person fell by an average of 1% a year during the 1990s. An Oxfam report published in April 2002 stated that if Africa increased its share of world trade by just 1% it would earn an additional £49 billion a year – five times the amount it receives in aid.

The terms of trade

The most vital element in the trade of any country is the terms on which it takes place. If countries rely on the export of commodities that are low in price and need to import items that are relatively high in price they need to export in large quantities to be able to afford a relatively low volume of imports. Many poor nations are primary product dependent; that is, they rely on one or a small number of primary products to obtain foreign currency through export. The world market price of primary products is in general very low compared with that of manufactured goods and services. Also, the price of primary products is subject to considerable variation from year to year, making economic and social planning extremely difficult. The terms of trade for many developing countries are worse now than they were a decade ago. Thus, it is not surprising that so many nations are struggling to get out of poverty.

North–South trade flows

Because the terms of trade are generally disadvantageous to the poor countries of the south, many developing countries have very high trade deficits (Figure 13.10). Among lower-income countries the average trade balance is a deficit of 12.3% of GDP. Such a level is a rarity amongst developed nations.

Key terms

The terms of trade — the price of a country's exports relative to the price of its imports, and the changes that take place over time.
Trade deficit — when the value of a country's exports is less than the value of its imports.

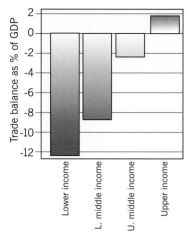

▲ **Figure 13.10:** Trade deficit by income group.

Conventional neoliberal economists generally welcome the large transfers of capital linked to high trade deficits. They say that trade deficits are strongly related to stages of economic development. The argument is that capital inflows swell the available pool of investment funds and thus generate future growth in the south. However, Marxist and Populist writers argue that:

- if the expansion of trade volumes brings benefits to developing countries, the accompanying expansion of trade deficits may bring considerable problems
- trade deficits have to be financed. One way is to borrow more money from abroad, but this will increase a country's debt. Another is to divert investment away from important areas of the economy such as agriculture, industry, education and health
- high trade deficits in the south constrain growth and produce a high level of dependency.

A report by the Dutch Tea Institute in 2006 drew particular attention to:
- the problems of falling prices and rising input costs
- the consequent pressure to limit labour costs of tea production workers
- the urgent need for improvement of labour, social, ecological and economic conditions throughout the tea sector in the developing countries.

The global tea market is dominated by a small number of companies including Unilever and Sara Lee. About half of all the tea produced is traded internationally. Annual export sales of tea in its raw material state are worth almost $3 billion. The retail value of the global tea business is of course much higher. The large tea companies wield immense power over the industry. As many countries now produce tea they have to compete with each other in an increasingly competitive market. Global supply is rising at a faster rate than consumption, keeping prices low. Tea producers complain that the global trading system prevents them from moving up the value chain by processing and packing the tea they grow. This is mainly because:
- they would have to compete with very powerful brands
- they would find it very difficult to achieve the economies of scale of the global tea companies.

Taking it further

The World Investment Report (UNCTAD) is published annually. Look at the latest report to see how much foreign direct investment is flowing into each world region.

Summary

In this chapter, you have learnt:
- the meaning of development and the development gap.
- about traditional and more recent measures of development.
- about the Millennium Development Goals.
- about modernisation, dependency and world systems theories.
- about the roles of major global organisations in the development process.
- about the relationship between trade and investment
- about the emergence of NICs.
- about the terms of trade and trade deficits.

MCQ

CHAPTER 14 What are the consequences of the development gap?

Learning objectives

After studying this chapter, you will be able to discuss these ideas and concepts and provide located examples of them:

- The social, economic, environmental and political consequences of the development gap.
- The increasing concentration of poverty in developing megacities.
- The ethnic dimensions of the development gap and their consequences.
- The positive and negative consequences for countries which are developing.

Key terms

Externalities
Indigenous population
Industrial revolution
Least developed countries
Megacity
Privatisation
Slum

How the development gap affects the most disadvantaged countries and people

The development gap has significant consequences for people in the most disadvantaged countries. The consequences of poverty can be economic, social, environmental and political (Figure 14.1).

	Consequences of poverty
Economic	Global integration is spatially selective: some countries benefit; others, it seems, do not. One in five of the world's population lives on less than a dollar a day and almost half on less than two dollars a day. Poor countries frequently lack the ability to pay for food, agricultural innovation and investment in rural development.
Social	More than 850 million people in poor countries cannot read or write. Nearly a billion people do not have access to clean water and 2.4 billion to basic sanitation. Eleven million children under five die from preventable diseases each year, especially from the inability to combat the effects of HIV/AIDS.
Environmental	Poor countries have increased vulnerability to natural disasters. They lack the capacity to adapt to climate change-induced droughts. Poor farming practices lead to environmental degradation. Often, raw materials are exploited with very limited economic benefit to poor countries and little concern for the environment. Landscapes can be devastated by various uses: mining, vast areas of rainforest being felled for logging and clearance for agriculture, and rivers and land being polluted by oil exploitation.
Political	Poor countries which are low on the development scale often have non-democratic governments or they are democracies that function poorly. There is usually a reasonably strong link between development and improvement in the quality of government. In general, the poorer the country, the worse the plight of minority groups.

▲ **Figure 14.1:** Economic, social, environmental and political consequences of poverty.

Synoptic link

Look at the following sections in Edexcel AS Geography:
(1) page 227 for an interesting case study of Katine village in Uganda, one of the most deprived villages in the world
(2) pages 45–6 for a consideration of the vulnerable position of Africa with regard to climate change.

Examiners' tip

If the wording of a question gives you the opportunity, try to classify your information into clear sections along the lines of Figure 14.1.

Case study: Sub-Saharan Africa – the world's poorest region

A UN progress report in 2007, at the midpoint between the adoption of the Millennium Development Goals and the 2015 target date for their achievement, stated that sub-Saharan Africa is not on track to achieve any of the eight goals. Amongst other conclusions, the report noted the following points:

- While the region is making progress towards universal primary school enrolment, there is still a long way to go. This goal is viewed by the UN as fundamental to the success of other poverty-reduction strategies.
- Girls and children from poorer or rural families are least likely to attend school.
- Disabled children miss out far more than most on receiving any kind of education.

Figure 14.2 shows that sub-Saharan Africa has by far the lowest GDP per capita of any world region. While all other regions experienced considerable income improvements, Africa's income declined between the 1970s and the 2000s. However, there has been some catching up in very recent years. South Africa and Nigeria together account for 54% of the region's total GDP.

HIV/AIDS has had a devastating impact on the region. At the end of 2007 an estimated 22 million adults and children were living with HIV in sub-Saharan Africa. During that year about 1.5 million died from the disease in the region.

Organisations such as Christian Aid and Oxfam argue strongly that trade is the key to real development, being worth 20 times as much as aid. However, the trading situation of Africa will only improve if the trading relationship between MEDCs and LEDCs is made fairer to bring more benefits to the latter. In fact, Africa's share of world trade has fallen in recent decades. According to Oxfam, if sub-Saharan Africa had maintained its exports at the same level as 1980, its economy would be worth an extra $280 billion a year.

IMF-World Bank loans are usually conditional on African countries opening their markets. Historically, African trade barriers have been high but they have been reduced significantly in recent years. Although the situation varies across the continent, some countries such as Mali, Mozambique and Zambia are more open to trade than the EU and the USA. However, many countries complain that MEDCs, in particular the EU and the USA, are not implementing at home the free-trade policies they expect African countries to follow.

Region	1975–80	1981–85	1986–90	1991–95	1996–2000	2001–05
GDP per capita						
Sub-Saharan Africa	1,928	1,844	1,782	1,648	1,668	1,768
East Asia & Pacific	905	1,227	1,686	2,407	3,399	4,595
Latin America & Caribbean	6,020	6,295	6,315	6,450	6,978	7,205
Middle East & North Africa	4,179	4,180	4,055	4,326	4,651	5,197
South Asia	1,132	1,268	1,505	1,745	2,110	2,530
Low & middle income	2,278	2,560	2,881	3,045	3,513	4,219
Growth						
Sub-Saharan Africa	−0.06	−1.60	−0.21	−1.64	0.79	1.79
East Asia & Pacific	5.26	6.12	5.76	9.10	5.63	7.06
Latin America & Caribbean	3.31	−0.95	−0.43	1.61	1.53	1.21
Middle East & North Africa	−0.20	2.41	−1.20	1.18	1.91	2.78
South Asia	1.03	3.14	3.89	3.01	3.59	4.65
Low & middle income	2.79	1.99	1.93	1.56	3.23	4.58

Note: All sub-Saharan African countries are included in calculations.

▲ **Figure 14.2:** GDP per capita and growth by region (weighted data).

Least developed countries

While the newly industrialised countries are an important part of the successful side of globalisation, the least developed countries have been largely bypassed by the processes of wealth creation. Many of the least developed nations are in sub-Saharan Africa. Others are concentrated in the poverty belt of Asia (including Nepal and Afghanistan) or are small island nations in the South Pacific.

As the gap between the richest and poorest countries in the world widens, LDCs are being increasingly marginalised in the world economy. Their share of world trade is declining and in many LDCs national debt now equals or exceeds GDP. Such a situation puts a stranglehold on all attempts to halt socio-economic decline.

Reasons for the concentration of poverty in megacities

The numbers of people living in urban poverty are increased by a combination of economic problems, growing inequality and population growth, particularly growth due to in-migration. Urban poverty is heavily concentrated in slums. Such poverty is multidimensional in nature (Figure 14.3).

As The Challenge of Slums (United Nations, 2003) states, 'Slums result from a combination of poverty or low incomes with inadequacies in the housing provision system, so that poorer people are forced to seek affordable accommodation and land that become increasingly inadequate.' The report identifies women, children, widows and female-headed households as the most vulnerable among the poor. In urban African slums, women head over 30% of all households.

The UN recognises that the focus of global poverty is moving from rural to urban areas; a process known as 'the urbanisation of poverty'. Without significant global action the number of slum dwellers will double over the next 30 years. The urban poor live in inner city slums, peripheral shanty towns and in almost every other conceivable space such as on pavements, traffic roundabouts, under bridges and in sewers.

• Inadequate income (and thus inadequate consumption of necessities including food and, often, safe and sufficient water; often problems of indebtedness, with debt repayments significantly reducing income available for necessities).
• Inadequate, unstable or risky asset base (non-material and material including educational attainment and housing) for individuals or communities.
• Inadequate shelter (typically poor quality, overcrowded and insecure).
• Inadequate provision of 'public' infrastructure (e.g. piped water, sanitation, drainage, roads, footpaths) which increases the health burden and often the work burden.
• Inadequate provision of basic services such as day care/schools/vocational training, healthcare, emergency services, public transport, communications, law enforcement.
• Limited or no safety net to ensure basic consumption can be maintained when income falls; also to ensure access to shelter and healthcare when these can no longer be paid for.
• Inadequate protection of poorer groups' rights through the operation of the law, including laws and regulations regarding civil and political rights, occupational health and safety, pollution control, environmental health, protection from violence and other crimes, protection from discrimination and exploitation.
• Voicelessness and powerlessness within political systems and bureaucratic structures, leading to little or no possibility of receiving entitlements.

Eight per cent of the world's urban population live in the 'megacities' which have populations over 10 million. Figure 14.4 shows the megacities recognised by the UN in 2005 and their predicted populations for 2015. As with all predictions, these are revised on a regular basis. Of the 20 cities shown in the table only Tokyo, New York, Los Angeles, Osaka and Moscow are in MEDCs. Nine of these megacities are in Asia. In 1950 only New York had a population over 10 million.

Key terms

Least developed countries (LDCs) — the poorest and weakest economies in the developing world. LDCs are a subset of the LEDCs.
Megacity — a city with a population of 10 million people or more.
Slum — a heavily populated urban area characterised by substandard housing and squalor.

Taking it further

Look at www.unctad.org to find out the latest information about least developed countries.

▲ **Figure 14.3:** The constituents of urban poverty.

115

▶ **Figure 14.4:** The world's megacities.

Urban agglomeration		Population (millions)				Average annual rate of change (%)	
		1975	2000	2005	2015	1975–2005	2005–2015
1	Tokyo	26.6	34.4	35.2	35.5	0.93	0.08
2	Mexico City	10.7	18.1	19.4	21.6	1.99	1.05
3	New York-Newark	15.9	17.8	18.7	19.9	0.55	0.60
4	São Paulo	9.6	17.1	18.3	20.5	2.15	1.13
5	Mumbai	7.1	16.1	18.2	21.9	3.15	1.84
6	Delhi	4.4	12.4	15.0	18.6	4.08	2.12
7	Shanghai	7.3	13.2	14.5	17.2	2.28	1.72
8	Kolkata	7.9	13.1	14.3	17.0	1.98	1.73
9	Jakarta	4.8	11.1	13.2	16.8	3.37	2.41
10	Buenos Aires	8.7	11.8	12.6	13.4	1.20	0.65
11	Dhaka	2.2	10.2	12.4	16.8	5.81	3.04
12	Los Angeles	8.9	11.8	12.3	13.1	1.07	0.63
13	Karachi	4.0	10.0	11.6	15.2	3.56	2.67
14	Rio de Janeiro	7.6	10.8	11.5	12.8	1.39	1.07
15	Osaka-Kobe	9.8	11.2	11.3	11.3	0.45	0.04
16	Cairo	6.4	10.4	11.1	13.1	1.82	1.66
17	Lagos	1.9	8.4	10.9	16.1	5.84	3.94
18	Beijing	6.0	9.8	10.7	12.9	1.91	1.82
19	Manila	5.0	10.0	10.7	12.9	2.53	1.90
20	Moscow	7.6	10.1	10.7	11.0	1.12	0.34

Note: Urban agglomerations are ordered according to their population size in 2005.

Synoptic link

Look at pages 116–17 of Edexcel AS Geography for a detailed case study of Mumbai, a megacity in Asia.

Synoptic link

Look at pages 74–5 and 115 of Edexcel AS Geography. The former examines the factors affecting migration, with Figure 4 providing a useful classification of push and pull factors. The latter discusses rural-to-urban migration in more detail.

Taking it further

Look at www.unhabitat.org (United Nations Human Settlement Programme) for recent information on the world's megacities.

Push and pull factors

A variety of push factors in the countryside have encouraged out-migration. The main factors include: population pressure, unemployment and underemployment, the poor conditions of rural employment, poor social conditions (housing, health, education) and environmental degradation.

People are attracted to urban areas (pull factors) because they feel life in towns and cities will provide at least some of the following: a higher standard of accommodation, a greater likelihood of employment, a better education for their children, improved medical facilities, the conditions of infrastructure often lacking in rural areas and a wider range of consumer services.

The scale of rural-to-urban migration in LEDCs is not surprising given the great concentrations of wealth and economic activity in the cities compared with the countryside. For example:

- in Mexico, the capital Mexico City creates 30% of the country's Gross Domestic Product each year
- half of all the motor vehicles in Thailand are in Bangkok, the capital city
- Caracas accounts for 75% of all the manufacturing industry in Venezuela.

The United Nations regards the Kibera district of Nairobi, housing three-quarters of a million people, as the largest slum in the world. The Dhawari district of Mumbai and the Orangi area of Karachi are not far behind in extent. Some slums are now as large as cities. For example, the Ashaiman informal settlement in Ghana is now larger than the city of Tema from which it grew.

Case study: The Kibera slum

Kibera, recognised by the UN as the world's largest slum, houses over three-quarters of a million people. Located at the edge of downtown Nairobi, Kibera is about 4 km² in area. It is the oldest and largest informal settlement in Nairobi. The government of Kenya does not recognise Kibera as an official entity, as it is illegal in status with title deeds never having been issued, and provides minimal services to the area. The quality of life is extremely poor:

- Most people lack sanitation, running water and electricity
- Access to healthcare is severely limited
- An estimated 20% of the population is HIV positive
- Women, and young women in particular, are treated as second-class citizens
- Approximately half of the population are under the age of 15.

▲ **Figure 14.5:** Kibera slum, Nairobi.

There is an ongoing water crisis in Kibera. On a daily basis, residents, particularly women, walk to nearby streams, wells and boreholes to collect water while others queue at water kiosks. Tap water is rare in Kibera and water vending has become a lucrative business. Girls take the burden of collecting water, often missing out on school as a result.

Kibera was part of the recent slum-upgrading initiative. Initially residents were told that some of them would be relocated to Athi River on the outskirts of the city to make room for the upgrading project. Residents strongly opposed the plan for a number of reasons but particularly because it would mean travelling longer distances to work. Landlords also objected because of their resultant loss of rental income. Both groups formed their own associations to resist relocation.

Social and political consequences of large disparities in wealth and opportunity

The development gap often has an ethnic and/or religious dimension where some ethnic groups in a population have income levels significantly below the dominant group(s) in the same population.

This is invariably the result of discrimination which limits the economic, social and political opportunities available to the disadvantaged groups. Examples include South Africa (Figure 14.6), Indonesia and Bolivia. Because of such obvious differences in status, tensions can arise between majority and minority groups resulting in:

- social unrest
- migration
- new political movements.

In South Africa the wide gap in income originated in the Apartheid era, but since then it has proved extremely difficult to close for a variety of reasons. Political change often occurs well in advance of significant economic and social change.

MEAN PER CAPITA INCOME (2007 CONSTANT RAND PRICES)			
	1995	**2000**	**2005**
African: mean	615.36	575.64	775.46
African: median	333.23	278.46	406.95
Coloured: mean	935.65	1141.80	1384.95
Coloured: median	583.72	655.11	651.47
Asian: mean	2299.15	2021.84	2785.50
Asian: median	1596.02	1306.92	1583.09
White: mean	4436.18	5129.21	7645.56
White: median	3442.72	3544.50	5331.61
Total: mean	1101.48	1074.29	1514.81
Total: median	428.74	356.27	483.87

◀ **Figure 14.6:** South Africa – income differences by ethnic group, 2007.

Inequality of wealth distribution is higher in Latin America than in any other part of the world. Indian and black people make up a third of the population, but have very limited parliamentary representation. Figure 14.7 shows the situation in five Latin American countries in 2005, prior to political transformation in Bolivia.

Country (ethnic group)	% of population	% representation in lower house
Bolivia (indigenous)	61	26
Ecuador (indigenous)	34	3
Guatemala (indigenous)	60	12
Peru (indigenous)	43	1
Brazil (African descent)	44	3

Case study: Bolivia

The indigenous population of Bolivia has always had to endure a much lower quality of life than those of Spanish descent. Two-thirds of Bolivia's population are indigenous, the largest number of any country within the region. However, the advent of 'participative democracy' in the last decade or so has resulted in a startling transformation of political power in the country. The key to this change was the indigenous population organising itself in an increasingly sophisticated manner. An important staging post was the success of Bolivia's poor in major protests over water and gas privatisation.

The privatisation of water has been a major issue. The resulting large increases in water bills provoked huge demonstrations such as in Cochabamba, Bolivia's third largest city. The Bolivian government withdrew its water contract with the TNC Bechtel and its operating partner Abengoa. As a result the companies sued the Bolivian government for $50 million. However, in 2006 the companies agreed to abandon their legal action in return for a token payment.

The indigenous population has been particularly susceptible to:
- a lack of economic opportunities in rural areas where there are particularly high concentrations of indigenous peoples. This has resulted in large-scale migration to urban areas
- low employment rates in the formal sector and thus heavy reliance on the informal sector
- a lack of access to land
- a lack of access to basic social services (education, health, energy)
- continued discrimination and stereotyping
- higher adjustment costs to the economic reforms of the 1990s (e.g. privatisation).

Figure 14.8 shows the indigenous/non-indigenous schooling gap for Bolivia and four other Latin American countries. Figure 14.9 shows the considerable gap between incomes achieved in the formal and informal sectors. The indigenous population is heavily over-represented in the latter.

Country	Non-indigenous	Indigenous	Schooling gap in years
Bolivia	9.6	5.9	3.7
Ecuador	6.9	4.3	2.6
Guatemala	5.7	2.5	3.2
Mexico	7.9	4.6	3.3
Peru	8.7	6.4	2.3

◀ **Figure 14.8:** The indigenous/non-indigenous schooling gap (average years of school).

The main driving force of political change was the Movement towards Socialism (MAS) party led by Evo Morales. He became the first fully indigenous head of state when he was elected president in December 2005. He was elected on a pledge to challenge the free market reforms that most people felt the country had been pressurised into adopting. There was widespread concern that these policies benefited large TNCs and the rich in Bolivia to the detriment of the poor and the environment. The party's stated aims were to give more power to indigenous and poor people by means of land reforms and the redistribution of gas wealth.

CHAPTER 15 How can we reduce the development gap?

Learning objectives

After studying this chapter, you will be able to discuss these ideas and concepts and provide located examples of them:

- The theories and approaches that underpin the development gap.
- The different types of aid and the strategies that different organisations adopt to deliver aid.
- The controversial nature of trade and investment.
- The future of the development gap.

Key terms

Appropriate technology
Fair trade
International aid
Microcredit
Resource nationalisation
Social business

Theories and approaches for reducing the development gap

Public, private and voluntary organisations often have different philosophies about narrowing the development gap. It is thus not surprising that the initiatives they develop reflect these philosophies.

Modernisation theory

This approach, which was very influential in the late 1950s and 1960s, relies heavily on the philosophy of the free market and the historical development of the MEDCs. It postulated that lack of development in poor countries was mainly down to pre-modern socio-economic structures. These prohibited the adoption of efficient modes of production. Thus, developing countries needed to make significant internal changes in order to follow the economic history of the industrialised nations.

Neoliberal economic theory

This approach developed in the 1980s and 1990s as the process of globalisation intensified. Abolishing tariff barriers should encourage international trade. Unrestricted markets would lead to development through trade. Privatisation, deregulation and cutting public expenditure are important elements of neoliberalism. This approach has been at the heart of the actions of the World Bank, the International Monetary Fund and the World Trade Organisation.

▼ **Figure 15.1:** Model of cumulative causation.

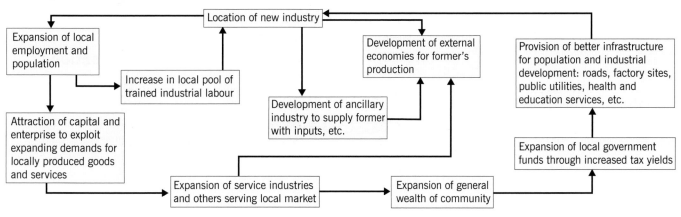

Supporters of neoliberalism point to the emergence of successive generations of newly industrialised countries as proof of the success of the free market in generating development. They argue that countries that can attract significant foreign direct investment are able to widen their range of economic activities and increase their volumes of trade. FDI sets off a chain of cumulative causation (Figure 15.1) whereby a phase of economic growth generates even more growth in the future. This process begins in the economic core region of a country. Eventually economic growth should 'spread' to spatially selected areas in the periphery (Figure 15.2).

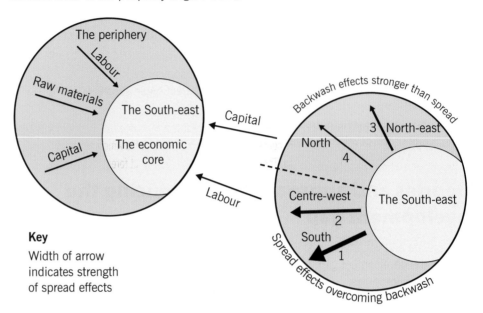

Figure 15.2: The polarisation of growth in the core region and the spread of growth to the periphery in Brazil.

Key
Width of arrow indicates strength of spread effects

Marxist and populist approaches

Critics of free market approaches argue that only a relatively small number of LEDCs have developed into NICs. For most LEDCs the development gap has widened rather than narrowed. They argue that the operation of the free market can often have devastating consequences for the fragile economies of poor countries. Internal policies require a certain level of government intervention to ensure a fairer distribution of wealth within countries, while external policies lobby international bodies to change the world's financial and trading systems to try to distribute the benefits of globalisation in a more equitable way.

The Marxist approach has historically been based on a very high degree of central planning (a top-down approach). In contrast, the populist approach is based on participatory bottom-up planning. So-called 'grassroots action' is an important element of 'bottom-up' planning. Such ideas began on the fringes of NGOs. Both the Marxist and populist approaches are left-wing, but they view development from a different perspective.

Non-governmental organisations

Non-governmental organisations (NGOs) generally adopt a very pragmatic approach in an effort to maximise the development impact of the funding available to them. They emphasise the local and the small-scale, putting significant emphasis on sustainability. Figure 15.3 shows WaterAid's approach to development.

Figure 15.3: WaterAid's approach to development.

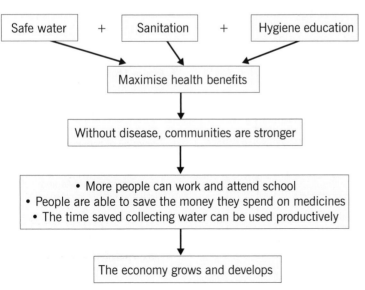

Case study: Bolivia and resource nationalisation

Bolivia is an example of a country challenging the free market philosophy. Bolivia has recently introduced a resource nationalisation policy. Along with Cuba and Venezuela it forms the so-called 'radical block' of nations in Latin America, which are concerned about US economic power in the region and the exploitative action of TNCs in general.

In May 2006 President Morales of Bolivia nationalised the country's gas and oil industries. Bolivia has the second largest natural gas reserves in Latin America, but produces only a small amount of oil for domestic use. The foreign energy companies were told they had six months to sign new operating contracts or leave the country. All signed, which should result in higher revenues for the government. Now, all foreign energy companies have to deliver all their production to the state-run YPFB for distribution and processing. Overall, Bolivia has taken control of 82% of the oil and gas in the country, leaving the remainder to foreign companies.

Bolivia is adopting a socialist model of regional commerce and cooperation as opposed to what it sees as 'US-backed free trade'. Bolivia views the concept of the Free Trade Area of the Americas as an attempt by the USA to 'annex' Latin America. The government is trying to attract foreign investment while at the same time giving the state a larger role in managing the economy.

How effective are different aid strategies in development?

The distinction between investment and aid

Investment involves expenditure on a project in the expectation of financial (or social) returns. Transnational corporations are the main source of foreign investment. TNCs invest to make profits. Aid is assistance in the form or grants or loans at below market rates.

Why is international aid necessary?

Most LEDCs have been keen to accept foreign aid because of the:

- 'foreign exchange gap' whereby many LEDCs lack the hard currency to pay for imports such as oil and machinery, which are vital to development
- 'savings gap' where population pressures and other drains on expenditure prevent the accumulation of enough capital to invest in industry and infrastructure
- 'technical gap' caused by a shortage of skills needed for development.

Figure 15.4 shows how these factors combine to form the 'vicious circle of poverty'.

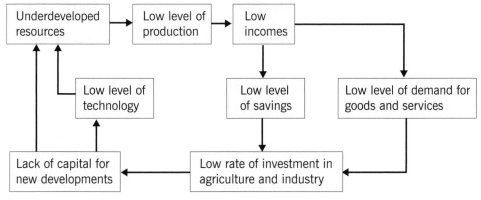

▲ **Figure 15.4:** The vicious circle of poverty.

Synoptic link

Look at page 234 of Edexcel AS Geography for more information on WaterAid's approach to development.

Key term

Resource nationalisation — when a country decides to take part, or all, of one or a number of natural resources under state ownership.

Examiners' tip

When revising case studies, write down what you consider to be the six most important points in bullet-point format. Learn these points off by heart and they will provide a 'trigger' to remember other information about the case study.

Taking it further

Look at the *Bolivia Times* website (www.boliviatimes.com) for information on some of the latest economic issues concerning Bolivia.

Examiners' tip

Learning a relatively simple diagram such as Figure 15.4 can help you produce a well-structured written answer.

▶ **Figure 15.5:** The different types
of international aid.

▲ **Figure 15.6:** Chinese aid project
in an African country.

The different types of international aid

Figure 15.5 shows the different types of international aid. The basic division is between the
following two types:

- Official government aid where the amount of aid given and who it is given to is
  decided by the government of an individual country. The Department for International
  Development (DFID) runs the UK's international aid programme.
- Voluntary aid run by non-governmental organisations (NGOs) or charities such as
  Oxfam, ActionAid and CAFOD. NGOs collect money from individuals and organisations.
  However, an increasing amount of government money goes to NGOs because of their
  expertise in running aid efficiently.

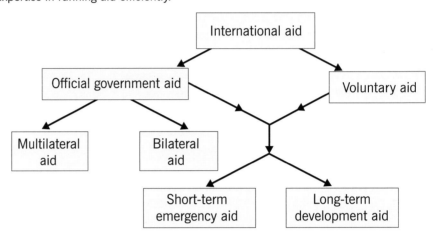

Official government aid

Official government aid can be divided into:

- bilateral aid, which is given directly from one country to another
- multilateral aid, which is provided by many countries and organised by an international
  body such as the United Nations.

Aid supplied to poorer countries is of two types:

- Short-term emergency aid, which is provided to help cope with unexpected disasters
  such as earthquakes, volcanic eruptions and tropical cyclones.
- Long-term development aid, which is directed towards the continuous improvement in
  the quality of life in a poorer country.

Critics of international aid argue that:

- too often, aid fails to reach the very poorest people and when it does the benefits are
  frequently short-lived
- a significant proportion of foreign aid is 'tied' to the purchase of goods and services from
  the donor country and often given for use only on jointly agreed projects
- the use of aid on large capital-intensive projects may actually worsen the conditions of
  the poorest people
- aid may delay the introduction of reforms: for example, the substitution of food aid for
  land reform
- international aid can create a culture of dependency.

Many development economists argue there are two issues more important to development
than aid: changing the terms of trade so that developing nations get a fairer share of the
benefits of world trade and writing off the debts of the poorest countries.

NGOs: leading sustainable development

Non-governmental organisations have often been much better at directing aid towards
sustainable development than government agencies. The selective nature of such aid has
targeted the poorest communities using appropriate technology and involving local people
in decision-making.

Taking it further

To read more about contrasting top-down and bottom-up aid models, read 'The effectiveness of aid' on your Student CD-ROM.

The effectiveness of aid: top-down and bottom-up approaches

Over the years most debate about aid has focused on the amount of aid made available. However, in recent years the focus has shifted somewhat to the effectiveness of aid. This has involved increasing criticism of the traditional top-down approach to aid.

Financing the Pergau Dam in Malaysia with UK government aid is an example of a capital-intensive government-led aid programme, set up without consulting the local population. Work began in 1991 and around the same time Malaysia bought £1 billion worth of arms from the UK, leading many people to believe that the £234 million in aid was 'tied' to the arms deal.

The Hunger Project is one of several organisations that have adopted a radically different approach. The Hunger Project has worked in partnership with grassroots organisations in Africa, Asia and Latin America to develop effective bottom-up strategies. The key strands in this approach have been:

- mobilising grassroots people for self-reliant action
- intervening for gender equality
- strengthening local democracy.

Case study: Local democracy in Kerala

In 1996 the government of the Indian state of Kerala launched a campaign (The People's Campaign for Decentralised Planning) to make village democracy a major development mechanism. The 'Kerala Model', hailed for its very high rate of political participation, has resulted in high levels of literacy and life expectancy and low levels of infant mortality and caste discrimination. Initial concentration was on:
- building development infrastructure
- improving public services
- creating jobs
- involving local people in planning and decision-making
- channelling resources to women and to the poorest castes and classes.

In 2002, the People's Campaign was extended to a follow-up project known as the Mararikulam Experiment.

How effective are different trade and investment strategies?

Trade, investment and economic growth undoubtedly have a role in reducing the development gap. These important elements of globalisation have been fundamental in the emergence of different generations of newly industrialised countries. The very high growth rates of the recently industrialised countries (RICs), which are the latest generation of NICs, are strongly related to their increasing share of global trade. However, the majority of LEDCs have not fared so well.

At one end of the ideological spectrum are those who see trade as a force for good that will lift people out of poverty, while at the other end are those who argue that trade is responsible for widening the gulf between rich and poor. Oxfam has pointed out what it thinks needs to be done to make trade fairer to poorer countries.

Fair trade products

Key term

Fair trade — producers of food, and some non-food products, in developing countries receive a fair deal when they are selling their products.

Many supermarkets and large stores in Britain and other MEDCs now stock some 'fairly traded' products. Most are agricultural products such as bananas, orange juice, nuts, coffee and tea but the market in non-food goods such as textiles and handicrafts is also increasing. The fair trade system operates as follows:

Taking it further

To find out more about what Oxfam are doing to make trade fair read 'Oxfam's "Make Trade Fair" campaign' on your Student CD-ROM.

- Small-scale producers group together to form a cooperative or other democratically run association with high social and environmental standards.
- These cooperatives deal directly with companies such as Tesco and Sainsbury's in MEDCs, thus cutting out 'middle men'.
- MEDC companies (through their customers) pay significantly over the world market price for the products traded. The price difference can be as large as 100%. This might mean, for example, supermarket customers paying a few pence more for a kilo of bananas.
- The higher price achieved by the LEDC cooperatives provides both a better standard of living, often saving producers from bankruptcy and absolute poverty, and some money to reinvest in their farms.

Advocates of the fair trade system argue that it is a model of how world trade can and should be organised to tackle global poverty. This system of trade began in the 1960s with Dutch consumers supporting Nicaraguan farmers. It is now a global market worth £315 million a year, involving over 400 MEDC companies and an estimated 500,000 small farmers and their families in the world's poorest countries. Food sales are growing by more than 25% a year with Switzerland and Britain being the largest markets.

The heavily indebted poor countries (HIPC) initiative

The HIPC initiative was first established in 1996 by the IMF and the World Bank. Its aim is to provide a comprehensive approach to debt reduction for heavily indebted poor countries. To qualify for assistance, countries have to pursue IMF- and World Bank-supported adjustment and reform programmes. By early 2008, debt reduction packages had been approved for 33 countries, 27 of them in Africa. Eight additional countries are eligible for HIPC initiative assistance.

Structural adjustment programmes (SAPS)

The conditions attached to IMF-imposed structural adjustment programmes are extremely controversial. Supporters of SAPs argue that they help prepare countries to compete in the world market. Critics say that SAPs hinder rather than promote development. A major issue is the speed with which countries have been forced to open up their markets to foreign imports. Very often they have been unprepared for the intense level of international competition. As a result, local producers have lost market share. This has led to a loss of income and jobs. Another big issue has been the forced privatisation of sectors of the economy such as water supply and energy. As foreign TNCs have bought out public corporations, the prices charged to the public have often increased steeply.

Taking it further

To find out more about the HIPC initiative read 'Countries concerned with the HIPC initiative' on your Student CD-ROM.

The development gap: what are the possibilities for the future?

'Looking ahead to 2015 and beyond, there is no question that we can achieve the overarching goal: we can put an end to poverty. We know what to do. But it requires an unswerving, collective, long-term effort.' (United Nations Secretary General Ban Ki-moon, 2008.)

Figure 15.7 shows the share of people by world region living on less than $1 or $2 a day in 2004, and projections for 2015. The most recent global projections anticipate that the proportion of people living in extreme poverty on less than $1 a day will fall from 29% in 1990 to 10% in 2015. Figure 15.7 shows that all regions except sub-Saharan Africa are on track to achieve MDG 1 by 2015. However, as Figure 15.8 shows, there is a range of factors which could either enhance or hinder the processes of development.

The global economic situation

The future of the development gap is uncertain, particularly in the light of the recent global credit crisis. It remains to be seen how much this will impact on much-needed investment in LEDCs. The significant increases in the prices of energy and food were already creating

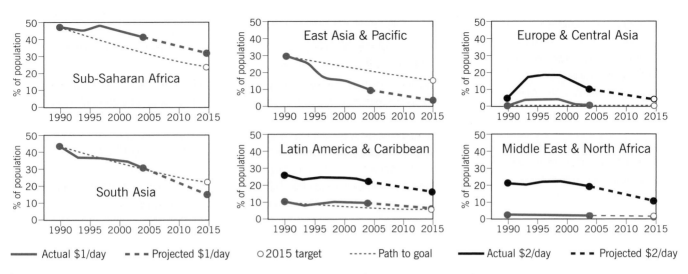

Legend: ——— Actual \$1/day   - - - Projected \$1/day   ○ 2015 target   ------ Path to goal   ——— Actual \$2/day   - - - Projected \$2/day

▲ **Figure 15.7:** The share of people living in poverty and projections for 2015 (by world region).

Factors encouraging future development in LEDCs	Factors hindering future development in LEDCs
MEDCs as a whole increasing international aid to the 0.7% of GDP agreed in 1970	Declining international aid in real terms
Reform of the WTO to allow developing countries greater access to the benefits of world trade	High food and energy prices drawing money away from other investment priorities
Reform of World Bank/IMF policies to fit better the individual circumstances of LEDCs	Adverse climate change reducing agricultural production and increasing the impact of climatic hazards
The wider spread of good governance in the developing world	Deterioration in the terms of trade for LEDCs
Significant technological advances in agriculture to bring food security to more people	The existence of a significant number of anti-democratic and corrupt governments
Increased levels of investment in LEDCs from TNCs	MEDCs increasing barriers to trade to protect their own industries
A reduction in the barriers to migration from LEDCs to MEDCs	MEDCs increasing the barriers to migration from LEDCs

▲ **Figure 15.8:** The factors affecting development in LEDCs.

considerable problems in many poorer countries before the full extent of the global credit crisis unravelled. Many countries are struggling more than ever before to pay for vital imports. While significant reductions in poverty have already taken place, the global problems that have emerged in the latter part of the first decade of the 21st century must cast doubt on further progress in a number of countries, at least in the short term. For example, a newspaper article in the *Daily Telegraph* in October 2008 was entitled 'Rising oil prices push Pakistan to verge of bankruptcy'. The article noted that Pakistan's foreign exchange reserves were so low that it could afford only one more month of imports.

The level of official development assistance

At the UN General Assembly in 1970 the rich donor governments promised to spend 0.7% of GNP on international aid. The deadline for reaching the target was the mid-1970s. However, the reality has been that almost all donor countries have consistently failed to reach this target. International aid is more of a priority in some countries than others.

Sustainable development

If the development gap is to narrow in the future, sustainable strategies will be of vital importance. Reducing poverty in rural areas will take the pressure of poverty off urban areas by dampening down rural-to-urban migration.

▲ **Figure 15.9:** Sustainable agriculture.

Microcredit and social business

The development of the Grameen Bank in Bangladesh has illustrated the power of microcredit in the battle against poverty.

The Grameen Foundation uses microfinance and innovative technology to fight global poverty and bring opportunities to the poorest people. The bank provided tiny loans and financial services to poor people to start their own businesses. Women are the beneficiaries of most of these loans. A typical loan might be used to buy a cow and sell milk to fellow villagers or to purchase a piece of machinery which can be hired out to other people in the community. The concept has spread beyond Bangladesh to reach 3.6 million families in 25 countries. Muhammad Yunus highlights 'social business' as the next phase in the battle against poverty in his book *Creating a World Without Poverty*. He presents a vision of a new business model that combines the operation of the free market with the quest for a more humane world. Yunus argues that poverty is created by economic, social and political systems and not by the laziness, ignorance or moral failings of the poor. He sees the role of women as 'drivers' of the 'coming revolution' and technology as a crucial enabler.

Summary

In this chapter, you have learnt:

- about the theories that help to explain the development gap.
- about the way that Bolivia has tried to manage globalisation.
- about the role of international aid in development.
- about the distinction between top-down and bottom-up approaches to development.
- about the factors that could impact on the development gap in the future.

MCQ

Exam Practice – Section A

Bridging the Development Gap

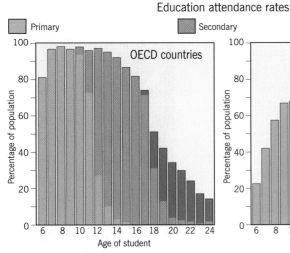
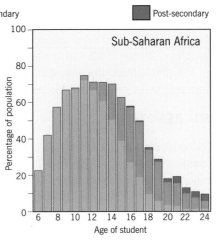
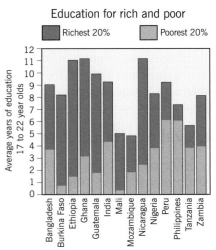

▲ **Figure 5:** The education gap

(a) Explain how Figure 5 shows inequality of educational opportunity between countries and within developing countries. [10]

(b) Evaluate the role of trade in bridging the development gap. [15]

CHAPTER 16 Why is there inequality in access to technology?

Learning objectives

After studying this chapter, you will be able to discuss these ideas and concepts and provide located examples of them:

- There are different levels of technological development and people's access to more advanced technologies varies.
- Access to modern technology is related to the level of development and shows significant global and regional contrasts.
- There is a clear divide between those who are able to access new technology and those whose access is restricted as a consequence of where they live.
- There is a range of reasons for the disparities in access to technological innovations.

Key terms

Digital divide
Environmental determinism
Global shift
Information technology
Intellectual property
Patent
Technical fix

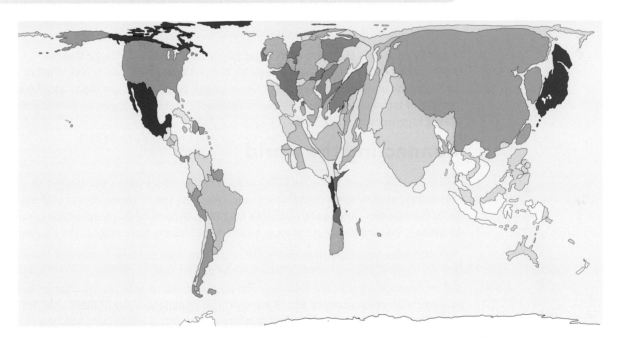

Imagine life without electricity. It drives most of the technology we habitually use. The map in Figure 16.1 shows the percentage of people with access to electricity in their homes from a power grid and self-generated sources. The percentage is over 97% in eastern Asia, eastern Europe, North America, western Europe and Japan, but is significantly lower in parts of Africa. Whereas countries of the former Soviet bloc enjoy near-universal access to electricity, in sub-Saharan Africa only 8% of the rural population have access to electricity and just over half the urban population. Moreover, the quality and regularity of the service are low.

▲ **Figure 16.1:** Access to electricity. The size of the territory shows the proportion of all people with some electrical power in their homes living there.

Powering the world

Technology has been defined in different ways. In the simplest of terms, it is the ability to control nature, which could include the use of any kind of tool from the most basic prehistoric axe. It may also be defined as the practical application of science to industry or commerce or the application of scientific advances to benefit humanity. We may think of it in terms of the electrical equipment upon which we now rely so heavily but, more generally, technology is the application of knowledge to meet the wants of people and this implies the need for learning in the understanding and use of technological tools.

Taking it further

Write down some of the recent technological advances that have occurred and discuss their benefits and drawbacks. Are they likely to benefit some at the expense of others?

The generation of electricity and the internal combustion engine are probably two of the most significant developments in the history of technology, followed later in the 20th century by the invention of computers and the growth of microtechnology. These advances have revolutionised the way in which we live, radically altering people's relationships with the geography of their lives.

In the affluent Western world, we take technology for granted. You may be reading this electronically or using the attached CD to follow up the Taking it further work, on your laptop, while listening to your iPod, with the television on in the background. You have plenty of light, you are comfortably warm (or cool if there is a heatwave) and you can grab something to eat or drink from the kitchen as and when you need. You probably cannot imagine life without all of the techno-gadgets upon which you rely. Now imagine you live in a Mumbai slum or the semi-desert of the Sahel or the Peruvian Andes. What technological aids do you think are readily available in these places?

A technical fix is the idea that there is a technologically 'correct' solution to any situation. The judgement as to the 'correctness' of any solution may be based upon an evaluation of the economic, social or environmental outcomes. It will also depend upon your perspective and this may be influenced by your cultural outlook. There may well be no satisfactory judgement and you should be prepared to argue the case from several viewpoints. In the wider world, there are different levels of technology and an appropriate technological solution may differ according to the level of knowledge and understanding (or education), as well as the level of economic development.

Today technology is pervasive, as is dependency on modern technology. It varies significantly between countries and regions, but practically everyone is now affected by technological advances to a greater or lesser extent. Great claims are made about the benefits of technology and breakthroughs are mostly greeted with glee as enabling the steady improvement of our lives.

Connecting the world

The major innovations of the past 200 years, such as steam power, electricity and telephones, exist to some degree in virtually every country. However, access to these older technologies varies widely between countries, depending on the affordability of the technology and the ability of the local culture to absorb the technological development.

Railways were built extensively in the UK in the mid-19th century, connecting the ports and the rapidly growing industrial towns. Their impact was revolutionary and played a key role in developing the British economy. Railways were constructed in the colonies to ensure strategic and military control and to transport raw materials. Many of these lines are now falling into disrepair, due to a lack of investment, and this is hindering development. In Latin America, notably Argentina, Brazil and Mexico, the railway system is better integrated and this has enabled industrialisation.

Car ownership has grown rapidly since the 1970s. The more affluent OECD countries have the highest number of vehicles per 1,000 people, but developing countries are rapidly catching up. In 2005 Luxembourg, New Zealand and Iceland had over 600 passenger cars per 1,000 people, whereas countries such as Somalia had less than 1 car per 1,000. Two-thirds of the world's population currently lives in countries with an average of less than 1 car per 20 people. Privately owned passenger vehicles in China have increased from 20,000 in 1985 to 18.24 million in 2006. Since the 1990s China has built a road network that is second in length only to the interstate highway system in the USA. But upkeep is costly and there are limited funds for investment. Feeder roads to rural communities are rarely constructed, making it difficult for rural communities to transport goods to urban markets.

Region	Vehicles/ 1000	Cars/ 1000
North America	648	441
Western Europe	491	427
Latin America	144	109
Middle East and Africa	35	24
South Asia	13	9
South-east Asia	144	85
China	24	15
OPEC	55	37

▲ **Figure 16.2:** Vehicle and passenger car ownership in 2005.

© Mike Baldwin / Cornered
BALdwin

"And this little warning light flashes when the outside air becomes too polluted to breathe."

▲ **Figure 16.3:** The cartoon shows how some people can afford to protect themselves from the environmental consequences of their actions.

The transport industry is a primary force in the shift from separate national economic systems to the global economy and shipping is a catalyst of economic development. Economies of scale, high-speed cargo handling systems (including the use of containers) and integrated transport systems have reduced the cost of shipping. Transport networks encourage trade and economic activity and each technological advance has encouraged economic growth. Air passenger transport has enabled the growth of travel and tourism. This has brought valuable income to many poorer parts of the world and has been used as a means of development, although it has also had damaging cultural and environmental impacts in some places. There is also a substantial business sector, often using private aircraft from more local airports.

Year	Number of passengers (million)	Passenger km (billion)
1955	68	61
1965	177	198
1975	534	697
1985	899	1,367
1995	1,304	2,248
2005	2,022	3,720

Passengers on scheduled airlines only; military aviation, private and business flights are excluded.

▲ **Figure 16.4:** The growth in air travel.

The volume of food transported in containers by sea doubled between 1985 and 2000. Traffic is particularly heavy between Asia, Europe and North America (see Figure 16.5). Cargo includes raw materials such as iron ore, fossil fuels and bauxite, agricultural goods such as grain and sugar, industrial materials such as rubber, cement, chemicals and textile fibres, and manufactured goods such as machinery, motor vehicles and consumer goods. Short sea shipping transfers goods within regions, and deep sea shipping transfers between regions. In contrast, air freight accounts for only 0.1% of goods transported, covering cargo such as engineering goods, processed textiles, livestock and automotive spare parts – the more time-sensitive items – but the cost of air transportation of goods is generally prohibitive.

Taking it further

Find a map of air travel in your school atlas and notice which countries are connected by the largest volumes of traffic.

Key term

Global shift — transfer of manufacturing from western Europe and North America, which involved trade across the North Atlantic, to the newly industrialised countries (NICs) and the growth of trade around the Pacific Ocean. This has been facilitated by the growth of transnational companies (TNCs).

Taking it further

Using Figure 16.4, calculate the distance travelled per passenger to find out how this changed between 1955 and 2005. Divide the number of passenger km (which is the total distance travelled) by the number of passengers.

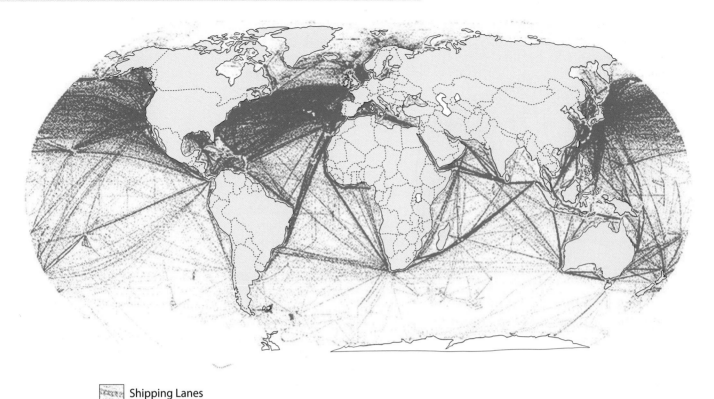

Shipping Lanes

▲ **Figure 16.5:** The shipping lanes show a noticeable concentration in the northern hemisphere transporting goods to and between the more affluent countries.

The digital divide

Key terms

Information technology — the electronic means of capturing, processing, storing and communicating information.

Digital divide — the gap between richer and poorer parts of the world in terms of ICT access. It can be measured by dividing the ICT penetration rate in the developed world by the ICT penetration rate in the developing world.

Communications technology commenced with the patenting of the first telegraph machine in 1830. By 1900, submarine cables connected Europe and North America and telephones were common in more affluent homes. Television commenced in the USA in 1928, but it was only in the 1950s that it became an economically viable option and its use spread rapidly. The first satellite images were relayed in the 1960s. Now we take telephones and televisions for granted. News is transmitted instantly, not only by professional journalists but also by amateurs recording incidents as they happen on their mobile phones. The news of the American Airlines flight landing in the Hudson River in January 2009 was circulated around the world via Twitter half an hour before the journalists arrived.

Yet in this shrinking world where telecommuting (working from home) is enabled by internet connections and teleconferencing facilities, many west Africans still receive news by word of mouth as they lack access to TV, newspapers and telephony and are unable to afford motor vehicles to drive on their unmade roads. Information technology (IT) has enabled the transfer and processing of information throughout the world and has therefore facilitated globalisation. IT has the potential to alleviate poverty through its use in encouraging small enterprises but, at the end of the 20th century, four-fifths of the world's population did not have access to telecommunications and one-third had no access to electricity.

The problem of disseminating technology is most acute in African countries. In 2000, while three-quarters of the population of Africa had access to radio and 40% to television, the internet was available to fewer than 1 in 1,000 people and over half had never used a telephone. The best way to spread information to the poor about agriculture or business, for example, was via newspapers, radio and television, but even these media did not reach the whole population and possibly those who most needed it were least likely to receive the information. LEDCs need IT to facilitate development but internet access is concentrated in the affluent north.

Use of the internet has grown exponentially from its origins in 1984. At the end of 2006, there were 1.2 billion internet users representing about 18% of the world's population. Access to IT continues to grow at high speed and the digital divide is shrinking. Internet users were initially concentrated in the United States, western Europe, Australia and Japan, but people living in eastern Asia, southern Asia, South America, China and eastern Europe are increasingly online. Fewer people are connected in northern Africa, south-eastern Africa and the Middle East. There are major disparities in access to IT; despite the high growth rates in some regions, many developing countries risk falling behind in the use of newer technologies and this will hinder their social and economic development.

Seeking explanations for disparity

Geography is essentially about people and the environment. There have been two major themes in the study of the people–environment relationship: the first emphasises the role of the physical environment in structuring human activities, whereas the second underlines the role of culture in structuring the physical environment. Technology plays an essential role in enabling people to overcome the constraints imposed by their environment and also allows people to control at least some aspects of the environment. Access to technology now varies in different parts of the world and there is a contrast between those who can access new technologies and those who are left behind.

Region	Percentage of world total
Canada and USA	65.3
Europe	22.4
Australia, Japan, New Zealand	6.4
Developing Asia-Pacific	3.7
Latin America/ Caribbean	1.9
Africa	0.3

Source: Potter, Binns, Elliott & Smith (2004)

▲ **Figure 16.6:** The distribution of internet hosts in 1999.

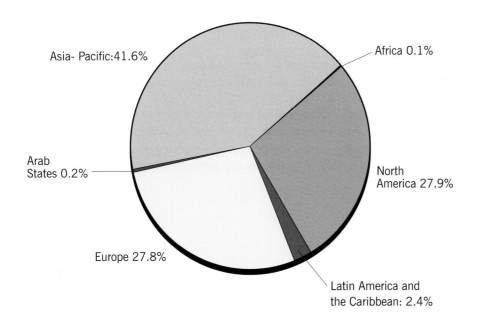

Distribution of broadband subscribers by region, 2004, in percent

Asia- Pacific:41.6%

Africa 0.1%

Arab States 0.2%

North America 27.9%

Europe 27.8%

Latin America and the Caribbean: 2.4%

◀ **Figure 16.7:** The pie chart shows the digital divide very clearly as Africa hardly registers.

▲ **Figure 16.8:** Searching for a mobile phone signal in the Egyptian desert. Satellite technology enables people in remoter regions to overcome the digital divide, removes geographical constraints and also crosses cultural barriers.

The poorest people may be said to suffer from environmental determinism. Environmental or geographical determinism is the view that the physical environment, rather than social conditions, determines culture. Essentially, the physical geography of an area, particularly the climate, affects the behaviour of the people living there, so the environment determines culture rather than social conditions. This idea was popular in the early 20th century but fell out of favour as it was used to justify racism.

Another approach suggested that the economic base is determined by environmental conditions. This holds some validity if the definition of environmental conditions includes the availability of useful raw materials. It may then follow that the type of economy that develops will influence the society and culture of the area. Another viewpoint holds that culture operates independently and this will determine the relationship between people and their environment.

When technology is transferred from one society to another, associated social and cultural values are also often transferred. For example, machinery might be introduced for a task traditionally done by women (such as collecting water or firewood) but men then take over the operation of the machinery while women are relegated to more menial tasks. On the other hand, the introduction of rice mills in Java, replacing milling in the home, enabled women to receive literacy training while they waited for their rice to be ground. Development in one sector can, therefore, affect other sectors of a community.

Crucially, the efficient use of technology requires knowledge and the ability to learn, not just about how to use it, but also about how it can be utilised effectively. Poor countries differ from rich ones as many inhabitants have less advanced technical knowledge as well as less wealth. Knowledge may be owned: indigenous people may have knowledge handed down about the medicinal uses of local plants, but pharmaceutical companies based elsewhere may research and then patent plant properties. In this way ownership of knowledge is related to economic and social power. People in developing countries need to know not only about how the technology works, but also about its purpose and value.

Just as migrants may meet intervening obstacles on their journey, there are barriers preventing people from accessing technology and the benefits it brings. These include:
- Cost barriers – new technology is initially very expensive as its producers need to cover their research and development costs
- Intellectual property rights and the patent system – used by inventors and innovators to protect their work
- Poor access to education and training – many countries cannot afford to provide full-time education for everyone throughout their childhood; also, some countries deny access to education, particularly for women
- Political denial of access – some political leaders fear they may be undermined if their people have full access to information on the internet, so denial is a means of control
- Religious denial of access – certain religious groups similarly seek to restrict their followers' access to the range of controversial arguments now available online.

Key terms

Patent — sole and exclusive right for a number of years to the proceeds from the sales of an invention. Intellectual property rights — cover ownership of creations of the mind, both artistic and commercial; they include copyright, trademarks, patents and trade secrets.

Case study: Affordable medicinal drugs

Millennium Development Goal 8, Target 4 aims to provide affordable essential drugs in developing countries in cooperation with pharmaceutical companies. In most developing countries the availability of low-cost or free medicines at public health facilities is often limited because of inadequate funding and inefficient procurement, stock control and distribution. Some drug manufacturers have lowered their prices in developing countries in line with local purchasing power, and international health charities also help to provide medicines to public health facilities. However, the poor availability of medicines in the public sector often forces patients to buy more expensive medicines in the private sector.

The pharmaceutical companies effectively control people's access to affordable drugs. They have been criticised for an alleged reluctance to invest in treatments for diseases common in developing countries such as malaria. They also receive criticism for the prices they charge for patented medicines, such as the AIDS drugs that are most needed in developing countries. Two-thirds of all people living with HIV and over 70% of deaths from AIDS are in sub-Saharan Africa. The research and development of medicinal drugs are costly and they can take many years to develop and test. New drugs are patented to prevent other companies from copying them. This enables the patent owner to recover the costs of research and development. A drug patent typically lasts for about 20 years, after which time a generic drug may be produced and sold by other companies at a lower price.

The World Trade Organisation rules permit a developing country to obtain essential medicines by importing cheaper versions of the drugs before patents expire and pharmaceutical companies do sometimes offer such medicines more cheaply to developing countries. However, over 40 pharmaceutical companies sued South Africa in 2001 because it allowed the import and generic production of cheap AIDS drugs. The case was later dropped after protests around the world. The big pharmaceutical companies do run charitable programmes such as Merck's donation of river blindness drugs to Africa, Pfizer's gift of free or discounted drugs for AIDS in South Africa and Novartis' Access to Medicine projects, including donations of medicines to patients affected by leprosy, tuberculosis and malaria.

HealthStore in Kenya has set up a network of franchises (comparable to fast-food chains) that are owned and run by nurses to provide poor communities in more remote rural areas with essential, affordable medicines. It has government support and provides training programmes, while giving the nurses a sustainable income. This innovative scheme is able to bypass the inefficient health systems that prevent essential drugs from reaching those who most need them.

Taking it further

The top pharmaceutical companies are GlaxoSmithKline (UK), Pfizer (US), Johnson & Johnson (US), Bayer (Germany) and Novartis (Switzerland). China's Sinopharm is the only developing world company in the top 50 but its revenue is one-tenth of that of the major companies.

Summary

In this chapter you have learnt:

- that there are different levels of technological development and people's access to more advanced technologies varies.
- that access to modern technology is related to the level of development and shows significant global and regional contrasts.
- that there is a clear divide between those who are able to access new technology and those whose access is restricted as a consequence of where they live.
  - that there is a range of reasons for the disparities in access to technological innovations.

MCQ

Chapter 17 How far does technology determine development and resource use?

Learning objectives

After studying this chapter, you will be able to discuss these ideas and concepts and provide located examples of them:

• Economic development and technological innovation are closely connected.
• There is a widening gap between traditional and knowledge-based economies, but this can be overcome through technology and knowledge transfers.
• There are unforeseen social, economic and environmental consequences of technological innovation that may be beneficial or costly.
• The challenge of achieving equitable levels of technology for people and the environment is clearly demonstrated in the rising demand for agricultural produce.

The role of technology in economic development

After the Second World War, it was thought that technology was the solution to economic development, therefore aid was poured into major infrastructure projects such as large dams in developing countries. The prevailing view was that poverty could be alleviated if poorer countries adopted the technology and knowledge of the advanced economies, and the change from simple and traditional techniques could be achieved with the application of scientific knowledge. More recently, there has been considerable criticism of major building projects due to their negative social and environmental impacts. In addition, they have not always brought economic benefits for local people.

This idea of a technological fix to solve social and economic problems does have some basis in history as each new wave of technological innovation has generated economic growth:
• textiles in the late 18th century
• railways and steel in the mid-19th century
• motor vehicles and chemicals in the early 20th century
• information and communications (micro–electronics) in the late 20th century.

It could be that the next economic cycle will be kick-started by developments in biotechnology and/or nanotechnology. But, economic development is so closely linked to technological development, those with the best access to knowledge are best placed to achieve wealth and others will fall on the wrong side of a widening information and technology gap.

There are several indicators that show how this gap is reinforced between richer and poorer nations. Obviously, more affluent countries are able to invest more in education, and participation rates in higher education (HE) are revealing. About 105 million students were enrolled in tertiary education (at university or in vocational training) in 2002, but young people in Finland were 140 times more likely to be in tertiary education than those in Mozambique. Over 60% of spending on tertiary education is concentrated in North America and western Europe compared with only 1.5% in central and south-eastern Africa, yet investment in such education greatly benefits society both socially and economically.

Taking it further

Compare the Worldmapper map number 346 on Proportion of People Enrolled in Tertiary Education with the Worldmapper map number 211 on Tertiary Education Spending at www.worldmapper.org/atozindex.html. Are there any significant differences between the maps?

China — 65,049
Switzerland — 83,973
Belgium — 87,891
Australia — 98,707
Sweden — 98,833
Russian Federation — 102,568
Netherlands — 125,038
Spain — 137,526
Canada — 173,782
United Kingdom — 326,194
France — 358,387
Germany — 376,744
Japan — 1,096,031
United States — 1,474,028

0   500,000   1,000,000   1,500,000

Source: http://data.un.org/data/

▲ **Figure 17.1:** Country of registration of patents in force in 2002, showing only countries with over 50,000 patents (out of a total of 53 countries).

The north–south divide in spending on research and development (R & D) is stark. To maintain their competitive edge, scientific and technological industries must invest in R & D to develop new and improved products. This can be expensive as it requires expertise, time, specialised equipment and materials. The findings of academic research are usually published (unless they are commercially sensitive) and the majority of scientific papers are published in western Europe, North America and Japan. Similarly, these regions apply for the majority of patents for new and improved products and processes and receive the greatest income from royalties and licence fees.

The level of technology can affect the extent to which resources are exploited as well as determining the volume of accessible reserves as a proportion of the total resource base. The level of technology will also determine, to some extent, the size of a population that can be supported in an area; for example, access to improved medical services will lower death rates. There is, therefore, an interrelationship between population, resources and technology – sometimes called the three-sided wheel – and this is illustrated in Figure 17.2.

Taking it further

Look up map number 165 showing the Location of Worldwide Research and Development Expenditure at www.worldmapper.org/atozindex.html and compare it with map number 205 on Science Research. Why is the distribution so skewed?

Leapfrogging

Technological leapfrogging may be one way of overcoming some of the barriers to development. Mobile phones are beginning to achieve this in many more remote parts of the world. It is cheaper and easier to put up mobile phone masts than to construct a cabled telecommunications network. Broadband technologies such as Wi-Max, GSM and Wi-Fi have the potential to provide a cost-effective communications infrastructure in developing countries, leapfrogging traditional land-based cable and fibre-optic connections. Internet bandwidth consumption and the number of broadband subscribers more than doubled between 1999 and 2004 in both middle- and low-income countries. Much of this growth has been in shared internet connections, such as through internet cafés, as personal computers are too expensive for most people in developing countries to buy.

The internet and mobile phones enable people to leapfrog stages in technological development such as landline phones and terrestrial television. Providing internet access in developing countries will help to achieve the Millennium Goals for health, education, employment and poverty reduction. Growth of mobile phone use has been strongest in regions with fewest fixed telephone lines. In Africa, over 60 million new mobile subscribers were added in 2006, by which time 22% of Africa's population had a mobile phone compared with 3% with fixed telephone lines and 5% who were internet users.

Key term

Leapfrogging — the term used to describe how some newer technologies, such as mobile phones and the internet, are penetrating developing countries much faster than older technologies like landline telephones.

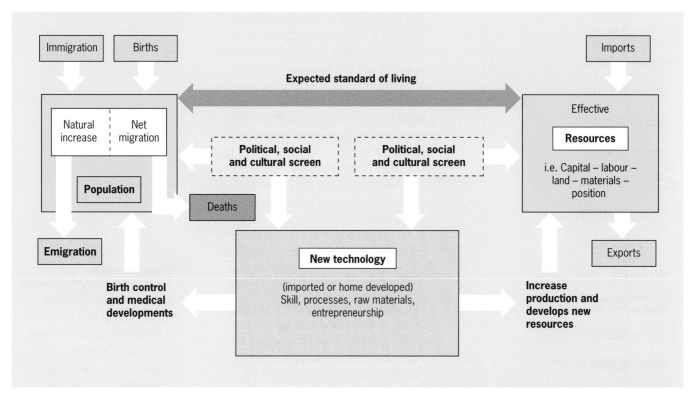

▲ **Figure 17.2:** The relationship between population, resources and technology.

The expansion of wireless broadband is closing the communications gap between poorer and richer countries, but the digital divide is still wide. In developed countries, 58% of the population used the internet in 2006 compared with 11% in developing countries and only 1% in the least developed countries. For many countries in sub-Saharan Africa, broadband is still inaccessible to the majority of the population because of its high cost. There are also institutional and legal barriers created by existing telecommunications providers reluctant to lose out to the new technology and restrictive intellectual property arrangements. More written languages need to become available on mobile phones to enable people to write in their native tongue.

The rapid increase in mobile phone ownership in low-income countries has significant social and economic benefits for poor people in rural areas who have previously been handicapped by poor communications infrastructure.

- Teba Bank in South Africa has developed a smart card that uses mobile phone technology to provide low-cost electronic banking services to low-income customers.
- The Bangladesh Welltracker project enables villagers to ensure the safety of their water supply. They send messages to identify their location and then receive information as to how deep to dig the well to avoid arsenic contamination.
- Ekgaon Technologies' innovative online application system enables rural people in Tamil Nadu in India to access their financial information by mobile phone, so maintaining accounts is now easier and bank loans can be arranged more quickly.
- In Sri Lanka, text messages alerting police officers, village chiefs and other important officials will enable them to warn people the next time a disaster such as a tsunami threatens, to give them time to seek safety.
- OneWorld South Asia has launched a phone-based academic support service for teachers and students in Rajasthan in India.
- In Delhi, IBM has tested a new mobile phone technology: a network of different VoiceSites will help rural communities which cannot read or afford a computer to access relevant information. Farmers will be able to sell their own produce directly, without going through a middle man, and villagers will be able to access health information.

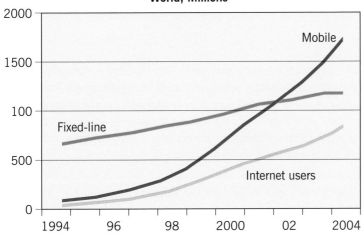

**Telephone subscribers
and Internet Users
World, Millions**

◀ **Figure 17.3:** The graph clearly shows how mobile phone usage has overtaken fixed-line telecommunications

Case study: Kenya connected

Africa is the fastest growing mobile phone market in the world. The continent's mobile phone use is increasing at twice the global average. In 1999 Kenya had 15,000 mobile phone subscribers. By 2008 there were 5.6 million subscribers, despite the fact that only 200,000 Kenyan households had electricity.

Mobile phones in Africa are used for a wide variety of tasks, from sending money to family members to buying a fish from the market:

- Fishermen check the local fish market prices on their phones to determine where it's best to sell the day's catch.
- Contract labourers can now provide their phone numbers to potential employers instead of having to wait for hours at a workplace in case a job arises.
- Crop growers can obtain up-to-date commodity information allowing them to get fruit and vegetable prices daily from a dozen markets. Many farmers have quadrupled their earnings because they have access to information about potential buyers and prices before making the journey into urban centres to sell their produce.

Case study: China online

China's online population expanded to 298 million in 2008, 23% of the population, many accessing the internet via their mobile phones. Internet use in the countryside was increasing faster than in the cities and the charges for the service have been falling fast, making it more accessible for poorer people. Students are the largest group of mobile internet users, using their phones to read online news, download music and check emails. By 2011, 3G services should be available all over China and this is expected to encourage massive growth in mobile internet use. 3G phones enable faster data transmission and services such as television, online games and websurfing.

China's booming internet use comes despite the government's censorship of the web's vulgar and pornographic content. Sites which are considered politically sensitive are blocked, including the BBC's Chinese-language news site. Google has been criticised for agreeing to restrict search results on some topics such as human rights and political reform under pressure from the Chinese government, which prefers to use the internet to promote its own ideological viewpoint.

Taking it further

Compare the Worldmapper maps showing telephone lines (number 332) and cellular (mobile phone) subscribers (number 334) in 2002 at www.worldmapper.org/atozindex.html. Identify which countries are pictured larger for telephone lines and which are larger for mobile phones. From this you should be able to work out which countries are leapfrogging the older telecommunications technology.

Taking it further

Other widely used products that subsequently proved to have unforeseen consequences include asbestos, DDT, Teflon, CFCs and HFCs. Investigate the expected uses and unintended consequences of these products.

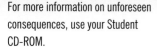

Taking it further

For more information on unforeseen consequences, use your Student CD-ROM.

Unintended consequences

Technological innovations can have unintended consequences, that is, unforeseen social, environmental and economic costs and benefits of new technology. These are known as externalities.

Positive effects include:

- Facebook, which had 150 million users by its fifth birthday in February 2009 and was translated into 35 languages with a further 60 in development. Mark Zuckerberg started the network in his Harvard dormitory simply as a way of keeping in touch with his friends. Within 24 hours 1,200 Harvard students had signed up and the network quickly extended to other colleges and universities. It has now become the world's biggest online social network.

Negative effects include:

- PCBs, which were developed in the 1930s and used for cooling and lubricating and as ingredients in many household products such as paint. However, they interfere with the hormone system in animals causing pre-natal damage leading to birth defects or stillbirth. PCBs remain in the environment for decades or even centuries and can now be found in every living organism. They accumulate exponentially through the food chain, becoming most heavily concentrated in the fat tissue of top carnivores.

Unintended consequences are invisible or seem unimportant at the time of technological development, but rigorous testing and environmental impact statements are now required to avoid unwanted externality effects.

Social benefits

The exponential growth of information technologies has engendered changes that have profound effects for people and organisations. Fifty years ago, there were no web designers or solar panel salespeople; new and unexpected professions are needed when an innovation spreads. There have been many social gains from the improvements in access to knowledge and information including the widening of education and the spreading of democratic ideas, although some regimes have seen this as a threat.

Social costs

The reasons for unintended consequences can include ignorance, error, greed and arrogance. Technology is not neutral because it can benefit some and cost others. The mechanisation of agriculture enabled more food to be produced, which improved people's diets, but farm labourers lost their jobs, having been replaced by the machines. Mechanisation and computerisation have caused unemployment for many people, but have created work for others. The social cost has been the need for a major skills change.

Economic benefits

There is a positive multiplier effect attached to any new economic development. The growth of new industries, ancillary companies and service businesses, involving new technologies directly or indirectly, has created work and generated wealth throughout the world. Edge-of-city retail parks, service stations and drive-through fast food outlets developed to serve the new car-driving population in the later decades of the 20th century.

Economic costs

Environmental costs inevitably have economic consequences. These will arise from the costs of environmental waste and degradation, reduction in natural resource stocks leading to an increase in the market value and the costs of recycling. The rapid economic growth in China has required the modernisation of its communications infrastructure and has encouraged a building boom. The huge demand for raw materials generated by this growth pushed up the market price of copper, for example, encouraging expansion of copper ore quarrying and copper recovery and recycling, creating both costs and benefits for those involved.

▲ **Figure 17.4:** Opencast copper mining at Parys Mountain in Anglesey, North Wales. World demand for copper has increased with the growth of the Chinese and other south and east Asian economies but there are inevitable environmental impacts.

Environmental benefits

The rise in energy prices has encouraged the development of technologies to enable a more efficient use of fuel. This has the added benefit of reducing per capita pollution levels. Clean water supplies and improved sanitation benefit people and ecosystems. More efficient resource use and recycling technologies reduce the degradation of the environment. Consider, for example, the reuse of aluminium, lessening the impact of bauxite extraction.

Environmental costs

Most industrial activities produce waste. The degree to which it is hazardous varies widely and, in advanced economies, legislation and waste management procedures minimise the impact on people and the environment. Industries that produce hazardous waste have a 'duty of care' to ensure it is disposed of properly. Hazardous waste from mining and processing metals, the petrochemical industry, pesticides and plastics manufacturing, for example, may have an immediate harmful effect or may become harmful over an extended period of time.

Metals are required to manufacture many microelectronic products. The extraction and transportation of the raw materials entail environmental costs, as does the manufacturing of the products: Figure 17.5 identifies some of the inputs required to produce a mobile phone. Mobile phones have an average life of 18 months before they are disposed of and there are environmental impacts associated with their disposal. Much of the obsolete high-tech equipment from the USA and Europe is shipped to China, India and Japan where copper, gold, lead, mercury and cadmium are salvaged. This work causes health and environmental problems as some of these components are toxic; 23% of the weight of a laptop is comprised of harmful metals such as lead, cadmium and copper.

Taking it further

The Environment Agency is responsible for overseeing the management of waste and its website provides a lot of technical detail about the classification of waste for industries, including a detailed glossary of terms.

Resources	Amounts	Equivalents	Other components
Water	160.2 litres	More than 1 person's daily water use in Britain.	The resources and energy needed to make the plastic case, antenna and battery and the energy used during the phone's lifetime to recharge the battery.
Chemicals	364 grams	In weight, equal to $6^{1}/_{4}$ Mars bars!	
Energy	6.59×10^{-6} kWh	Enough to run a low-energy light bulb for 2 seconds.	

▲ **Figure 17.5:** Resources required to manufacture a mobile phone.

Feeding the world

One of the greatest challenges in the 21st century will be to feed the increasing number of people, possibly 9 billion by 2050. In the last century, green revolution techniques enabled food production to rise in line with population growth, confounding the Malthusian theorists, but providing tangible support for Esther Boserup (see Figure 17.7). From 1961 to 1985, the population in developing countries grew by 2.3% per year, whereas agricultural production grew by 3.3%. China used improved varieties and more fertiliser to increase rice yields by 57% between 1974 and 1988, achieving 40% more production from 11% less land to feed the growing population. Figure 17.8 weighs up the outcomes of the green revolution.

Malthus versus Boserup: pessimism or optimism?

▲ **Figure 17.6:** Thomas Malthus.

An Essay on the Principle of Population (1798)

Malthus said that unchecked population growth increases geometrically: 2, 4, 8, 16, 32... while food production increases arithmetically: 1, 2, 3, 4, 5... Thus he said that 'The power of population is indefinitely greater than the power in the Earth to produce subsistence for man'. Malthus' theory is considered pessimistic because it is based on the belief that food supplies are fixed rather than expanding, but conditions during the past half century have not supported his theory.

▲ **Figure 17.7:** Esther Boserup.

The Conditions of Agricultural Growth (1965)

Boserup said it was possible to overcome environmental limits through culture and technology. Thus population increase is the main factor driving technological change and creating a better world for many more people: 'necessity is the mother of invention'. She argued that a larger population could stimulate economic growth and the production of more food, so her ideas are considered to be optimistic; they seem to have been justified with regard to the green revolution.

The outcomes of the green revolution	
Benefits	**Costs**
• Increased yields of staple crops such as wheat and rice • 2 or 3 crops per year can be grown where climatic conditions permit • Increased farm incomes raising farmers out of subsistence • Increase in food production kept pace with population growth	• Poorer farmers could not afford the higher-yielding varieties (HYVs), agricultural chemicals or machinery • Many farmers got into debt in order to buy HYVs, chemicals, etc. • Increased rural unemployment due to mechanisation • Damaging environmental impacts from increased use of fertilisers and pesticides • Salinisation of soil due to increase in irrigated land

▲ **Figure 17.8:** The green revolution debate.

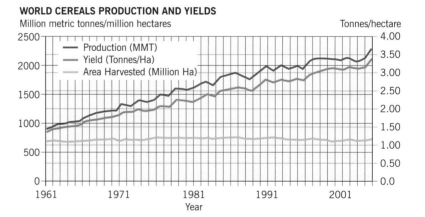

WORLD CEREALS PRODUCTION AND YIELDS

▲ **Figure 17.9:** World cereals production and yields – the impact of the green revolution.

The law of diminishing returns applies to the use of agricultural chemicals. As inputs increase, the proportional gains in terms of yield decrease until the cost of the additional chemicals exceeds the income from the additional yield. So the economic and environmental costs of using fertilisers and pesticides exceed the socio-economic benefits of more food. In low-input farming the chemical inputs are reduced; this increases the environmental benefits but does not seriously alter the social and economic costs and benefits.

Case study: Conflicting views on GMOs

GMO producers, Monsanto: 'We're excited about the potential for genetically modified food to contribute to a better environment and a sustainable, plentiful and healthy food supply. We recognise, however, that many consumers have genuine concerns about food biotechnology and its impact on their families.'

French farmer: 'Today there are 102 million hectares sown with GMO seeds around the world. What we fear is that if France rejects GMOs we will be left behind and be dependent on other countries' technology.'

US farmer: 'I think genetically modified seed is the way and future of farming. It's not harmful and it seems to benefit farmers. We have actually planted some GM cotton, which is resistant to some insects and bugs. There is nothing wrong with it. Seriously, I think some people aren't thinking practically.'

Biotech engineer: 'Many people who oppose GMOs do not even know what DNA stands for. Most GMO modifications allow farmers to grow more produce per unit of land making them more efficient. Many of the objections to GMOs are unfounded. It is a relatively new science and not all the risks are understood. However, it has the potential to become a huge asset for mankind, especially as we face a global population that is rapidly approaching our planet's carrying capacity.'

Organic farmer: 'Who's responsible if it isn't on a leash? I'm a certified organic seed grower and if my crops were to get contaminated with any detectable amount of transgenic sugar beet pollen, my product would become worthless.'

Kenyan ecologist: 'We are not opposed to GMOs, but they are a danger to food security and our indigenous gene pool.'

Greenpeace: 'The introduction of GM food and crops has been a disaster. The science of taking genes from one species and inserting them into another was supposed to be a giant leap forward, but instead they pose a serious threat to biodiversity and our own health. The real reason for their development has not been to end world hunger, but to increase the stranglehold multinational biotech companies have on food production.'

Low-input farming, which is less intensive and more sustainable, lies between the extremes of agri-business and permaculture. Agri-business exploits the land and its produce to maximise output and profit and it includes aspects of farming that are increasingly regarded as unacceptable such as monoculture and factory farming. Permaculture is an agricultural system that works with nature by recognising that places differ in terms of local climate, landform, soils and the combinations of species. Permaculturalists aim to design permanent high-yielding agricultural ecosystems enabling people to be self-sufficient on as little land as possible, in effect reducing reliance on technology to a minimum. Both systems involve the application of technology but, whereas one uses industrial techniques to maximise output, the other applies knowledge of ecology to work the land as efficiently as possible.

Key term

Biotechnology — any technological application that uses biological systems, living organisms or derivatives of them to make or modify products or processes for specific use. The term is often used to refer to 21st century genetic engineering technology, but it covers a wide range of procedures for modifying biological organisms from the earliest cross-breeding of native plants to artificial selection and hybridisation.

Summary

In this chapter you have learnt:

- that economic development and technological innovation are closely connected.
- that there is a widening gap between traditional and knowledge-based economies, but this can be overcome through technology and knowledge transfers.
- that there are unforeseen social, economic and environmental consequences of technological innovation that may be beneficial or costly.
- that the challenge of achieving equitable levels of technology for people and the environment are clearly demonstrated in the rising demand for agricultural produce.

Taking it further

To look at arguments for and against using genetically modified organisms in agriculture read 'The GMO debate' on your Student CD-ROM.

MCQ

143

CHAPTER 18 What is the role of technology in the management of the contested planet?

Key terms

Appropriate technology
Biocapacity
Ecological footprint
Environmental sustainability
Extended polluter
  responsibility
Externalities
Geo-engineering
Inter-cropping
Intermediate technology
Planetary engineering
Technological absorption

Learning objectives

After studying this chapter, you will be able to discuss these ideas and concepts and provide located examples of them:

- Technology operates at different levels and has different social and environmental consequences.
- Technology has the potential to fix major environmental problems but the solutions may have negative impacts.
- Technology needs to be employed sustainably and used to achieve sustainable development.
- The future may see a continuing divergence between the technologically advanced core and the technologically impoverished periphery.

Valuing technology

Optimists view the adoption and spread of technology such as IT as having positive impacts such as the creation of wealth and improvements in the provision of social and welfare services. Pessimists, on the other hand, emphasise negative impacts such as unemployment and the alienation of those who do not possess the skills to benefit from technological advance. There is also a problem in that those with access to and understanding of new technologies may underestimate and overlook the value of traditional local or indigenous knowledge and experience.

It has been suggested that the introduction of advanced technology from more economically developed countries into less developed economies has destroyed traditional work faster than new employment has been created, leaving the poor worse off. The green revolution used to be regarded as a prime example of this negative impact as poor farmers did lose out initially but, by the end of the 20th century, it was clear that even the poorest of rural workers had eventually benefited from higher incomes, a better diet and greater demand for their labour.

The building of large dams to control water supply and to supply electricity (HEP), as well as a variety of other purposes, employed the expertise of rich countries and has largely been funded by grants and loans from them. The Aswan Dam on the River Nile, for example, was paid for by the former Soviet Union. Many of these schemes have been highly contested due to their negative environmental and social impacts such as the enforced migration of local people. It is now thought that the global-warming potential of methane emissions from decaying organic matter in reservoirs for HEP may be several times greater than that of oil-powered electricity generation.

In *Small is Beautiful* (1973), E.F. Schumacher called for 'technology with a human face' so that the poor could help themselves by using intermediate technology. He founded the Intermediate Technology Development Group (ITDG) that set out criteria against which a technology could be tested for its appropriateness in a given socio-economic situation. Intermediate technology enables communities to produce the less complex goods that poorer people need such as building materials, clothing, household goods and agricultural tools. It has the advantages of being:

Taking it further

Identify the positive and negative impacts of technological innovations such as large dams, the internet, or wind turbines.

Taking it further

To view the criteria set by the ITDG to judge the appropriateness of technology read 'The appropriateness of technology' on your Student CD-ROM.

- geographically accessible with more locally-based and smaller factories
- educationally accessible as lower-level skills are required
- organisationally accessible as it is small-scale with no need for complex administration systems.

The equipment used is simpler so it is easier to maintain and repair, and requires less training and supervision. Intermediate technology represents a 'technical fix' in that it attempts to identify the most appropriate technology in a developing economy. It is sometimes referred to as appropriate technology, although this refers more to the way in which it is organised, that is, at a more local level.

Using technology

Unit 3 examined some of the issues that people will have to deal with in the 21st century including the provision of energy and clean water, the sustainable development of resources, and the threats to biodiversity. Technology will have an important role to play in overcoming global environmental issues such as global warming and land degradation but some of the proposed technological fixes may not be feasible or desirable.

Any technological fixes will need to be socially and economically equitable as well as environmentally sustainable. As Figure 18.1 shows, the world's ecological footprint is not shared equally as some countries are making a far deeper impression than others. The USA has less than 5% of the world's population, for example, but uses 25% of the world's fuel resources. The World Commission for Environment and Development (WCED, 1987) suggested the need to develop new technologies that will reduce the amount of energy and materials used in every aspect of economic life.

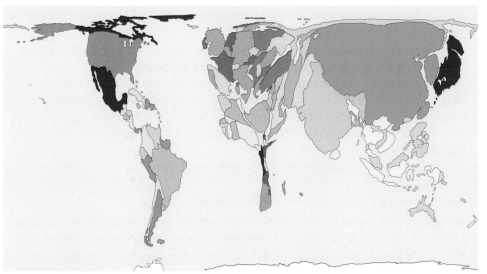

▲ **Figure 18.1:** The world's ecological footprint. The territory size shows each country's share of the global ecological footprint.

Unsustainability occurs when an area's ecological footprint exceeds its biocapacity. This is a useful measure of the earth's carrying capacity as it shows the biological productivity of the land including cropland, pasture, forests and fisheries, and also built-up or degraded land. The biocapacity of an area is affected by physical conditions and human activity such as agricultural practice and urbanisation. In effect, what is being measured is the ability of biologically productive land to provide renewable resources and absorb waste. In ancient times, the Mesopotamian marshes (now Iraq) were part of the 'fertile crescent' where farming techniques were first developed, but this area has been drained and desertified and it is now one of the least productive regions in the world.

Key term

Intermediate technology — labour-intensive and small-scale technology. It is 'a technology that recognises the economic boundaries and limitations of poverty' (Schumacher, 1973) and is regarded as more productive than indigenous technology but less capital-intensive (cheaper) than advanced technology.

Appropriate technology — seen as giving control of technology to individuals and communities at a local level rather than to the technocrats of large companies or governments; it is a people-centred technology.

Ecological footprint — a measure of the area needed to support a person or population's lifestyle. It includes the consumption of food, fuel, minerals and other resources, as well as pollution such as carbon dioxide emissions.

Taking it further

Calculate your ecological footprint at www.ecologicalfootprint.com. What can you do to reduce your footprint?

Taking it further

Look up map number 321 showing the distribution of the world's biocapacity at www.worldmapper.org/atozindex.html. Compare this map with that of the ecological footprint and account for the differences.

Fixing global warming

According to Greenpeace, the solutions to global warming are 'renewable energy, energy efficiency and new environmentally sound technologies'. There is a considerable range of proposed solutions from the obvious to the apparently absurd including:

- Improving the energy efficiency of vehicles, appliances and machinery
- Improving vehicle efficiency through aerodynamic design, using lighter materials for the chassis and body and more fuel-efficient engines
- Changing transport patterns from air and road to rail, and reducing the distances travelled by goods (such as reducing 'food miles')
- Extending renewable sources such as wind, tidal and solar power and geothermal energy sources, and developing wave and ocean power technologies
- Producing biofuels from crops, although this does reduce land available for food production
- Using natural gas (CH_4) in place of coal to generate electricity as methane is 21 times more harmful as a greenhouse gas than carbon dioxide, which is a by-product in this process
- Nuclear power is a highly contentious option but it is a zero carbon alternative, although it is expensive with potentially severe environmental impacts
- Constructing greener buildings with smart meters, double glazing, high-specification insulation, solar panels, more efficient appliances and 'passive solar design' (i.e. making use of sunlight)
- Carbon sequestration by storing carbon underground in geological reservoirs as a gas or in solid form (gas hydrate), for example, it can be used to force out and replace the North Sea oil
- Carbon sequestration through afforestation or protecting threatened forests in the higher northern latitudes as well as tropical forests
- Agricultural carbon sequestration which occurs when manure and crop waste are used instead of chemical fertilisers to maintain soil fertility organically
- Seeding oceans with iron to encourage growth of phytoplankton, although this may reduce oxygen levels and lead to the release of more methane when the plankton decays
- Injecting sulphate particles into the upper atmosphere could reflect solar radiation but it may also damage the ozone layer and would not reduce other problems caused by rising CO_2 levels;
- Burning sulphur in the stratosphere could create a hazy cloud that would reflect solar radiation.
- Constructing giant mirrors in space to reflect sunlight.

These are all technological means of stabilising or reducing carbon emissions or mitigating the effects of increased carbon in the atmosphere. There are also social and political solutions such as population control, lifestyle changes (using bicycles, buses and trains more and cars less), energy conservation campaigns, and tax credits for electric or hybrid vehicles. The Kyoto Protocol, which came into force in 2005, enables countries to offset their carbon emissions by purchasing carbon credits from countries producing less. The more ambitious schemes to fix global warming, such as releasing sulphur particles or seeding the ocean, are called geo-engineering solutions.

Fixing land degradation

In many parts of the world, the land is being degraded by monoculture, over-cultivation and over-grazing, and desertification is spreading. Essentially, it is the soil that is being damaged and this is sometimes due to the over-use of advanced agricultural technology. Soil salinity may be caused by inappropriate irrigation, salt incursion into groundwater in the coastal zone, or poor drainage leading to the build-up of brackish (salty) water.

Taking it further

Classify the list of global warming solutions according to their feasibility. You could do a cost-benefit analysis in social, economic and environmental terms for each proposed solution.

Taking it further

Look up the Worldmapper map number 297 showing Carbon Emissions Increases at www.worldmapper.org/atozindex.html. Identify the countries showing the largest increases and explain why carbon emissions are increasing in these places.

Key terms

Geo-engineering — the use of planetary engineering techniques on earth.
Planetary engineering — the use of technology to influence global processes; has been proposed in order to make other planets habitable.

High levels of soil salinity can be tolerated by salt-tolerant plants (called halophytes) and this can be reduced by washing the soluble salts out of the soil, provided there is good drainage. Soil may be poorly drained because it is compacted, preventing percolation, because there is an impermeable layer such as a plough pan, or because it has a high clay content. Good drainage is essential for reclaiming saline soils as water must move through the soil in order to leach salts to below the plant root level.

In a natural ecosystem, soil texture, structure and fertility are maintained by natural processes including the nutrient cycle. Removal of vegetation cover makes the soil more vulnerable to erosion and reduces its fertility, repeatedly growing the same crop reduces the nutrient content, and drainage is hindered when the soil is compacted by livestock or farm machinery. Artificial fertilisers replace the macro-nutrients, nitrogen, phosphorus and potassium, but there are many other essential nutrients that are also becoming depleted.

Increasing the organic content of the soil by adding manure and crop wastes improves its structure and drainage. The residues from previous crops can be worked back into the soil in a system called conservation tillage. Leaving land fallow, as in traditional agricultural systems, allows the soil to recover, and crop rotations balance out the nutrient budget as well as preventing pests from taking long-term hold. Alternating legumes, such as peas, soybeans or lentils that add nitrogen to the soil, with cereals, such as wheat or corn, that remove it, helps to maintain soil fertility. Planting shelterbelts (rows of trees or hedges), terracing, and ploughing along contours (instead of up and down slopes) prevents the soil from being washed or blown away.

In tropical countries, inter-cropping increases yield, prevents the spread of pests, and maintains soil quality. Planting cereal crops in strips with a soil-saving cover crop such as grass or a legume ensures that the ground is completely covered and reduces moisture loss through surface runoff. Similarly, alley-cropping alternates crops with trees and bushes that can provide fruit and wood for fuel. The trees also provide shade, thereby reducing water loss by evaporation and the leaf litter can provide green manure or fodder for livestock.

These are intermediate technological solutions and their use is more appropriate for the long-term maintenance of land resources. Generally, conservation technologies are popular if they are low cost with high returns on the investment (including investment in labour terms). Organic farming does not use agricultural chemicals and so achieves lower yields, but it works because it can charge a higher price for the produce. In poorer countries, constructing lines of stones is easier than terracing as it slows runoff and prevents soil erosion but requires much less labour. Rows of stones can be laid along contour lines, allowing enough water through to irrigate the fields below and reversing desertification.

Fixing energy demand

Technological change could meet the energy needs of development at a lower cost as more advanced technology cuts energy use per person. But existing solutions present significant problems, for example, large dams provide energy without atmospheric pollution but flood valleys, displace people, destroy wildlife habitats and silt up as alluvium is trapped behind the dam. Biofuels are regarded as a substitute for oil, but it would require as much as 40% of cropland to replace current world fuel use. In order to achieve the biofuel targets set by the European Union, which call for a replacement of liquid fuel for transportation by 10% in 2020, the available biomass in Europe will need to increase significantly. Cultivating energy crops on set-aside land and non-cultivated land will help but this will not be enough to meet demand; it will also be necessary to increase output per hectare. Crop quality must also be improved by using biotechnology and improved crop protection.

▲ **Figure 18.2:** Soybeans growing next to a bio-diesel manufacturing plant in Iowa, USA.

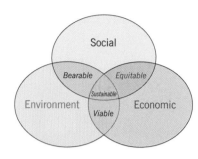

▲ **Figure 18.3:** This Venn diagram shows how sustainability requires coordination between the social, economic and environmental spheres and also that this relationship should be bearable, equitable and viable.

Taking it further

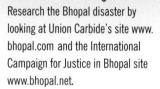

Research the Bhopal disaster by looking at Union Carbide's site www. bhopal.com and the International Campaign for Justice in Bhopal site www.bhopal.net.

Key term

Externalities — third-party effects that can be positive or negative. They occur when the actions of one individual, group or organisation affect the standard of living or quality of life of another individual, group or organisation without any direct interaction between the two.

Achieving sustainability

The term sustainable development was defined by the WCED as development that 'meets the needs of the present without compromising the ability of future generations to meet their own needs'. It has been criticised as a simple message adaptable to a wide range of agendas suiting corporate image-makers and revolutionary deep ecologists alike. 'Technocentric' theorists advocate rational, technical solutions to environmental problems using better planning and cleaner technologies to achieve sustainable resource management. At the other extreme, 'ecocentric' theorists propose radical changes to society and economic structures aiming for zero growth and local self-sufficiency.

Gains in terms of technological efficiency are being overtaken by rising standards of living and population growth, increasing the environmental impacts of human activity. The size of an environmental impact is the product of population size times the rate of consumption times the technology employed. Whether improvements in technology can keep up with the growth in population and fulfil people's desire for rising living standards is asking a lot of the technicians. This makes it hard to see how increasing use of technology and an environmentally sustainable future can be achieved. Technology does not necessarily have to create waste and pollution because there are more sustainable forms of technology.

The externalities of technology use include social, economic and environmental impacts and there have been impacts ever since the wheel was invented! A great deal of law has been created to protect people and the environment from the undesirable and often quite dangerous consequences of the extraction and processing of raw materials, and the manufacture, use and disposal of technological products. Ironically, while many things have been designed to improve standards of living and quality of life, they have had the reverse effect for some people.

The externalities of technology use are accounted for in some economies but not in others. Legislation has been enacted to protect people and the environment from the harmful effects of the use of technology, but this is not universal and people in poorer countries are too often less well protected that those in more affluent countries. In Britain, there is a considerable amount of environmental protection, health and safety legislation, and risk assessment requirements designed to minimise such impacts, yet accidents still occur as at the Buncefield oil depot in 2005. In Bhopal, India in 1984, over half a million people were exposed to toxic gases following an explosion at a chemical factory and at least 8,000 people died.

The 'polluter pays' principle is intended to make those who cause pollution pay for the damage they do to the environment. It is enforced through environmental law in the form of ecotaxes, for example, by making people with bigger cars pay higher vehicle tax. When Severn Trent Water accidentally allowed untreated sewage to flow into the River Erewash in Derbyshire in 2007, scores of fish were killed and the company was fined £10,000 plus court costs. A more precise definition of the 'polluter pays' principle is extended polluter responsibility (EPR), which holds manufacturers and traders responsible for the environmental impacts of their products throughout the product life-cycle, from the extraction of the raw materials, through the manufacturing process and product use, to their disposal.

Pollution often occurs at the waste disposal stage of the production cycle, so manufacturers are now being encouraged to make a greater proportion of their products recyclable and to reduce the volume of harmful materials. For example, Apple Computer Inc. claims to have eliminated many harmful toxins from its products such as mercury and arsenic, increased the proportion of recyclable parts, reduced packaging by more than a third (which cut transport costs as the boxes are smaller) and made its products more energy-efficient with longer-lasting batteries.

In effect, the cost of waste disposal is internalised into the cost of the product, encouraging the producers to reduce waste and increase reuse and recycling. Nevertheless, in many parts of the world, the environment is treated like a sink, expected to absorb the detritus of human activity. Old computers discarded in the USA often end up in developing countries, illegally exported by e-waste dealers to places like China and West Africa. Unlike European nations, the USA allows export of most e-waste, such as computer hard drives, printers and old cell phones. As much as 80% of US electronic waste collected for recycling ends up abroad, although it contains mercury, lead, cadmium and dangerous flame retardants.

International agreements exist to protect people and the environment, though unscrupulous people will always find loopholes. The Montreal and Kyoto Protocols are designed to protect the atmosphere, the London Convention governs the dumping of waste into the oceans, the Basle Convention covers the trans boundary movement of hazardous wastes, and there are several agreements on nuclear safety.

Technology for the future

Will the world become technologically united or divided in the 21st century? Some developing regions have been able to leapfrog towards technological equality with the advanced world, whereas others seem to be locked in technologically impoverished economies. It may be that the division is cultural rather than spatial and some groups within societies are excluded or choose to be excluded. There are no certain answers in this debate and you should be aware of the differing viewpoints for there is a range of technological futures ranging from 'business as usual' divergence to global technological convergence. Quite possibly, an untidy mix of the two will continue as disparity is not necessarily spatial.

The World Bank has developed a summary index of technology that combines the extent of scientific invention and innovation, the diffusion of older and of newer technologies and the intensity with which foreign technologies are employed in domestic production. Technological progress separates the faster-growing developing economies from the slower ones where poverty persists. In the last 20 years, it has been strongest in east Asia, south Asia and eastern Europe, whereas it has been much weaker in Latin America, the Middle East and Africa. This has enabled the proportion of people living in absolute poverty in developing countries overall to fall from 29% in 1990 to 18% in 2004.

Migration assists technology transfers by establishing links between richer and poorer regions. Networks are developed through which money for investment, knowledge and skills can be transferred. The successful adoption of new technology depends on a country's ability to absorb the technology and there are obvious differences between the lagging regions of sub-Saharan Africa compared with the rapid modernisation of economies in south and east Asia such as Taiwan and Singapore. Countries are exposed to foreign technologies through trade, investment, or migration, but technological absorption in a region depends on many local factors including:
- how receptive the economy is to change
- people's level of technical literacy
- the availability of investment funds
- how receptive the political culture is to technology.

Technology spreads more easily in cities; in India, for example, the availability of telephones in urban centres is eight times that in rural areas. Wireless technology is now spreading rapidly and was established in 400 cities by mid-2006, growing particularly in countries such as Taiwan, Singapore, Hong Kong and Mexico. Regarded as the fifth utility (after electricity, gas, water and sewerage), provision of municipal infrastructure for wireless communication is seen as a goal for social development as it will narrow the digital divide. It is also much cheaper than providing cable telecoms. City governments are pushing for the provision of wireless technology in their urban areas as this will encourage economic growth. This can be financed, built and operated in several ways:
- by municipal government agencies who seek to provide a free service but this may be a financial burden and does not enable public participation or market controls
- by private industry, removing the burden from government and enabling the market to respond rapidly to demand, but this is run for profit: it may not provide a full service as only profitable areas are targeted, and the companies need to be regulated

Taking it further

To read a case study about China's plan to halt the advance of the Gobi Desert read 'The green wall of China' on your Student CD-ROM.

Key term

Technological absorption — a measure of the ability of a country or region to accept and adopt new technology.

Taking it further

Download the World Bank's summary report, Technology and Development, at http://siteresources.worldbank.org/INTGEP2008/Resources/GEP08-Brochure.pdf.

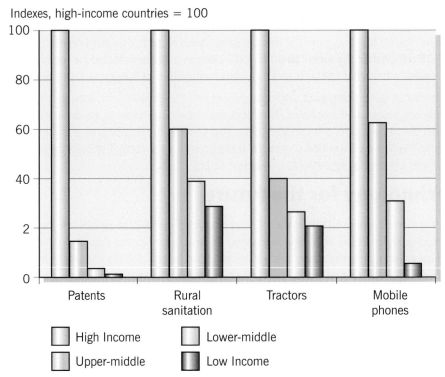

Indexes, high-income countries = 100

High Income
Upper-middle
Lower-middle
Low Income

▲ **Figure 18.4:** These data clearly show the wide gaps in the use of technology in 2004.

- by a private monopoly corporation; this gives control to the government, but may cause conflict between them and the corporation and it lacks the efficiency of market dynamics
- by 'grass roots' communes; these involve public participation, they are well placed to serve social interest by operating free of charge, and they provide no burden for the government, but such systems tend to grow very slowly.

Economic growth in east Asia may have been based on perspiration (using available labour) and not on inspiration (technological development) but economic development is increasingly based on innovation and knowledge. In the end, access education may be the key. Within societies, technological progress may benefit some groups of workers more than others. It may also mean significant short-term losses for competitors who are still using older technologies but conflict caused by technological progress can benefit economies by encouraging domestic competition. The Millennium Development Goal 8, Target 5 aims to, 'In cooperation with the private sector, make available benefits of new technologies, especially information and communications'. In the next few years you will be able to assess the success or failure of this aim.

Taking it further

Look up the latest MDG report at http://mdgs.un.org and track the progress of the goals.

Summary

In this chapter you have learnt:

- that technology operates at different levels and has different social and environmental consequences.
- that technology has the potential to fix major environmental problems but the solutions may have negative impacts.
- that technology needs to be employed sustainably and used to achieve sustainable development.
- that the future may see a continuing divergence between the technologically advanced core and the technologically impoverished periphery.

MCQ

Exam Practice – Section A

The Technological Fix?

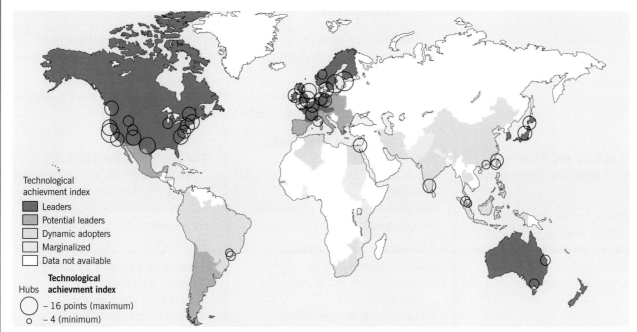

▲ **Figure 6:** The geography of technological innovation and achievement.

(a) Explain the distribution of technological innovation and achievement shown. [10]

(b) To what extent is technology capable of narrowing the development gap? [15]

Exam Practice – Unit 3 Section B

Pre-release materials

On your Student CD-ROM you will find a sample of pre-release materials that are the Issues Analysis resources for Unit 3 Section B.

They are based on one of the six Unit 3 core topics, in this case Superpower Geographies. They also contain synoptic links to other Units at AS and A2 level.

'Real' versions of the resources will be published by Edexcel in the format shown on your CD-ROM, with integrated figures and tables. The resource booklet will not exceed five sides.

Examples of the questions students would be expected to complete in the exam are:

Questions

1a Compare the level of human and economic development in India and China. [12 marks]

1b To what extent does China meet the criteria for 'superpower' status? [14 marks]

1c Assess the political and environmental risks of continued, rapid growth in India and China. [14 marks]

(TOTAL = 40 marks for Section B)

Introduction to Unit 4

General information

The aim of the unit is to allow you to have more flexibility in your geographical studies, by researching a major topic in depth, and in doing so mastering a range of independent learning and study skills.

You will focus on this option for a couple of months, researching all four enquiry questions from one of the chosen themes shown below in Figure 0.5.

Tectonic Activity and Hazards
Risk and Vulnerability. Patterns and Players.

1 Definitions, causes, event profiles, role of plate margins
2 Impacts on landscape
3 Impacts on people
4 Responses and issues

Life on the Margins – the Food Supply Problem
Too much too little
Food insecurity and range of management methods – trade, high tech, organic debates.

1 Issues and spatial patterns
2 Causes of inequalities
3 Desertification and dryland ecosystems
4 Management techniques and strategies

The World of Cultural Diversity
Diversity in cultures and geographical patterns. Conflicts in viewpoints of consumerism, environmentalism, conservation, protection, role of globalisation.

1 Nature and value of culture
2 Spatial patterns
3 Impacts of globalisation
4 Cultural attitudes to the environment.

Strong physical focus

Strong social and cultural focus

Cold Environments – Landscapes and Change
Changing distribution. Role of climate-active and relict landforms. Challenges and opportunities, threats and management.

1 What and where
2 Climate and meteorological processes
3 Geomorphological processes and distinctive landscapes
4 Challenges, opportunities and management

Consuming the Rural Landscape – Leisure and Tourism
Shifts from production to tourism and leisure from urban fringe to wilderness. Threats and fragility needs management. Preservation of ecotourism.

1 Relationship between leisure and tourism and rural landscape.
2 Physical significance and fragility of some landscapes
3 Changing impacts of leisure and tourism, positive and negative, hotspots
4 Management issues

Pollution and Human Health at Risk
Health risk. Link to economic development. Geographical patterns and role of pollution. Management options.

1 Range of health risks, patterns, epidemiology model, impacts
2 Causes of health risk, including pollution – role of geographical features, models e.g. diffusion
3 Link between health risk and pollution incidents and sustained, role of economic development, pollution fatigue
4 Managing health risks local–global, sustainability?

▲ **Figure 0.5:** Details of the spectrum of choice in Unit 4.

Centres will differ on the degree of choice afforded to students depending on size of groups, skills and interests of teachers and students, resource availability, etc. The end result is however that you will be researching only one theme, culminating in a long report-style essay done under examination conditions without any form of notes. The exam is marked out of 70 and is worth 20% of the A level award, i.e. 40% of A2. Preparing for success in the Unit 4 exam therefore includes three main phases:

1 Carrying out the research.
2 Organising research for the exam once the pre-release focus is made available four working weeks before the final exam.
3 Performing well in the exam itself, which is 1½ hours long.

Advice on carrying out the research

What makes a good researcher?

- Working with your teacher as a mentor – your teacher will guide you as to useful sources and focus.
- Being systematic and well organised by documenting and cross-referencing all sources and always trying to follow a structure.
- Managing time effectively by learning how to make efficient summaries and notes.
- Being prepared to work outside class time – a minimum of 4 hours of your own time each week.
- Being self-disciplined. Keeping up a sustained interest can be very hard. Why not try all sorts of ways of presenting your research? – blogs, video diaries, PowerPoint presentations, etc.
- Try to do some individual, possibly primary research linked to your option. Even if you cannot get to Iceland try some virtual fieldwork sites to see volcanoes and glaciers live! Or seek out relevant lecture notes from university websites.
- Take the initiative by keeping up to date on the latest events and incidents by reading newspapers.
- Try to meet all the deadlines your teacher will have set as these are here to help you develop as a researcher. In particular practice questions are very important as they build up your skills.
- Be a sharer of ideas and websites with your class group; discussing ideas could be a great motivator.
- Be flexible – sometimes you have to change tack as you do not seem to be getting anywhere.
- Take all the advice provided on how to research, e.g. on using search engines, etc.

Planning and organising your research

Creating a really useful file is essential. Separate your research folder (paper or computer) into the four key enquiry questions from the spec for your chosen option to ensure good coverage.

▼ **Figure 0.6:** shows an example for Tectonic Activity and Hazards.

Option	Enquiry questions			
Tectonic Activity and Hazards	Causes sub Enquiry Qs • range of events, hazards, disasters • event profile • plate movement causes • plate margin causes	Physical impacts sub Enquiry Qs • extrusive activity • volcanoes + hotspots • intrusive activity • earthquakes	Human impacts sub Enquiry Qs • reasons for habitation in tectonically active areas • range of impacts • impacts in differing economic development stages • trends frequency + impact over time	Response sub Enquiry Qs • varying approaches in differing economic areas • strategies – modification of loss/event/vulnerability • effectiveness, changes over time, future strategies

- Create case study fact files, for example on particular types of tectonic hazards/activity or pollution incidents/health risk. These are shortened notes ready for learning.
- Create a case study grid to ensure a wide coverage of examples of players and people and of places, from across the range of World Bank economic groupings. Remember to include examples from BRICs as well as LDCs.
- Compile a glossary of key terms for each enquiry question as you go along. You may find the MCQs in the Active Teach section useful here to test yourself. Start with the specification, for example Life on the Margins yields the following terms:
  - Food security
  - Food miles
  - Food globalisation
  - Famine
  - Over- and under-nutrition
  - Neo-Malthusian
  - Technocentric
  - Desertification
  - Dryland
  - Ecosystems
  - Fair trade
  - Organic farming
  - Salination
  - Aquaculture
  - Sustainable production.

Then you can add as many others as you need.

Make a list of key concepts, theories and models – for example, carrying capacity, resilience models, eco-values, fragility index, Butler's model and rural urban continuum are all key to the Consuming the Rural Landscape option.

Information on sources

- Keep an ongoing bibliography of all the books (give author, pages, key quotations), articles (give journal, author and date) and websites (give bias, viewpoints and exactly what it was used for) you use.
- When you are reading always check relevance, bias, age of source, reputation of source.
- Try to achieve a balance between books, articles and websites (BAW).
- You could create a research wall, as shown below, to help you.

Books	Articles	Others and Websites	
Textbooks Basic A2 texts or standard text	Geography magazines Geofile Geofactsheet Geography Review Geographical Magazine National Geographic	GIS system, e.g. using Google Earth, local authority websites	Internet YouTube good for video clips and pressure groups
Specialist Advanced textbooks Try contemporary case studies or access series and books for undergraduate use		Geography dept videos, DVDs, possibly streamed onto internet	Bookmark key websites for your unit, use the Edexcel website to get a reading list starter and of course Google!
	Other magazines: Economist New Scientist New Society Scientific American	Internet gateways and meta search engines e.g. www.search.com www.bubl.ac.uk	Check whether your centre buys into the Athens system for university journals

▲ **Figure 0.7:** How a research wall can help you track sources.

Looking for Synopticity

Figure 0.8 summarises this for Unit four. In your chosen unit you will find three key linkages entitled Global Synoptic Content so make sure you put these in your research folder.

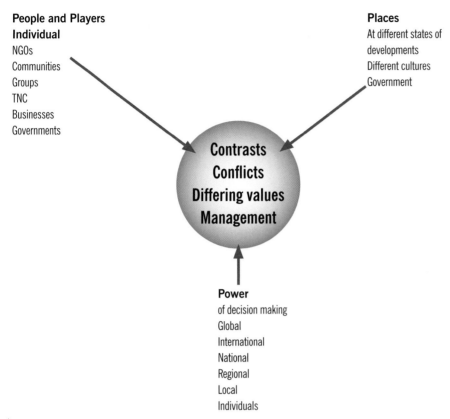

People and Players
Individual
NGOs
Communities
Groups
TNC
Businesses
Governments

Places
At different states of developments
Different cultures
Government

Contrasts
Conflicts
Differing values
Management

Power
of decision making
Global
International
National
Regional
Local
Individuals

▲ **Figure 0.8:** Synopticity in Unit 4.

In your research folder it is worth setting aside a place for this. You need to be aware of the different values and attitudes of the people involved in making decisions within your chosen option. A table is a useful way of doing this.

For more guidance on preparing for Unit 4 assessment see pages 302–7.

For more information on the question, student plan and mark scheme for Unit 4 assesment go to your Student CD-ROM

Chapter 19 What are tectonic hazards and what causes them?

Key terms

Active volcano
Asthenosphere
Avalanche
Block
Bomb
Continental crust
Continental Drift
Convergent boundary
Disaster
Divergent boundary
Earthquake
Lahar
Landslide
Lapilli
Lava
Lithosphere
Liquefaction
Magma
Natural hazard
Oceanic crust
Plate margin
Pyroclast
Pyroclastic flow
Richter scale
Saturation
Seismologist
Tectonic hazard
Tectonic plate
Transform boundary
Tsunami
Volcano
Volcanic ash

Learning objectives

After studying this chapter, you will be able to discuss these ideas and concepts and provide located examples of them:

• Tectonic hazards generate significant risk to human populations and their possessions.
• There is a range of tectonic hazards associated with earthquakes and volcanoes.
• Tectonic hazards vary in their profile, based on their frequency, magnitude, duration and areal extent.
• Tectonic hazards are caused by the movement of the earth's tectonic plates.
• Different types of tectonic activity are associated with the plate margins, affecting the spatial distribution of tectonic hazards.

Both earthquakes and volcanoes can be described as tectonic hazards. Tectonic hazards are closely related to the movement or deformation of the earth's tectonic plates. These movements involve both the thin, basaltic oceanic crust, which underlies most of the world's ocean basins, and the thicker continental crust, which is composed of granite and underlies the earth's continental areas (Figure 19.1).

Tectonic hazards such as these do not always result in natural disaster. Whilst earthquakes and volcanoes have the potential to cause damage or harm, it is important to remember that natural disasters occur only when a significant impact on people or infrastructure results from a hazard event.

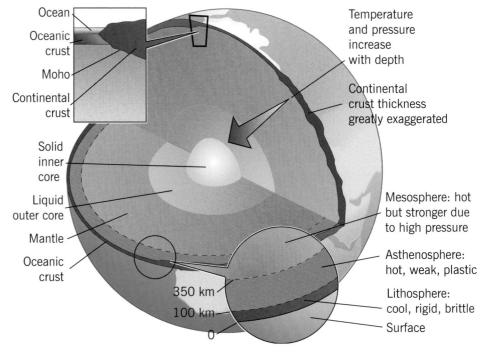

▲ **Figure 19.1:** The structure of the earth. Volcanoes provide us with clues as to what lies directly below the crust, in the asthenosphere.

Synoptic link

Look at Edexcel AS Geography pages 6–15 to examine the main types of physical risk facing our world.

The impact of volcanoes

Around the world, there are more than 500 'active' volcanoes, not including those that occur on the floor of the ocean. Volcanoes are recognised for the spectacular violence of their eruptions; however, they are rather more complex than this stereotypical image. There is a number of types of volcano and a number of types of volcanic eruption, from almost serene to incredibly destructive. Volcanoes also give us a unique glimpse of what lies below the cool, brittle rock of the earth's lithosphere (Figure 19.1). Volcanoes produce a range of impacts on the landscape.

A window to the earth's interior

Below the earth's crust, temperature and pressure increase with depth. Because of this, rock-like material within the asthenosphere (the upper mantle) is hot and structurally weak. The material found here is referred to as magma, and at these great temperatures and pressures, it exists in a 'plastic' molten or semi-molten state. The rigid pieces of the earth's lithosphere (the tectonic plates) lie on top of the asthenosphere and, as we will see later in this chapter, are subject to movements within it. Heat and pressure can eventually force magma onto the surface of the earth, where it combines with the rocks that form the volcano itself to create a range of volcanic materials.

Lava

Arguably, lava is the best known volcanic material. Lava flows can emerge from the vent of a volcano or from fissures along its flanks, and can spread many kilometres from their source.

Pyroclasts

Whilst lava remains in a liquid-like, molten state until it cools, other volcanic materials are solid. These are the 'pyroclasts', a word from ancient Greek which can be translated as 'fire fragments'. These fiery fragments are generated when heat and pressure within a volcano blast rock into smaller-sized particles.

Pyroclastic materials are categorised into different groups by their size, as shown in the following table.

Pyroclastic material	Description	Size
Volcanic ash	Very small particles, usually of a fine grain	Less than 2 mm
Lapilli	Medium-sized particles, sometimes referred to as 'cinders'	2 mm to 64 mm
Blocks and bombs	Large aggregates of volcanic material	Greater than 64 mm

▲ **Figure 19.2:** Categories of pyroclastic materials.

Pyroclastic flows
A pyroclastic flow is a mixture of superheated rock (some of which may be semi-solid) and hot gases that rapidly flows down the side of a volcano. Moving extremely quickly, pyroclastic flows are impossible to outrun, and completely destroy anything in their path (Figure 19.3).

Examiners' tip

Make sure that you can explain the difference between a 'hazard' and a 'disaster'. Use a dictionary to help you get a clear definition of each term. Remember, not every hazard turns into a disaster!

Key terms

Volcano — an opening in the earth's crust from which material from below the earth's surface is ejected. The word derives from the name of the Roman god of fire, Vulcan, blacksmith to the other gods.

Active volcano — one which is in the process of erupting or showing signs that an eruption is imminent.

Lava — when magma flows onto the surface of the earth, it is referred to as lava.

Synoptic link

Look at Edexcel AS Geography pages 16–25 to examine how and why natural hazards are becoming seen as an increasingly global threat.

Taking it further

The incredible speed of a pyroclastic flow occurs because the materials within it are superheated. This means that the whole mass moves and behaves more like a liquid than a solid. Pyroclastic flows can cover large distances from their starting point. Scientists have discovered that the 6,000-year-old Koya flow, in southern Japan, moved over a distance of 60 km from its starting point, with 10 km being over water!

▲ **Figure 19.3:** An incredible pyroclastic flow, as seen from ground level.

Key terms

Lahar — this word comes from the Indonesian language, and refers to a volcanic mud flow.

Seismologists — people who study earthquakes.

Tsunamis — waves generated in the ocean by the displacement of the sea-bed during an earthquake.

Taking it further

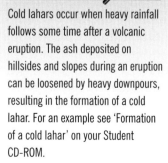

Cold lahars occur when heavy rainfall follows some time after a volcanic eruption. The ash deposited on hillsides and slopes during an eruption can be loosened by heavy downpours, resulting in the formation of a cold lahar. For an example see 'Formation of a cold lahar' on your Student CD-ROM.

Lahars

Lahars comprise water and volcanic ash and result from the mixing of water with volcanic materials either during or after an eruption. Lahars can be just as deadly as other types of volcanic materials, often resulting in the destruction of infrastructure or the burying of people and homes.

Volcanic gases

The volcanic materials covered so far have been highly visible aspects of volcanic eruptions. There are, however, unseen volcanic materials with the potential to cause injury and death. These are the volcanic gases that emerge from a volcano during an eruption. Chief among these is the relatively harmless water vapour, which comprises between 70 and 90% of all the volcanic gases emitted. Of greater concern are the next most common volcanic gases: carbon dioxide (CO_2) and sulphur dioxide (SO_2). In sufficient quantities, both of these gases have the potential to kill.

The impact of earthquakes

Like volcanoes, earthquakes are a tectonic hazard. We experience earthquakes as a series of vibrations at the surface of the earth. The most noticeable effect of earthquakes is the ground shaking during the earthquake itself. These 'tremors' are caused by various movements of rock within the earth's lithosphere, as will be covered in more detail towards the end of the chapter. Like volcanoes, earthquakes produce a range of impacts on the landscape.

Ground shaking

Large earthquakes have the potential to flatten buildings and to destroy infrastructure. Famously, the magnitude of earthquakes can be measured using the Richter scale. This scale was developed by Charles F. Richter in 1934.

The work of seismologists

Seismologists use sensitive recording devices called seismographs to record the amplitude of shock waves during an earthquake event and to help them assign a magnitude to the earthquake. Seismographs can record vibrations of the earth that are so small that they go unnoticed by humans.

Tsunamis

Earthquakes, particularly those that occur beneath the sea bed, also have the ability to generate tsunamis. Tsunami is a Japanese word which means 'bay or harbour wave', and this is an apt description, as this is where tsunamis can do most of their damage. Tsunamis can also be generated by events such as the collapse of volcanoes or coastal landslides.

Case study: Tsunami devastation

Tsunamis can bring vast volumes of water ashore in coastal areas. The tragic Boxing Day Tsunami in 2004 resulted in more than 200,000 deaths throughout the Indian Ocean region. Small, relatively defenceless, coastal communities were the hardest hit, as revealed in the before and after aerial photographs of Banda Aceh, in Indonesia (Figure 19.4).

▲ **Figure 19.4:** Before and after photographs from Banda Aceh province in Indonesia bear witness to the terrible effects of the tsunami that was generated by an earthquake on 26 December 2004.

Displacement

The shaking of the ground during earthquakes can also result in landslides and avalanches. Earthquakes can cause or exacerbate a structural weakness within a body of soil, rock or snow, which in turn can lead to the complete loss of structure that we call a landslide or avalanche. These 'after-effects' can sometimes result in significantly more casualties and damage than caused by the earthquake itself.

Liquefaction

Earthquakes have many obvious effects above ground. A relatively silent but insidious process that can occur below ground as a result of an earthquake is liquefaction.

Liquefaction can cause the loss of soil from hill slopes or the collapse of the walls of earth that support dams. It can also result in the disruption of building foundations, leading to the 'tipping' of buildings into the earth (Figure 19.5).

Liquefaction occurs when soils are turned into a 'suspension' and in soils that are 'saturated'. Saturation means that all of the available 'spaces' within the soil profile (that is, between soil particles) are filled with water. This water exerts a pressure on the soil. This pressure increases during the shaking of the ground that accompanies an earthquake. When pressure builds up in this way, the water molecules can effectively 'push' the soil particles apart. This is liquefaction, and it leads to the complete loss of soil strength and stability.

▲ **Figure 19.5:** A famous example of liquefaction, which followed the Niigata earthquake in Japan in 1964.

The effects of tectonic hazards

Tectonic hazards vary in their effects

Not all tectonic activity is dangerous. It is also important to remember that tectonic activity is an earth-building process – that is, it results in the creation of 'new' land and various landforms that can be utilised by humans. Much tectonic activity occurs on earth without any loss of human life and poses no threat to our infrastructure or our way of life. There can be a number of reasons why this is the case, related to the cause of the tectonic hazards.

▶ **Figure 19.6:** The earth's major tectonic plates, and the three different types of tectonic plate boundaries that can be described.

The causes of tectonic hazards

Overwhelmingly, the greatest factor influencing the exposure of any given community to tectonic hazards is its geographical location. Tectonic activity is closely related to the pattern of the earth's tectonic plates (Figure 19.6). The tectonic plates in effect 'float' on the layer of semi-molten rock, or mantle, lying below them.

Heat generated by the earth's core causes movements within the mantle, known as convection currents. The tectonic plates respond to the movement of these convection currents and move with them. Most of this movement is imperceptible to humans, but, over time, it has resulted in significant changes in the lithosphere of the earth, as first proposed in a theory known as Continental Drift.

Tectonic activity associated with different types of plate margin

As tectonic plates move, they can collide, drift apart, or slide past each other. The force of the processes involved in this movement is responsible for the vibrations that we detect as earthquakes and also for the formation of volcanoes.

Most tectonic activity occurs at the boundaries or 'margins' of the tectonic plates. Based on the crustal movement that occurs at the margins of the plates, there are three types of plate boundary that can be described – divergent, convergent and transform (Figure 19.6).

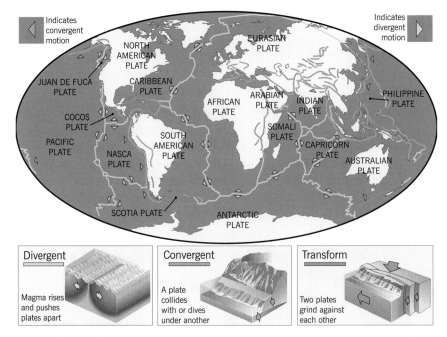

Divergent boundaries

Divergent boundaries are also known as extensional or constructive boundaries. At these locations, the tectonic plates are moving apart from one another. Earthquakes in these locations are relatively shallow and usually have a magnitude of less than 8.0 on the Richter scale. On earth, divergent boundaries are found beneath the oceans. As plates of oceanic crust pull apart from one another, magma from below the lithosphere can well up into the space created and lead to the formation of underwater volcanoes.

Convergent boundaries

Just as the sea-floor is spreading at divergent boundaries and new land is being created, it stands to reason that some of the earth's crust must be being destroyed at other locations. This occurs at the convergent boundaries, which are also known as compressional or destructive boundaries.

Case study: The Mid-Atlantic Ridge

The spectacularly long Mid-Atlantic Ridge is perhaps the best known example of a divergent plate boundary. Stretching 16,000 km through the Atlantic Ocean, the Mid-Atlantic Ridge marks the zone where the North American and South American Plates are pulling away from the African Plate. Along the Mid-Atlantic Ridge, underwater mountains stretch 1,600 km wide either side of the diverging boundary. Here, the sea-floor is spreading at about 2.5 cm per year. Whilst this sounds incredibly slow, over millions of years the sea-floor has spread many thousands of kilometres, taking the piggy-backing oceans and continents along for the ride!

At convergent boundaries, the tectonic plates are moving towards each other. In effect, plates are colliding at these locations. As a result, convergent boundaries are the locations of the earth's largest quakes. There are in fact three types of convergent boundary, depending on the combination of crustal types involved. This results in the formation of different landform features, as shown in Figure 19.7.

Types of crust involved		Landforms
Oceanic	Continental	Ocean trenches, volcanic mountain ranges
Oceanic	Oceanic	Ocean trenches, volcanic island arcs
Continental	Continental	Fold mountains

Transform boundaries

At transform boundaries, crust is neither created nor destroyed, as the tectonic plates simply slide past one another. Sometimes referred to as fracture zones, these boundaries tend to have a 'zigzag'-shaped pattern and can connect two divergent boundaries or two convergent boundaries.

The spatial distribution of tectonic hazards

As a result of tectonic activity occurring at plate boundaries, it is possible to map the spatial distribution of the earth's volcanoes and earthquakes. It is clearly evident that people living closest to the plate boundaries are at greatest risk of tectonic hazards.

Plate margin	Earthquake depth	Types of volcano
Divergent	Shallow (0–70 km below surface)	Shield / Cinder
Transform	Shallow (0–70 km below surface)	Rare
Convergent	Intermediate (70–300 km below surface) / Deep (300–700 km below surface)	Composite / Cinder

Summary

In this chapter, you have learnt:
- that tectonic activities pose a threat to life and property.
- that earthquakes and volcanoes are significant tectonic hazards that confront human populations.
- how the theory of plate tectonics can be used to understand better where tectonic hazards are likely to occur.
- how knowledge of plate margins can help us to understand the nature, magnitude and likely extent of tectonic hazards.

MCQ

Examiners' tip

There are many and varied names for the different types of plate boundary. For example, the zone where two tectonic plates move away from each other can be referred to as a 'divergent', 'extensional' or 'constructive' boundary. To assist your exam marker, choose whichever of these terms you are most comfortable with and stick with it during your exam.

Figure 19.7: There are three types of convergent plate boundary, each involving different combinations of oceanic and/or continental crust.

Synoptic link

Look at Edexcel AS Geography page 31 to read a case study about a well-known transform boundary in California.

Figure 19.8: The variations in earthquake and volcanic activity that are associated with the different plate margins.

Synoptic link

Look at Edexcel AS Geography page 11 to see a map showing the locations of the world's volcanoes and major earthquakes.

Taking it further

For information on hazard profiling, read 'Hazard profiling' on your Student CD-ROM.

CHAPTER 20 What impact does tectonic activity have on landscapes and why does this impact vary?

Key terms

Batholith
Cinder volcano
Composite volcano
Constructive boundary
Destructive boundary
Dike
Extrusion
Fault line
Fissure
Fold
Fumerole
Ground displacement
Hawaiian eruption
Hotspot
Intrusion
Laccolith
Lava plateau
Parasitic cone
Plinian eruption
Plutons
Rift valley
Ring of Fire
Shield volcano
Sill
Stock
Strombolian eruption
Vein
Viscosity
Volcanic cone
Vulcanian eruption

Synoptic link

Look at Edexcel AS Geography pages 26–35 to explore why some places are more disaster-prone and hazardous than others.

Taking it further

For information on the volcanic features of New Zealand, read 'The Land of the Long White Cloud' on your Student CD-ROM.

Learning objectives

After studying this chapter, you will be able to discuss these ideas and concepts and provide located examples of them:

- Extrusive igneous activity can lead to the formation of volcanic cones, fissures and lava plateaux.
- Volcanoes differ in terms of their formation and morphology.
- There are differences in the morphology and eruption characteristics of volcanoes, which link to variations in the processes that occur at different plate margins.
- Intrusive igneous activity can lead to the formation of a range of landform features including batholiths, laccoliths, stocks, dikes, sills and veins.
- Earthquakes have a range of effects on landscapes, including fault lines, rift valleys and ground displacement, due to the stresses that the ground is subjected to during such activity.

Despite first appearances, both volcanoes and earthquakes are part of the earth-building processes that exist on this planet. They play an important role in creating the rich variety of landscapes that can be found on the surface of the earth, and which have been utilised and exploited by humankind over millennia. As well as being incredibly explosive at times, volcanoes help to create new land surfaces as well as a range of landforms, including both extrusive and intrusive features.

Extrusive volcanic landforms

Once extruded onto the surface of the earth, magma is referred to as lava, which cools and hardens to form igneous rocks. Extrusive igneous activity leads to the creation of a variety of landform features above the surface of the earth.

Volcanic cones

The central vent of the volcano is connected to a store of magma below the surface, which is known as the magma chamber (Figure 20.1). The extrusion of lava from the vent leads to the creation of a volcanic cone. With each new eruption, new layers are added to the cone, in the first instance by the lava and pyroclastic materials which are ejected from the volcano, and then by the volcanic ash which later settles from the air.

Fissures

Fissures are cracks or openings within rock through which magma escapes onto the surface of the earth. They usually form because of weaknesses that exist within rock. Fissures can be connected back to the magma chamber below a volcano or to a secondary source of magma, such as the vent of the volcano itself (as in Figure 20.1).

Lava plateaux

A lava plateau is a raised area of land that has been formed by repeated lava flows in a given place over a period of time. Layered lava flows can form tablelands or flat-topped hills that can extend for hundreds or even thousands of square kilometres.

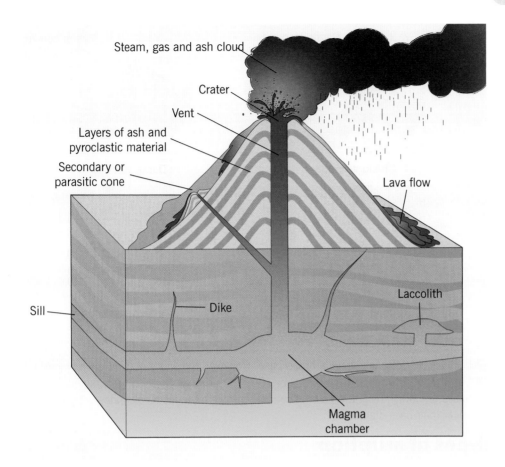

Examiners' tip

Although we think of volcanoes as highly destructive, it is vital that you demonstrate that volcanoes are actually responsible for earth-building. They help to create new land and new opportunities for populations. Iceland and the Hawaiian Islands are great examples to refer to.

Key term

Extrusion — the upward movement of magma through the earth's crust and onto its surface as lava. Extrusive volcanic landforms form once the lava has cooled and hardened.

◀ **Figure 20.1:** Magma chambers below the earth's surface are the source of the material which helps to create the generally conical shape of volcanoes.

Types of volcano

Volcanic cones differ in terms of their morphology (or 'shape'). This is because of the highly varied nature of volcanic eruptions, which will be explored in more detail in the next section.

Cinder volcanoes

The most common type of volcano is the cinder volcano (Figure 20.2). Also referred to as scoria volcanoes, they are the smallest type of volcano, often less than 300 m high. Cinder cones tend to have very straight sides. Despite their low height, they can be very steep, with the sides of some cinder cones inclining at as much as 35 degrees.

Cinder cones have a very consistent composition, being almost entirely made up of pyroclastic lapilli – volcanic material that is between 2 mm and 64 mm in size.

Composite volcanoes

Composite volcanoes are considered to be the most picturesque of all volcano types (Figure 20.2). Paradoxically, they are also the most deadly. The typical shape of a composite volcano is a tall cone with sides that slope gently at the base but that become increasingly steep towards the summit. The net result is a volcano with concave sides. The summit itself is small in comparison other volcanic cones. Japan's Mount Fuji is thought to be the archetypical example of a composite volcano.

Composite volcanoes are composed of different types of volcanic material, and these tend to exist in alternate layers throughout the volcanic profile.

Shield volcanoes

Shield volcanoes tend to be very broad and relatively flat (Figure 20.2). Having gentle slopes at their lower levels, shield cones increase in steepness mid-slope before flattening out again towards the summit. The net result is a convex shape.

Key terms

Parasitic cone — when fissures form along the flanks of an existing volcano, a 'parasitic' cone can develop, that draws magma from the vent of the volcano. These are also referred to as secondary cones.
Fumerole — the name given to a fissure which exudes volcanic gases.
Cinder volcano — a volcano composed mostly of lapilli-sized volcanic material, with a cinder-like feel.
Composite volcano — a volcano that is composed of different types of volcanic material including lava, pyroclastics and ash.
Shield volcano— the morphology of these volcanoes is thought to resemble a shield resting on the ground in an upright position – hence the name.

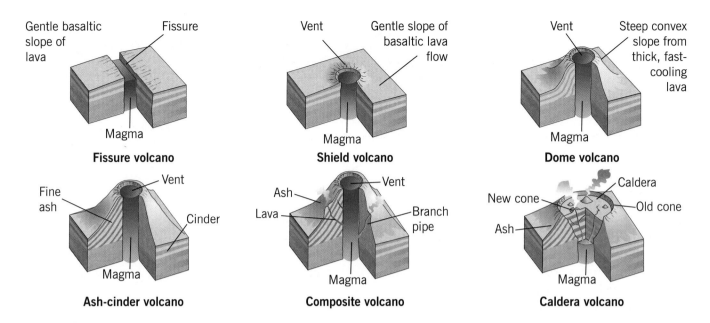

Fissure volcano

Shield volcano

Dome volcano

Ash-cinder volcano

Composite volcano

Caldera volcano

▲ **Figure 20.2:** Different types of volcano exist because of the variations that exist in the types of eruption.

Typically, shield volcanoes have a broad base. However, the width of the base can vary from as little as 2–3 km wide to well over 100 km. Although broad of base, shield volcanoes are low in height. As an indication, the height of shield volcanoes is typically 1/20th of their base diameter.

Types of eruption

The formation of the different types of volcano is closely linked to the different types of eruption. In turn, the type of eruption that occurs is largely dependent on the composition of the magma that is found within a given area.

Hawaiian eruptions

Hawaiian eruptions are the calmest of all volcanic eruptions. Generally non-explosive, they are so named because of their prevalence on the islands of Hawaii. Hawaiian eruptions tend to involve steady fountains of lava which run quickly away from the summit of the volcano through lava channels. This typically results in the formation of shield volcanoes.

Strombolian eruptions

Strombolian eruptions tend to occur in areas where relatively viscous basaltic magma is found. This viscosity of the magma prevents the escape of volcanic gases, leading to a build-up of pressure within the volcano. Episodic eruptions are the result, releasing the pressure build-up with a large 'booming' sound. Eruptions tend to feature vast amounts of lapilli, and as a consequence, cinder cones tend to build up around the volcanic vent.

Vulcanian eruptions

Vulcanian eruptions tend to be short-lived, lasting only a few hours. Found in areas where lava is highly viscous, a build-up of pressure within the volcano means that these eruptions are relatively intense. Pyroclastic blocks and bombs are ejected at high velocity, with much of the pyroclastic material being blasted from the sides of the volcano. A high degree of fragmentation of the volcanic material during the eruption leads to the formation of vast amounts of volcanic ash. Being more explosive than any of the other types of eruption covered so far, Vulcanian eruptions can result in the formation of eruption columns that reach between 5 and 10 km into the air.

Taking it further

Cinder cones tend to be found in basaltic lava fields. The cinder-like feel of the lapilli is a result of the low viscosity of basaltic lava. Due to its low viscosity, volcanic gases are able to pass through this lava easily. As a result, the lapilli are pock-marked by the bubbles of gas that have escaped through it during formation. It is said to feel just like 'cinders'. But what are cinders? Research this question using the library or internet resources.

Taking it further

An important subset of Hawaiian eruptions is 'fissure eruptions'. Investigate how fissure eruptions are created, and explore how they contribute to the formation of different types of volcano.

Case study: What's in a name? Stromboli and Vulcano

Strombolian eruptions are named after the small volcanic island of Stromboli, which lies between Italy and Sicily. This island has witnessed almost constant eruptions for many hundreds of years, leading to it being referred to as the 'Lighthouse of the Mediterranean'. During some periods of time, volcanic eruptions on the island have occurred as regularly as every 20 minutes. Vulcanian eruptions are named after the small Italian island of Vulcano. The fiery eruptions on Vulcano and the rumbling sounds were thought to be the Roman god of fire, Vulcan, going about his work as a blacksmith!

Plinian eruptions

Plinian eruptions are arguably the best known of all the volcanic eruption types. Most of the best-known historic eruptions, including Krakatau (1883) and Mount Pinatubo (1991), have been Plinian eruptions. These eruptions occur where magma is dacitic or rhyolitic in its composition. The high viscosity of these types of magma prevents the escape of volcanic gases, leading to highly explosive eruptions. During Plinian eruptions materials can be ejected from a volcano at speeds of hundreds of metres per second.

Where are volcanoes found?

Plate margins

Most of the earth's volcanoes occur at the boundaries of the tectonic plates, which are referred to as the 'plate margins'. At these places, the movement of the plates, either together (destructive boundaries) or apart (constructive boundaries), can result in the creation of volcanoes.

Case study: The Ring of Fire

Some of the plate margins are more tectonically active than others. For example, the edges of the Pacific Plate experience approximately three-quarters of all the earth's seismic activity. The destructive boundaries, and particularly the subduction zones, lying on the fringes of this particular plate also form the so-called 'Ring of Fire'. Here, volcanoes stretch out in a 'ring' around the Pacific Ocean, from Australasia and the Philippines on its western edge, through the Aleutian Islands to the coastlines of North and South America on the eastern edge of the Pacific.

Hotspots

Whilst most volcanoes are found along plate margins, there are some exceptions to this rule, with the volcanic islands found in the middle of tectonic plates being a good example. Lying roughly in the middle of the Pacific Plate, the Hawaiian Islands are 3,200 km from the nearest plate boundary! The theory of 'hotspots' is used to explain how volcanoes can form in places other than plate boundaries. The heat of the hotspot is enough to melt the crust lying directly above it, leading to the formation of volcanoes. It is thought that there are as many as 100 hotspots located below the earth's crust. Most of these can be found in the interior areas of the tectonic plates.

Taking it further

Composite volcanoes are most commonly found along convergent plate boundaries, particularly where one tectonic plate is being subducted beneath another. This gives rise to a vast supply of molten material which can form the eventual volcanic cone. Use this information to identify examples of well-known composite volcanoes. As a hint, you might begin your search along the Pacific Rim, and the so-called 'Ring of Fire'.

Taking it further

Mount Etna is well known for its Strombolian eruptions and the frequency of its volcanic activity. Use the internet to develop a profile of Mount Etna, including details of its location, eruptive history and any damage caused.

Key term

Plinian eruption — named in honour of Pliny the Younger, the Roman historian whose vivid description of the eruption of Vesuvius in 79AD is one of the reasons that we know so much about the devastation that was caused at Pompeii.

Examiners' tip

Names are important. Composite volcanoes are so-called because of the mixed nature of the materials of which they are composed. This links to the type of eruption that helps to form these volcanoes. Making these links obvious to your marker is a good way to demonstrate the depth of your knowledge.

Key term

Hotspots — thought to be small areas of abnormally intense heat lying below the earth's crust.

Examiners' tip

The Hawaiian Islands are a great example to use to help explain the theory of hotspots. Ensure that you study the varying ages of the islands and their location relative to one another (and the hotspot) in order to demonstrate a full understanding of the theory. Commit this information to memory and practise writing your explanation before the exam.

Taking it further

The theory of hotspots was proposed in 1963 by the Canadian J. Tuzo Wilson. How well accepted was the hotspot theory at the time, and how has the theory stood the test of time? Research these questions using the internet or library resources.

Taking it further

The theory of hotspots suggests that they remain relatively constant in terms of their location, whilst the overlying tectonic plates continue to move. As a result, volcanoes form above a hotspot in 'chains', with each 'new' volcano being carried away from the hotspot in turn by the motion of the plate on which it sits. By studying maps of the various volcanic island chains across the face of the earth, we can determine the direction in which the underlying tectonic plates are moving.

Case study: Evidence to support the hotspot theory

Evidence in support of this theory of hotspots is found by dating the rocks in the various peaks of any given volcanic island chain. The rocks on Kauai, at the north-western end of the Hawaiian chain (and furthest from the location of the hotspot), are dated at 5.5 million years old, whilst those on 'Big-Island' (or Hawaii, as it is more commonly referred to), at the south-eastern end of the chain and much closer to the hotspot, are just 0.7 million years old. With the Pacific Plate known to be moving in a north-westerly direction, the dating of the volcanic islands provides strong evidence in support of the hotspot theory.

Intrusive volcanic landforms

Intrusion

Just like extrusion, intrusive processes can also result in the creation of volcanic landforms. The only difference is that intrusion occurs when magma cools and hardens into rocks below the earth's surface. Over time, and after many years of weathering of the less resistant rock that surrounds them, intrusive features can become exposed at or above the surface of the earth, creating unique volcanic landforms.

Batholith

Batholith is the name given to the largest of the igneous rocks that form as a result of intrusive activity. They tend to be irregular in shape and are often composed of granite. Parts of a batholith can become exposed at the surface by processes such as tectonic uplift or weathering, but much of the rest may remain buried because of their enormous size.

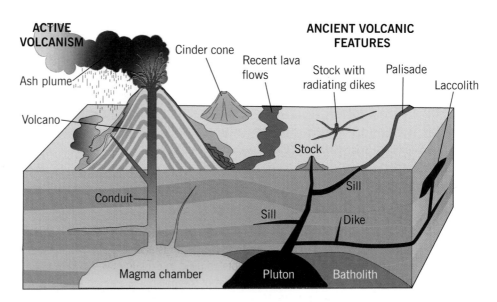

▲ **Figure 20.3:** Intrusive landforms are sometimes referred to as 'ancient volcanic features' because of the time it takes for them to become exposed above the earth's surface by weathering and erosion.

Stock

Stock is the term used to describe intrusive igneous rocks that are smaller in size and extent than a batholith. By definition, they must be less than 100 km² in areal extent. Often, stocks form as offshoots of larger batholiths.

Laccolith

A laccolith is a dome of igneous rock that is formed between two layers of pre-existing sedimentary rock. Laccoliths are created when slow-flowing, highly viscous magma is forced between the horizontal layers of existing strata. Eventually, the magma builds up into a dome or mushroom shape.

Dike

A dike is usually a vertical or near vertical sheet of rock that is created when magma is thrust into a body of pre-existing rock. By their nature, dikes cut across layers of existing rock. Sometimes, dikes form in fractures or weak points within rock strata. Most commonly, dikes are found near volcanic cones. Prior to the hardening of rock within the dike, it may be a conduit for magma to reach the surface of the earth. When exposed above the earth's surface, a dike can appear to be a 'wall' of volcanic rock.

Sill

A sill is the name given to a long, thin intrusion of igneous rock through pre-existing strata. Unlike dikes, which cut across layers of rock, sills intrude between other layers, forming a distinct layer of their own. The orientation of the sill is determined by the nature of the rocks themselves and the ease with which the magma can force its way through during the period of formation.

Vein

Sometimes, magma will find its way into the small cracks, fractures and openings that exist in the rock that lies below the surface of the earth. When this magma cools to form igneous rock, the vein-like patterns within the rocks can remain.

The effects of earthquakes on landscapes

Whilst volcanoes help to build the earth by creating new land, the human experience of earthquakes would more commonly associate them with destruction rather than creation. Whilst above ground we experience their relatively short-term impacts on life and infrastructure, earthquakes are also a reminder of the important, longer-term earth-building activities that are occurring below the surface of the earth. These processes help to create a number of landform features.

Taking it further

For information on batholiths read 'Large batholiths' on your Student CD-ROM.

Key terms

Intrusion — the movement of magma, below ground, into spaces that exist within rock strata. When this magma cools and hardens, intrusive volcanic landforms are created.

Plutons — the major types of intrusive igneous features (batholiths, stocks and laccoliths). Pluto was the Greek god of the underworld, or Hades. In keeping with this legend, it is the 'fires of the underworld' (in this case the asthenosphere) in the realm of Pluto which lead to the formation of the major intrusive features. Pluto is a general term used to describe any mass of rock that has formed by the hardening of magma below the surface of the earth.

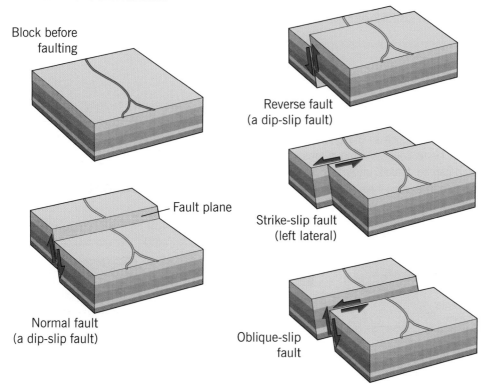

◀ **Figure 20.4:** Different types of fault can occur as a result of ground moving during earthquakes.

Faults

Sometimes rock can be broken by movements within the earth's crust, and then displaced sideways, up or down. When this occurs, it is referred to as a fault. They are so called because an error or 'fault' appears to have occurred within rock strata or surface features that are no longer in alignment on opposite sides of the fault line (Figure 20.4).

A fault zone is a region of the earth where the crust is relatively weak and where a fault is likely to occur. A fault line is a point of intersection within that zone. Fault lines are usually associated with earthquake activity, as abrupt earth movements can occur along them. The world's most infamous example is the San Andreas Fault in California.

Rift valleys

Rift valleys can form at the point where three tectonic plate boundaries meet. By their very nature, they tend to be large landform features. Rift valleys form when one arm of the three-plate boundary stops moving or spreading. The result is a valley between the plates, much like a canyon, only bigger. When rift valleys continue to grow between continents, new oceans can form.

Rift valleys help to form oceans

It is thought that rift valleys that developed in the ancient continent of Pangaea resulted in its break-up into the separate continents of Africa, Europe and North and South America, and the beginning of the Atlantic Ocean. This ocean continues to grow, spreading every year along the rift that is known as the Mid-Atlantic Ridge. The biggest rift valley on earth is the so-called Great Rift Valley in Africa, which is 6,000 km long.

Case study: Africa's Great Rift Valley

Known more formally as the East African Rift System, the Great Rift Valley is arguably the world's best-known geological example of its kind. The rift stretches from Jordan in south-western Asia, southwards through eastern Africa to Mozambique, covering 6,400 km on its journey. The East African Rift System began to form in the Tertiary Period, 65 million years ago, and is still active today. The rift is formed at the junction of three tectonic plates that are in the process of moving away from each other. The result is the formation of the rift, a scar across the surface of the earth that is up to 64 km across in some places. Far from being a single rift, the East African Rift System is in fact a series of rifts, including the well-known Ethiopian Rift, and a Western Branch and an Eastern Branch further to the south.

Taking it further

Folding can occur at many different scales, resulting in the production of folds that vary from being essentially symmetrical to extremely complex (Figure 20.5). Folds can be classified into various types according to the nature of their slopes and curves. Using the library and the internet, find examples of the folds described in Figure 20.5.

Ground displacement

Huge amounts of energy are involved in the movement of the earth's tectonic plates. When pressure is applied to rocks for long periods of time, especially in enclosed, below-ground environments such as those found beneath the earth's subduction zones, deformation can result. Under these enormous pressures, continental crust can be buckled, bent or broken. Land can be 'folded' into mountains, in much the same way that a piece of loose carpet will fold as it is pushed against a wall. As fold mountains are created, the land is also uplifted, increasing its height above the earth's surface.

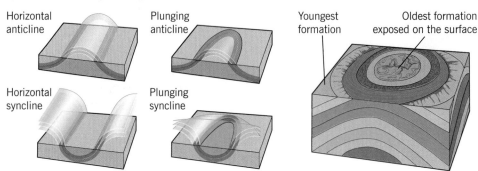

Horizontal anticline   Plunging anticline   Youngest formation   Oldest formation exposed on the surface

Horizontal syncline   Plunging syncline

▶ **Figure 20.5:** The development of folds.

Type of fold	Description
Monocline	A one-sided slope connecting two horizontal strata
Anticline	A symmetrical upfold
Syncline	A simple downfold
Overturned	The fold is over-steepened, and one side has a reverse orientation to the other
Overthrust	The pressure exerted has broken an overturned fold and caused it to shear

Figure 20.6: Many different types of fold can result from the tectonic pressures that are exerted on rock strata.

Summary

In this chapter, you have learnt:
- that volcanic activity produces a variety of landforms above the surface of the earth.
- how different types of volcano are formed by different types of eruptive processes.
- that there are processes occurring at plate margins that help to produce different landforms and landscapes.
- how volcanoes also help to create features below ground, which, after weathering and erosion of surrounding rock, can become landform features that are exposed at the surface of the earth.
- that the earth movements associated with the movement of the earth's tectonic plates can also result in the creation of unique landform features and leave their mark on entire landscapes.

MCQ

CHAPTER 21 What impacts do tectonic hazards have on people and how do these impacts vary?

Key terms

Centre for Research on the
  Epidemiology of Disasters
  (CRED)
Choice
Developed
Developing
Direct cost
Economic impact
Emergency Disasters
  Database (EM-DAT)
Environmental degradation
Ignorance
Indirect cost
Inertia
Less developed
Physical impact
Social impact
Socio-economic status
Tectonically active

Learning objectives

After studying this chapter, you will be able to discuss these ideas and concepts and provide located examples of them:

• There are reasons why people live in tectonically active areas, some of which are related to their level of economic development.
• Tectonic hazards can have a range of impacts on people, including physical, economic and social.
• The impacts of tectonic hazards will vary between locations, especially in countries at different stages of development.
• Trends are emerging in the frequency and impact of tectonic hazards over time.

If the causes of tectonic activity are so clearly understood and the spatial distribution of tectonic hazards so readily identifiable, it begs us to ask why people continue to live in areas that are so tectonically risky (Figure 21.1). This chapter will investigate this question in more detail, as well as considering trends in the frequency and impact of tectonic hazards over time.

Why do people live in tectonically active areas?

There are various reasons why people live in tectonically active areas, including ignorance, choice and inertia.

Lack of knowledge

Even in the world of today, there are people who live in tectonically active areas with a lack of understanding of the world that lies below their feet. As we have seen previously, it is incorrect to think that tectonic activity occurs only at plate boundaries, as these events can occur anywhere on the earth's surface. This leads to people being ignorant of the fact that they may be exposed to tectonic hazards.

There are also places where the knowledge of tectonic activity is limited or even unknown. In the less developed world, for example, the resources or expertise to study the environment and to identify areas at high risk from tectonic hazards may not exist.

▲ **Figure 21.1:** Despite the dangers, settlements continue to develop in areas of high tectonic risk, such as here, at the base of the notorious Mount Vesuvius.

Synoptic link

Look at Edexcel AS Geography pages 16–25 to explore why natural hazards are becoming seen as an increasingly global threat.

Case study: Pompeii – the classic case of ignorance to disaster

Sometimes, our perceptions can lead to ignorance. In ancient times, the lack of an eruption within 'living memory' led many people to believe that Mount Vesuvius, in modern-day Italy, was dormant. Therefore, when Vesuvius burst back into life in 79AD, there was absolutely no expectation that this would happen. As a result, residents in the Roman 'holiday town' of Pompeii were caught completely unaware as the town quickly became covered in a thick layer of volcanic material.

Choice

Strangely enough, there are people who choose to live in tectonically active areas.

In the process of a volcano erupting, new land is created as lava cools and hardens to form rock. Eventually, over time, the physical and chemical weathering of this volcanic rock leads to the formation of fertile volcanic soils. There are many well-known examples of productive agricultural regions that have developed in volcanic areas. Greek, Roman and Etruscan settlements were based on the rich volcanic soils of the Mediterranean and Aegean regions. In Indonesia, thousands of hectares of rice are grown on soils that have developed relatively quickly from the weathering of volcanic rock under tropical conditions.

Volcanoes also promote the establishment of mines. Ore deposits form near volcanoes because the heat that is being generated below the crust causes ore-bearing fluids to move and circulate. As this occurs, certain ores can become concentrated and deposited as veins. After they have cooled and hardened, rich deposits of valuable metals can remain. Copper, gold, zinc and lead deposits can be formed in this way, encouraging settlement on the slopes that surround volcanoes, which in many cases, are still active.

Inertia

Unfortunately, by the time that humans learned about tectonic plates and their movement, it was already too late for many centres of population that had been long established.

In these places, 'living with the hazard' becomes a way of life. However, with continued development over time, and particularly due to urbanisation, by their very nature settlement patterns have increased the likelihood of disaster. Increased population growth and the development of infrastructure in tectonically active areas only expose more people and their possessions to potential disaster.

The physical and economic impacts of different types of tectonic activity

Tectonic activity has a range of impacts upon people and their possessions, including the following.

Physical impacts

The earth experiences, on average, between 50 and 60 earthquakes each year, with the potential to have a significant physical impact. Most obviously, volcanic eruptions can endanger the lives of the estimated 500 million people who live in the region of the earth's active volcanoes. Incredibly, there are 60 large cities located in these regions and their populations and associated infrastructure would bear the brunt of significant eruptions.

The physical impact of volcanoes

Thankfully, three-quarters of all the lava that is erupted on earth actually emerges from volcanoes that are located underwater. Much of this volcanic activity occurs at the diverging plate boundaries, and especially along the length of the mid-oceanic ridges that characterise the separation of the plates, such as the Mid-Atlantic Ridge and the East-Pacific Rise. The physical impact of these volcanoes, in human terms, is minor.

Above the sea, the area of greatest volcanic risk occurs along the converging plate boundaries. Here, most of the world's active volcanoes are found in the less developed world. Latin America, the Caribbean, parts of Asia and the south-west Pacific are the regions at greatest risk of volcanic disaster. Rising populations and increased urbanisation in these areas serve to concentrate people and infrastructure, increasing the risk of disaster.

The physical impact of earthquakes

Like volcanoes, earthquakes can also have a significant physical impact. Most obviously, the shaking of the ground during an earthquake threatens infrastructure, both above and below the ground, and can also result in human casualties.

Key terms

Tectonically active — areas in which the likelihood of earthquakes and/or volcanoes is relatively high, due to the movement of the tectonic plates beneath these locations.

Inertia — the way in which objects tend to remain in their current state or form, unless acted upon by outside forces. In the case of human settlements, sometimes the forces inherent in the threat of tectonic hazards are not enough to shift people from their current location.

Examiners' tip

California's San Andreas Fault is the classic example used by many students to illustrate the nature of faults and the earth movement associated with them. Set your work apart from that of other students by being able to refer to examples of specific sections of the fault (it is part of a very large system of faults), supported by evidence of the extent and impact of movement across these sections.

Taking it further

For information on California's tectonically active nature, read 'Welcome to California – have a nice day' on your Student CD-ROM.

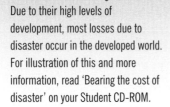

Taking it further

It is commonly known that the heat and pressure below the earth's surface can turn organic matter into deposits of oil and gas over a long period of time. In some places, the heat from below the surface also produces geothermal fluids. For examples and more information, read 'The benefits of tectonic activity' on your Student CD-ROM.

There is an incredible number of earthquakes each year, many of which are so small that they are not felt by humans. It is almost impossible to estimate how many earthquakes occur each year, as many are of such small magnitude that they are barely detectable. What can be measured more easily is the number of large earthquakes. Information from the United States Geological Survey puts the average number of earthquakes with a magnitude of 7.0 or greater at 19.4 per year (over the period from 1900 to 2005). It is important to remember that the worst of the quakes are not necessarily the largest in terms of magnitude, but instead the quakes that occur in heavily populated or infrastructure-dense regions, especially in areas of high vulnerability.

Economic impacts

The costs of natural disaster can be direct and indirect. The direct costs are those that occur when capital goods and equipment are destroyed by the disaster. This can either occur immediately during the disaster, or be as a result of follow-on damage or deterioration. Indirect costs arise as a result of the interruption to commercial systems, lost wages, or the lost opportunities to do business and/or earn money as a result of the disaster.

In response to the direct and indirect costs, there will also be some macro-economic effects which are felt across the whole economy of a community, region, state, or, in the worst case scenarios, nation.

Case study: The high cost of disaster in the developed world

An illustration of just how vulnerable human communities have become to the economic impact of tectonic activities is seen in the earthquake that occurred in Northridge, California, on 17 January 1994 (Figure 21.2). This quake had a magnitude of 6.6 and, sadly, 60 people were killed. However, because the quake occurred in the infrastructure-rich region of the San Fernando Valley, within the city of Los Angeles, the economic impact was a truly staggering $US 30 billion.

▶ **Figure 21.2:** The Northridge earthquake in California (1994) caused significant damage to infrastructure.

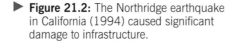

Taking it further

Due to their high levels of development, most losses due to disaster occur in the developed world. For illustration of this and more information, read 'Bearing the cost of disaster' on your Student CD-ROM.

The social impacts of different types of tectonic activity

Whilst infrastructure can be replaced and livelihoods re-established, undoubtedly the most devastating impact of tectonic activity is that it can result in the loss of human lives. As revealed in Figure 21.3, which considers the casualties caused by natural disasters in the first part of this century, earthquakes have a significant impact on human life. The threat posed by volcanoes would appear to be relatively smaller.

That said, volcanoes are estimated to have claimed 300,000 lives since 1600. Most deaths due to volcanic activity are caused by the deadly pyroclastic flows and lahars that were covered in previous chapters.

In March/April 1982, villages which lay within 8 km of the summit of the Mexican volcano El Chichón were struck by the pyroclastic flows which surged from it. More than 2,000 people lost their lives during this eruptive phase.

Earthquakes are well known for causing death and destruction by trapping people in collapsed buildings or burying them under tonnes of rubble. However, earthquake-generated tsunamis are perhaps even more terrifying.

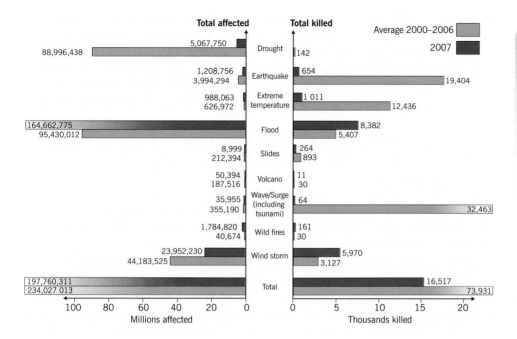

◀ **Figure 21.3:** Human impact by disaster type over the course of the 2000s. Earthquakes and tsunamis (shown as Wave/Surge in the diagram) take more human lives that any other disaster.

They are especially threatening to coastal and island communities, with those in Asia and the Pacific being particularly vulnerable. In 1883, the eruption of Krakatau (an island between Sumatra and Java, in Indonesia) set in motion a number of tsunamis, which devastated local communities: 36,000 deaths occurred as these tsunamis destroyed 165 coastal villages.

Impacts are linked to level of development

The degree of exposure of a community to tectonic hazards is intimately related to the socio-economic status of the community. In places where poverty is high, the capacity to reduce the impact of hazards or to recover from the destruction that they may cause can be non-existent. Additionally, environmental degradation removes or reduces the impact of the natural buffers which help to provide some protection against tectonic hazards. The removal of these buffers means that the impact of hazards will be much greater. At the same time, it also reduces the capacity of a community to cope with a hazard. This leads to a delayed recovery time. Sadly, 90% of all deaths due to natural disasters occur in the less developed or developing world.

Key term

Environmental degradation — the damage that humans do to various components of the ecosystem, including its soils, flora, fauna, water and air.

Responding to disaster

The 'Response Curve' (sometimes referred to as Park's Model) can help us understand how communities deal with and respond to disaster (see Figure 21.4 below).

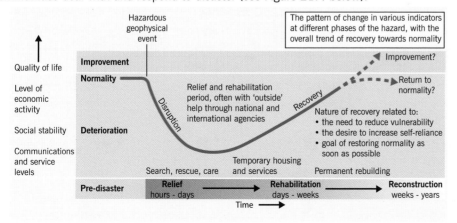

◀ **Figure 21.4:** The Response Curve is a model used to demonstrate how communities deal with and recover from disaster.

Taking it further

As a demonstration of the role that socio-economic status plays in determining our level of exposure to tectonic hazards, consider the following statistics. Of the 40 least developed countries in the world, 24 face a level of risk from disaster that would be considered 'high' by world standards. Incredibly, six of these countries have suffered between two and eight major disasters during each one of the last 15 years! The cycle of disaster–loss–recovery is almost continual in these locations, making it even harder to plan for and cope with the onset of hazards. Using the internet, research specific examples of countries like these.

Key term

EM-DAT — stands for the Emergency Disasters Database, an information-gathering programme that is run by the Centre for Research on the Epidemiology of Disasters (CRED).

Immediately after the occurrence of a geophysical event, communities enter a phase of intense disruption to their normal patterns of daily life. Amid the chaos and carnage of this phase, which can last from a period of hours to a number of days, the priority is to relieve the suffering of those people who have been affected by the disaster. In some instances, this can include locating those who are missing, rescuing those who are trapped, collecting and accounting for the injured and the dead, or providing emergency supplies of food and water.

The next phase of the Response Curve shows the beginning of a period of rehabilitation, and the gradual re-establishment of more 'usual' routines and patterns within the community. To allow this to happen, many temporary services are provided during this phase, which can last from days to weeks. This may include the provision of healthcare, sanitation and housing, as well as the establishment of an ongoing supply of food and water. Often, this phase is characterised by assistance from outside the affected region, sometimes including humanitarian aid from abroad.

Following rehabilitation is a period of recovery. During this period, which can extend from weeks, or months, through to years, the community is reconstructed and life is able to return to normal. Importantly, communities draw lessons from the events of the natural disaster they have experienced.

Trends in frequency and impact over time

Statistics gathered by groups such as EM-DAT show that the number of disasters is steadily increasing with each passing year. However, the number of people dying as a result of disasters is decreasing. This is thought to be because as a species we have learnt ways to help us avoid death due to natural hazards.

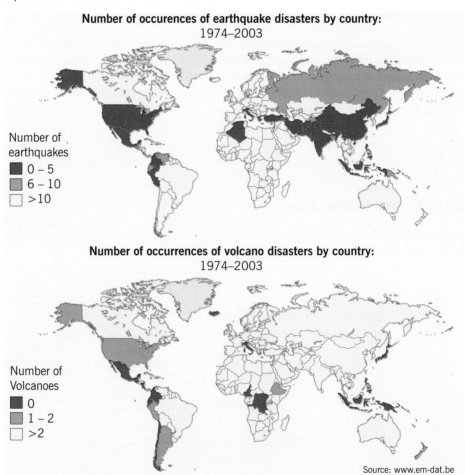

Number of occurences of earthquake disasters by country: 1974–2003

Number of earthquakes
- 0 – 5
- 6 – 10
- >10

Number of occurrences of volcano disasters by country: 1974–2003

Number of Volcanoes
- 0
- 1 – 2
- >2

Source: www.em-dat.be

▶ **Figure 21.5:** Maps such as these help us to understand the spatial patterns of disaster due to earthquakes and volcanoes.

In the case of tectonic activity such as volcanoes and earthquakes, better knowledge and understanding of the natural environment have helped to identify hazardous areas (Figure 21.5). At the same time, better building techniques and continued monitoring of the environment by sophisticated equipment have given us a better chance of survival in the event of a tectonic hazard.

Research has shown that the economic cost of disasters is increasing. Between 1950 and 1959, there were '20 great natural catastrophes'. The total cost of these disasters was $US 28 billion. Yet, by comparison, in the decade following 1990 there were 82 such disasters, with a combined damage bill of $US 535 billion.

Disasters have increased because humans and their infrastructure are more vulnerable than ever before to natural hazards. But while the number of disasters increased four-fold between 1959 and 1999, there was a corresponding 14-fold increase in the economic cost.

Case study: A deadly region

The Asia-Pacific region accounts for approximately one-fifth of the earth's land surface. However, the same region is home to more than 50% of the entire global population. Recent investigations have revealed that the frequency of natural disasters in on the increase within the Asia-Pacific region. Statistics from 2006 reveal that of the 457 natural disasters that took place that year, well over 40% occurred in this part of the earth. The effect on the population was severe, as in 2006 more than 88% of all those people affected by disasters called the Asia-Pacific home.

Summary

In this chapter, you have learnt:
- that, for a variety of reasons, mostly to do with lifestyle and livelihoods, some people live in areas that are at high risk of tectonic hazard.
- how the impacts of tectonic hazards are more than just injuries, death and destruction. They also include a range of longer-term effects on the fabric of societies and their economies.
- that the level of development within a community can determine the effect of a tectonic hazard upon it, with less developed communities at greater risk of disaster.
- how research shows that whilst the frequency of tectonic hazards is increasing, the number of deaths due to these hazards is declining. However, the costs associated with hazard events is increasing rapidly, as we become more developed and more urbanised.

MCQ

CHAPTER 22 How do people cope with tectonic hazards and what are the issues for the future?

Key terms

Capacity
Community memory
Cost–benefit analysis
Disaster Risk Equation
Federal Emergency
  Management Authority
  (FEMA)
Hazard profile
Infrastructure
International Decade for
  Natural Disaster Reduction
  (IDNDR)
Loss burden
Megacities
Natural buffers
Non-governmental
  organisation (NGO)
Prediction
Systemic approach
Vulcanologist
Vulnerability

Learning objectives

After studying this chapter, you will be able to discuss these ideas and concepts and provide located examples of them:

• Individuals and governments have varying approaches to coping with tectonic hazards, and these may be dependent on levels of development.
• There are specific strategies involved in adjusting to tectonic hazards, including modifying the event, modifying the loss burden and modifying human vulnerability.
• People attempt to cope before, during and after hazardous tectonic events.
• Approaches and strategies for coping with tectonic hazards have changed over time, and the effectiveness of these different approaches can be measured.

As we have seen in the previous chapters, tectonic hazards are a very real threat for many people, especially those living in the most tectonically active parts of the world. Therefore, it is important that we understand how to live with tectonic hazards and how to cope with the impact that they have upon our lives and our communities.

► **Figure 22.1:** A section of the Nishinomiyako Bridge which collapsed as a result of the Kobe earthquake in Japan (1995).

Approaches to coping with tectonic hazards

In the face of tectonic hazards that threaten their homes, communities and livelihoods, individuals have three basic choices: do nothing, adjust or leave.

Do nothing

There are some people who choose to do nothing to help them prepare for or cope with a potential tectonic hazard. On some occasions, this is due to complete apathy – the idea that 'it will never happen to me'.

At other times, sadly, people 'do nothing' about preparing for tectonic hazards due to ignorance of the dangers that are inherent in certain locations. This ignorance can be due to a lack of education or awareness about tectonic hazards, which is often not the fault of the person who is 'ignorant', but may be a factor of their circumstance, location or socio-economic situation.

The role of socio-economic status in disaster

Sometimes, of course, people may want to 'do something' about disaster preparedness, but simply do not have the social or economic means to do so. People living in the less developed world are at a much higher risk from natural disaster than those who are fortunate enough to live in the developed world. Victims of disaster are 150 times greater in the less developed world, whilst economic losses due to disaster are 20 times as great, when considered as a percentage of gross national product. Socio-economic status is a huge determinant of our ability to cope with hazards – and most especially earthquakes.

The impact of population growth in the less developed world

The world's population is expected to grow by another 3 billion people by the year 2050. Most of this population growth will occur in the countries of the less developed and developing world. Overwhelmingly, the continued trend towards urbanisation will see this growth concentrated in cities and towns. In fact by 2010, the 'local areas' found within these countries will collectively need to accommodate an extra 180,000 people a day. As the 'megacities' continue to develop, ongoing degradation of the environment will further reduce the natural buffers that protect populations against disaster.

Adjust

There is little, if anything, that humans can do to prevent the occurrence of volcanoes and earthquakes. However, if communities work together to prepare for the risks, then there is a good chance that the amount of suffering and loss that occurs as a result of one of these hazards can be reduced.

Preparing to adjust for hazards involves making an assessment of how vulnerable an area is to a given hazard. This requires a particular set of specialist skills, and needs to be based on accurate and reliable information.

Varying levels of government, including local, county/state and national, attempt to adjust to the reality of tectonic activity by preparing hazard profiles for their communities. In determining the likely impact of volcanoes and earthquakes, hazard profilers will take into account factors such as:

- location
- frequency
- magnitude
- duration
- areal extent.

Leave

There are times when people choose to abandon certain locations on the basis that they are 'too risky'. This can occur as a result of a formal hazard assessment, but more usually it occurs because of perceptions that are held within the community. Collective 'community memory' plays a role in determining how residents feel about the places that are 'safe' within the area that they call home. It is also very adept at recognising areas that are unsuitable for settlement or land uses that increase the level of risk to population and infrastructure in the event of a hazard. Tapping in to community memory is an important aspect of hazard mapping.

Leaving can occur on many different levels. People may leave for a short while, for example, during a high-risk period of volcanic activity. Residents may leave during or immediately after a disaster, such as an earthquake, to return at a later time when it has been declared safe to do so. After repeated hazards in a given location, or after one major disaster, people may decide to leave permanently.

Key term

Megacities — those cities with a population in excess of 10 million.

Synoptic link

Look at Edexcel AS Geography pages 64–71 to examine how we should tacke the challenges of increasing risk and vulnerability in a more hazardous world.

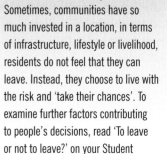

Taking it further

Sometimes, communities have so much invested in a location, in terms of infrastructure, lifestyle or livelihood, residents do not feel that they can leave. Instead, they choose to live with the risk and 'take their chances'. To examine further factors contributing to people's decisions, read 'To leave or not to leave?' on your Student CD-ROM.

Specific strategies involved in adjustment

It is therefore apparent that 'adjusting' is the preferred method of coping with tectonic hazards. Adjustment can take a number of different forms, based on the various modifications that can be made within communities.

Modifying the event

It is not possible for humans to prevent natural hazards such as earthquakes and volcanoes. What remains is for us to focus our efforts on predicting when such events are likely to occur. Predicting the occurrence of earthquakes and volcanoes is difficult and requires the use of expensive monitoring techniques, but it can afford populations with enough warning to allow them to escape from the danger zone.

Seismographs have long been used to record the vibrations of plate movements, with increases in the frequency of vibrations being the usual precursor to a ground movement of significant magnitude.

Predicting when a volcano is likely to erupt is based on regular monitoring of the volcano, including conditions inside its vent or around its perimeter (Figure 22.2). Warning signs that an eruption is imminent may include small earth tremors as magma moves below the surface, increases in ground temperatures or an increased discharge of volcanic gases from around the vent.

Assessing the impact of earthquakes and tsunamis

When completing a hazard assessment for seismic hazards such as earthquakes and tsunamis, hazard mappers will consider the degree of ground shaking and movement during the event as the most important factors. To assist with planning in practical terms, earthquake hazard assessments refer to the probability of a certain amount of shaking being exceeded during an earthquake. In this way, infrastructure can be 'rated' to a certain magnitude of earthquake, based on good records of past activity in a given location and its resultant effects. It is important to note that this process is more likely to be prone to errors in areas that experience little or no seismic activity, and where the records on seismic events are much thinner.

▲ **Figure 22.2:** Accessing volcanoes and studying them safely can prove very challenging. Here, a team of vulcanologists await extraction by helicopter from volcanic slopes.

Modifying human vulnerability

Protecting humans from the impact of natural hazards such as earthquakes and volcanoes is paramount. Recalling the Disaster Risk Equation, an assessment of the potential for disaster in any given community should be based on a consideration of its:

- risk of hazard
- vulnerability to the hazard
- capacity to cope with the hazard.

The objective of any such assessment is to assess the likelihood that a specific hazard will occur in a given area. In addition, these assessments focus on the likely intensity of such hazards, and consider the area that would be impacted by hazards of varying intensity. In this context, it will be possible to identify groups within the community who could be considered 'highly vulnerable'. The approaches that can be taken as a result can focus on reducing the vulnerability of a community to hazard, or increasing its capacity to cope.

Approaches used in different locations at different stages of development

Strategies to modify the vulnerability of communities are much more difficult to establish in the less developed world due to a range of factors. In general, chief among these factors are the:

- poorer quality of buildings
- weaker systems of communication

- limited funding pre- and post-disaster
- lack of central coordination to plan for/deal with disaster.

Serious effort put into planning for hazard events can significantly reduce the amount of damage that is likely to occur.

However, there are times when hazards cannot be accurately assessed because of a lack of technological infrastructure. At other times, the importance of hazard mapping may be ignored by planners and developers, or there may be no coordinated approach to planning and development. Sadly, these are factors which expose people in the less developed world to increased risk of disaster.

Modifying the loss burden

Some places within the environment are likely to experience greater damage as a result of an earthquake or a volcanic eruption. Modifying the loss burden refers to moving vulnerable communities, infrastructure or capital items out of harm's way, so as to reduce the overall losses due to disaster.

Proximity is a good guide, with increased distance from a volcanic vent or fault line likely to mean that the damage sustained during an event will be lower. Key resources should be located safe distances away, and the same is true of housing developments and buildings.

Sometimes, it is not possible to move land uses to safer locations, because of the time it would take or the costs that would be incurred. Other ways to modify the loss burden involve investing time and effort in protecting vulnerable resources which cannot be moved. This may include earthquake proofing buildings or specialist training programmes for people located in the high-risk areas.

Planning to cope with disaster

One of the fundamental principles underlying the ability of a community to cope with disaster before, during and after the event is that people have a responsibility for their own safety.

It is naïve to think that governments, at any level, can protect us from natural hazards. Governments do have a role to play – but it is to provide the policies that guide preparations that are made at local levels. These policies must be flexible enough to operate successfully in a variety of locations, and must encourage activities that help to reduce the risk of natural hazards resulting in disaster.

When planning for the management of volcanic eruptions, authorities usually consider factors such as:

- the establishment of an exclusion zone around the volcano
- creating plans that allow large numbers of people to be evacuated quickly
- supplying basic provisions and sanitation for large numbers of displaced persons
- maintaining effective systems of communication during and after the eruptive phase.

In general, earthquake events (and their associated tsunamis) are shorter-lived phenomena than volcanoes, therefore preparations for earthquakes tend to involve practice and drills for what to do in the event of an earthquake. Typically, this includes:

- emergency response team preparations and practice
- the preparation of emergency kits that can be used if essential services such as water, electricity and gas are cut by the earthquake
- earthquake proofing of infrastructure, so that it is able to absorb the movement generated by an earthquake.

The way that a community is able to prepare for disaster is dependent on its social and political context. It is important to recognise that what is achievable in one location may not be even remotely achievable in another.

Taking it further

For an example of a community-based risk assessment and a case study on reducing vulnerability in the Caribbean, read 'The progression of vulnerability' and 'Reducing vulnerability' on your Student CD-ROM.

Examiners' tip

The 'Progression of Vulnerability' is a very important concept that helps to show your depth of understanding about tectonic hazards and their impact on people. Although the magnitude and frequency of hazards in given locations are a factor, the overall level of impact will also be determined by other conditions and pressures that exist in the local community, including many examples linked to the level of development. Study the chart on the weblink in some detail – it is a good one to reproduce and explain in test conditions. This is included in the Taking it further activity 'The progression of vulnerabilty' on your Student CD-ROM.

Examiners' tip

The response of the global community in helping to establish a tsunami warning system in the Asia-Pacific Region following the Indonesian tsunami makes an excellent case study of disaster preparedness. Be prepared to provide evidence of international efforts to establish such a system in your exam.

Taking it further

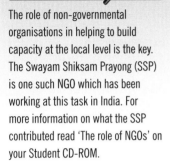

For information on the USA's Federal Emergency Management Authority go to your Student CD-ROM.

Taking it further

The role of non-governmental organisations in helping to build capacity at the local level is the key. The Swayam Shiksam Prayong (SSP) is one such NGO which has been working at this task in India. For more information on what the SSP contributed read 'The role of NGOs' on your Student CD-ROM.

Key term

Cost–benefit analysis — this generally compares the economic costs of a proposed course of action with the value of the benefits that it will provide.

For example, in the developed world, we are fortunate enough to have government agencies which promote awareness of disaster preparation and which encourage community involvement in the formulation and practice of emergency response plans.

Coping in the less developed world

In many parts of the less developed world, it is just not possible for families to prepare disaster plans in the same way, as they may not have the resources to do so, or the assistance of outside agencies such as FEMA. Instead, work to prepare for disaster in the less developed world focuses on raising the awareness of local communities about disaster and building the capacity of the community to cope.

Building the capacity of communities starts at the grassroots level, within villages and towns. The members of these communities are the people with the most to lose in any disaster, so naturally they are also the most willing to contribute to disaster preparedness. They are also the best source of local knowledge about the way that disaster plays out in their location and can advise on the best of the traditional coping strategies. Significantly, they are also the first people who will respond in a crisis, in the absence of a centrally coordinated government response, which may take days or even weeks to come, if at all.

Investigating the success of coping strategies

Not all coping strategies will be successful. Some, although effective in reducing the potential for disaster, will be so expensive as to be cost-prohibitive. Others, whilst relatively inexpensive, may not bring real or lasting benefits. This is where cost–benefit analysis can be used to help judge the effectiveness of varying coping strategies. Particularly in the less developed world, cost–benefit analysis plays an important role in helping to determine the best way to allocate limited resources.

Coping strategies have changed over time

In the past, central government, at either state/county or national level, had assumed that local communities were generally unaware of the risks they faced from natural hazards and that they were equally unprepared to face them. The focus of the central governments was on the work that they could do post-disaster, in terms of providing relief, aiding recovery and rebuilding. Within the less developed world, there was also a general reliance on the multi-millions of dollars that flowed to disaster zones from the international community post-disaster.

In the last three decades, a new mantra has emerged in terms of our approach to dealing with disaster. Whilst disaster risk management strategies must be coordinated centrally in any given nation, it is now evident that their success is dependent upon a wide spread of decision-making abilities, to take into account the variations that exist between locations within a country. Local decision-makers are also reliant upon the participation of people within their local community to help make disaster management plans truly effective.

'Policy direction and legal foundations assure legitimacy but it is the professional and human resources available, on the ground, that are a true measure of success.' (United Nations Living with Risk: A global review of disaster risk initiatives, 2004) This new thinking reflects a systemic approach to coping with disaster. The processes that exist at the local level must match the administrative approach and resources that are available at the next level of government, and dovetail into state/county or national risk reduction strategies.

These changes began to emerge during the 1990s, which were the International Decade for Natural Disaster Reduction (IDNDR). During this period, the basic policies of disaster reduction were introduced at a range of administrative levels, and the focus clearly shifted from post-disaster recovery to pre-disaster preparedness and mitigation.

Coping in the future

As the world grows increasingly hazardous, the accurate identification of risk scenarios will become paramount. Hazard assessments must incorporate people's perceptions of the risk that they face, as well as the socio-economic and environmental context of where they live.

Assessment methodologies will need to respond in appropriate ways. The systemic approach will become even more important, with a need to integrate processes and information between various levels of government, and in the face of increasing global disasters, between national governments.

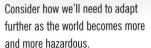

Taking it further

Consider how we'll need to adapt further as the world becomes more and more hazardous.

Summary

In this chapter, you have learnt:
- that there are many different approaches to coping with tectonic hazards; from doing nothing, to abandoning a settlement or location altogether.
- that, alternatively, communities can make a choice to try and cope with the hazards that they face.
- that coping with hazards is all about understanding what the risks are and the community making itself less vulnerable to their impacts.
- that, as a society, we are getting better at coping with tectonic hazards, but there is more work to be done, particularly in terms of sharing information and strategies between the more developed and the less developed worlds.

MCQ

CHAPTER 23 What are cold environments and where are they found?

Key terms

Alpine
Dynamic equilibrium
Glacier
Firn/névé
Fluvioglacial
Ice sheet
Periglacial
Permafrost
Pleistocene
Tundra

Learning objectives

After studying this chapter, you will be able to discuss these ideas and concepts and provide located examples of them:

- The location of a range of cold environments and how they differ.
- The idea of landscape as a system and the inputs, stores and outputs involved in the glacial system.
- How the distribution of cold environments has changed over time.

The location of cold environments

The cold environments of the earth can be divided into two major categories: high latitude (or polar) and high altitude (or alpine).

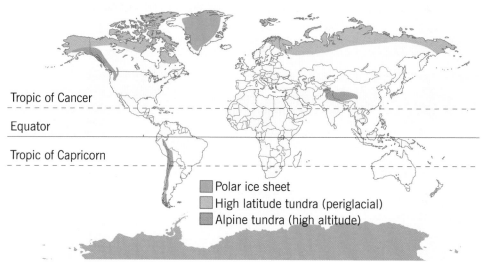

▶ **Figure 23.1:** Map showing polar, alpine and tundra/periglacial environments.

Polar ice sheet
High latitude tundra (periglacial)
Alpine tundra (high altitude)

Key terms

Alpine — high altitude areas within mountain ranges where glaciers and small ice caps can be found.

Ice sheets — masses of glacier ice that cover the surrounding terrain and are greater than 50,000 km².

Glaciers can be found in both locations. They are large bodies of ice formed by the compaction of snow that slowly move down-slope due to gravity and their own weight. Antarctica is the coldest region on earth and is covered by permanent ice in the form of a continental glacier or ice sheet. Located at the South Pole and having high altitudes, temperatures have been recorded as low as –89°C within its boundary. In the northern hemisphere, Greenland is also covered by a major ice sheet.

▶ **Figures 23.2 and 23.3:** Views showing typical (on left) alpine glacier, confined within a valley and with associated features and ice sheet (on right) showing the horizontal extent.

However, most of the ice in the Arctic is sea ice, without any land beneath. Almost 95% of glacier ice is locked up in the ice sheets of Antarctica and Greenland.

In high altitude areas such as the Alps, the Rockies and the Himalayas, snowfalls can build up and compact to form source areas for alpine glaciers. Alpine glaciers can be corrie or cirque glaciers when snow and ice have collected in hollows and eventually flowed over the edge. These are the smallest in scale. Valley glaciers may be fed by one or more corrie glaciers and flow down valleys that may have been initially created by rivers. When glaciers flow out from a mountain range as the valley empties onto a plain, they are known as piedmont glaciers.

In alpine locations there is summer melting that releases meltwater to feed many of the major world rivers such as the Rhône and the Ganges. The glaciers retreat, advancing again when temperatures have fallen. In polar regions, there is little or no melting in the continental glaciers or ice sheets as temperatures do not rise above zero.

In Greenland, not all the island is covered by the ice sheet. Its coastal edges, lying adjacent to the ice sheet, are not ice-covered, but are affected by the very cold conditions. These areas are called periglacial zones and are characterised by permanently frozen ground called permafrost. Although a harsh environment, periglacial areas can support some vegetation as the upper layers of soil thaw during the very short summer. The resulting ecosystem is known as tundra and the plants that grow in these areas are typically low-growing perennial shrubs. There are no trees as the growing season is so short and there is very little water available as most of it is frozen as ice or snow. There is also alpine tundra which is found below the snowline in mountainous areas.

The glacial landscape system

Glacial and periglacial landscapes are the result of the action of ice and freezing temperatures. In order to provide a framework for investigating the landscape, a systems approach is often used. Various inputs, outputs and stores, plus the linkages between them, can be identified and looked at individually while maintaining an overview of the system as a whole. A simple glacial system is shown in Figure 23.4.

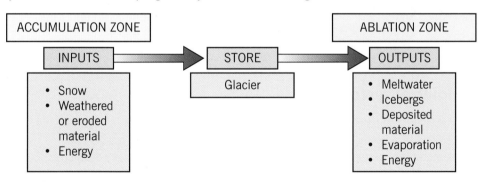

Figure 23.4: Simplified glacial system.

Glacier ice is made up of snow that has been compressed, driving out air. Fresh fallen snow is 90% air, but once it enters the glacial system it is covered by further layers. As a result, air is driven out of it, as well as some thawing due to pressure and refreezing. The snow loses its branching shape and becomes more granular. When two-thirds of the air has been removed, it forms firn (or névé). This occurs at least a year after the snow first fell and it will eventually form glacier ice when all the granules have cemented together. This process usually takes between 10 and 40 years.

The area where a glacier receives inputs of snow and ice and increases in mass is called the Accumulation Zone. The area where it loses mass by evaporation and melting, towards the end of the glacier, is known as the Ablation Zone. The relationship between input and output is known as the mass balance or the glacier budget. The size of the glacial system depends on this balance.

Key term

Dynamic equilibrium — literally, a moving balance, when a system's inputs and outputs balance one another out.

With the smaller alpine glaciers (those found at high altitudes in mountainous areas), in the upper zone of the glacier, accumulation exceeds ablation and in the lower zone ablation exceeds accumulation. The boundary between these two zones is the line of equilibrium. At this point within the glacier system, accumulation is equal to ablation over the year as a whole – there is balance. The glacier is said to be in dynamic equilibrium when the inputs in the Accumulation Zone match the outputs in the Ablation Zone and the glacier neither retreats nor advances overall. Recent higher summer and winter temperatures have meant that many alpine glaciers are retreating as their rates of ablation are higher than those of accumulation. This has meant that the dynamic equilibrium has been disturbed and the glacier may retreat up the valley it has carved for itself.

Case study: The retreat of the Grinnell Glacier, Glacier National Park, USA

This shows the impact of recent warming on a glacial landscape. The Grinnell Glacier is located in Glacier National Park in Montana, USA and is in the Lewis mountain range. Over the last century the glacier has lost an estimated 90% of its mass. As the glacier is reasonably accessible, many photos have been taken of it, beginning in the middle of the 19th century when photography was in its infancy. In 1850 the glacier measured 2.88 km². By 1993 this had reduced to 0.88 km² as ablation continued to be greater than accumulation within its glacial budget. It is now expected that by 2030 the Grinnell Glacier will have melted away, along with most of the others in the National Park. The images of the glacier show the changes to its glacial mass over time, as well as the impact on the landscape.

Grinnell Glacier 1850-1981
1850
1968 1937
1981

◀ **Figures 23.5 and 23.6:** Grinnell Glacier showing the amount of retreat since 1850 when it was photographed for the first time.

Taking it further

Investigate where in the world there are glaciers that are regularly accessed by tourists. Find out whether they are advancing or retreating. (Surprisingly, some will be advancing.)

Periglacial systems

The glacial landscape often also includes periglacial areas which are not permanently covered by ice, such as the coastal fringes of Greenland. Here there are very low temperatures and permanently frozen ground that give rise to some very distinctive landforms. Not all periglacial areas are adjacent to glaciers, for example, large expanses of Alaska and Siberia, but can be typified by the presence of permafrost. This can also apply in alpine environments where periglacial conditions exist at high altitudes.

Fluvioglacial systems

As glaciers melt during ablation, meltwater is produced that flows away from the foot of the glacier. Combined with sub-glacial streams which flow beneath the ice, this will carry large amounts of sediment that is deposited when the streams lose energy, creating depositional landforms including braiding. Fluvioglacial processes often link glacial and periglacial areas as the meltwater streams flow away from glaciated areas into the zone of permafrost.

Changes in the location of cold environments over time

Although today we are familiar with cold environments being located around the poles and in high mountain areas, in the past cold environments have covered both greater and lesser amounts of the earth's surface.

Taking it further

To learn to investigate glacial landforms read 'Be your own ice detective' on your Student CD-ROM.

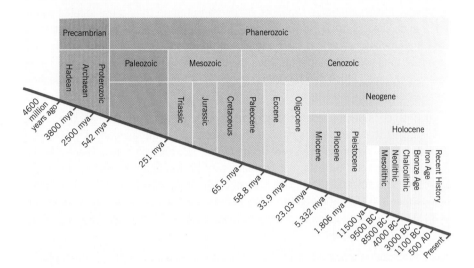

◀ **Figure 23.7:** Geological time and human history.

During the Quaternary period, there have been several glaciations or ice ages. This period covers the 2 million years since humans have lived on earth. It commenced with the Pleistocene epoch, which lasted from 2 million until 10,000 years ago when the Holocene epoch began. This coincided with the end of the last ice age, since which time there has been a net retreat of glaciers and ice sheets.

The ice ages of the Pleistocene period began about 1.5 million years ago and it has been estimated that during this time there is evidence of 17 glacial cycles.

A glacial cycle covers about 100,000 years and is a period of glaciation followed by a time when the climate warms and the glaciers and ice sheets retreat (an interglacial – usually of about 15,000 years).

During the last ice age, the ice was at its maximum extent about 18,000 years ago. At this time there was a continental ice sheet across much of North America with many glaciers in the mountains of the west.

▼ **Figure 23.8:** World map showing the extent of last glaciation.

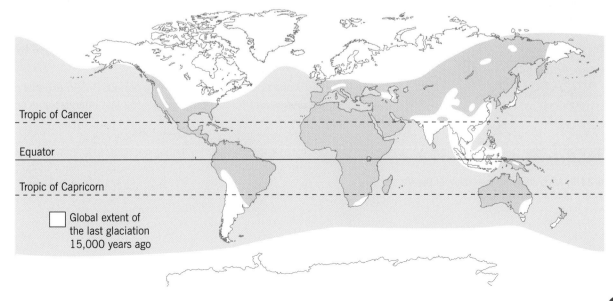

Synoptic link

Go to Unit 1 Chapter 4 of the Edexcel
AS Geography textbook for further
information on evidence of past
climatic changes.

In Europe the Scandinavian ice sheet spread over much of the British Isles and northern Europe. Glaciers and smaller ice caps were found in regions of high altitude and there was an extensive ice sheet over Siberia. Another ice sheet was located over the Himalayas and covered much of what is now India. In the southern hemisphere there were fewer ice sheets and glaciers as there was less land for them to develop on, but the majority of New Zealand was covered by ice and the Antarctic ice sheet expanded as far north as 50°S.

In Europe trees managed to grow in northern Spain, northern Italy (south of the Alps) and in Greece. There were large expanses of tundra to the north of these locations and south of the ice sheets, similar to those seen in Siberia today, with herds of reindeer and other grazing animals, as well as their dependent predators such as wolves and humans. Evidence that tundra/periglacial areas have existed in these areas is given by the patterned ground and polygons, which can be seen from the air as crop marks. Soil cross-sections also show evidence of ice wedges.

There has been considerable evidence from sea-bed sediment cores (see AS Unit 1 Topic 1.4) that suggest that the glaciers and ice sheets began retreating around 14,000 years ago, with the North American ice sheet disappearing 10,000 years ago. There have been some mini-advances and retreats, but overall the ice sheets and glaciers are reducing in size and depth and scientists state that we are in an interglacial period. As the climate became warmer and the ice retreated, it left behind evidence of its path in a variety of landforms, both erosional (such as deep glaciated valleys known as glacial troughs) and depositional (such as drumlins).

Previously glaciated landscapes can tell us about earlier climates and environments, but care is needed as non-glacial processes might have created them. The term used to describe the idea that similar landforms could be created by a mix of different processes is equifinality.

Taking it further

To learn more about the three major
glaciations during the Pleistocene
period over Britain, read 'The
Pleistocene period' on your Student
CD-ROM.

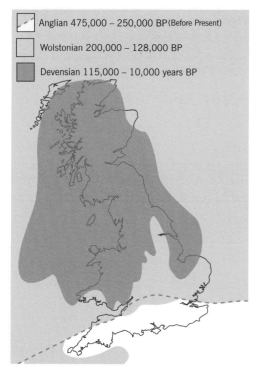

Anglian 475,000 – 250,000 BP (Before Present)

Wolstonian 200,000 – 128,000 BP

Devensian 115,000 – 10,000 years BP

▲ **Figure 23.9:** Map showing the extent of the three Quaternary glaciations in the British Isles.

British cold environments — past and present

We have already seen that Britain has experienced glaciations in the past. By looking at landforms and sediments and comparing them with glaciated landscapes today, many similarities can be seen. Studies of soil cores and the analysis of pollen grains in the British Isles have allowed a picture to be built up of past climate changes. The landscape of Britain bears scars of its glacial past, such as the deep scratches on rock surfaces caused by glacial abrasion called striations. As Britain is no longer glaciated, these landforms are known as relict (or fossil) landforms. As the most recent ice sheets retreated, the areas in front of the ice became periglacial.

It was at this time that the periglacial landforms we see today were formed. Over much of Britain earlier examples have been altered or destroyed by subsequent advances and retreats.

During the Pleistocene epoch of the Quaternary period, Britain experienced three major glaciations and three interglacials – the last interglacial is occurring at the present time.

The Anglian Glaciation 475,000–250,000 years BP (Before Present)
During this glaciation, the ice sheet blocked the north-eastern route of the River Thames so it was forced to flow into its present easterly channel. This ice sheet, as it retreated, left many of the glacial deposits to be found today in East Anglia.

The Hoxnian Interglacial 250,000–200,000 years BP
Temperatures warmed to such an extent during these 50,000 years that sea levels were 25 metres higher than today and oak forests grew in Britain. Humans lived in the Thames valley alongside elephants and rhino.

The Wolstonian Glaciation 200,000–128,000 years BP
Deposits from this glaciation can be found along parts of the Holderness coast and in the West Midlands. They are also found further south than the Anglian Glaciation in the South West and the Scilly Isles.

The Ipswichian Interglacial 128,000–115,000 years BP
Forests returned to Britain again and, with the rise in sea levels, Britain was an island, separated from the continent.

The Devensian Glaciation 115,000–10,000 years BP
This last ice age reached its peak about 18,000 years ago and obliterated or buried much of the evidence of earlier glaciations over the north and west of Britain.

For all of the glaciations, their ice sheet edges were bounded by periglacial areas where the intense cold led to permafrost and associated landforms. It is clear that over the last 400,000 years Britain has experienced many changes in climate and even within these glacial and interglacial periods there were smaller advances or retreats of ice that lasted for comparatively short lengths of time.

Examiners' tip

When referring to past glaciation, do not say 'During the ice age', but make it clear that you understand that there have been several advances and retreats of ice and say either 'During the most recent ice age' or 'During the Devensian advance'.

Summary

In this chapter you have learnt:
- why there are different cold environments and what is meant by glacial, alpine, periglacial and tundra.
- where these cold environments are located today.
- the idea of a glacier as a system.
- that Britain has undergone several climate changes during the Quaternary period and that the glaciations had different extents.

MCQ

CHAPTER 24 Cold environment climatic processes

Key terms

Albedo
Anticyclone
Continentality
Insolation
Kettle hole
Milankovitch cycles
Plate tectonics

Key terms

Insolation — the amount of solar radiation received at a particular point on the earth's surface. The solar energy also passes through more atmosphere at higher latitudes due to the curvature of the earth.

Albedo — a measure of the amount of reflectivity of a surface. Snow has a high albedo; green forests have a low albedo.

Anticyclones — stable areas of high pressure.

Learning objectives

After studying this chapter, you will be able to discuss these ideas and concepts and provide located examples of them:

- The causes of cold conditions in a variety of locations.
- That cold environments are not fixed in location.
- Weather processes in cold environments vary according to location.
- The location of glacial and periglacial landscapes.

Causes of cold climates

The polar regions of the Arctic and Antarctica receive less insolation per unit area than regions at lower latitudes. This is because the insolation received at high latitudes is spread over a wider surface area of the earth due to its curvature.

More solar radiation is absorbed, dispersed and reflected, so it vastly reduces the amount reaching the surface. With polar regions being covered in ice and snow, the albedo is also an important factor in keeping temperatures low as it gives a high surface albedo and does not heat the earth's surface.

Cold air is denser and it sinks at the poles, forming anticyclones. This cold air moves south from the Arctic and north from the Antarctic to become part of the global atmospheric circulation. The cold air flowing towards the Equator replaces warm air moving away towards the poles and thus heat is transferred to higher latitudes.

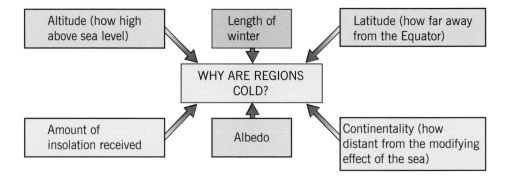

▶ **Figure 24.1:** Why are regions cold?

As the earth wobbles on its axis, during the winter the northern hemisphere is angled away from the sun and temperatures drop. For extreme northerly locations beyond the Arctic Circle, this means continuous darkness for several months, known as polar nights. However, during summer months when the northern hemisphere is angled towards the sun, these same regions experience daylight for 24 hours with the sun never setting below the horizon.

Polar areas receive limited precipitation because of the high pressure system keeping rain-bearing depression away and this also means there is a lack of cloud cover. This leads to a rapid loss of heat during hours of darkness.

Within Antarctica, locations in the central areas of the continent are much colder than coastal locations. Places that are distant from oceans do not benefit from the modifying influence of the sea. Land cools much more rapidly than oceans and coastal areas adjacent to the sea experience less extreme temperatures.

Alpine areas above the snowline also have cold climates, but this is due to temperatures falling with altitude. However, despite experiencing seasonality, these locations do not have the continuous periods of daylight and night of polar regions. Albedo in these locations is important in reflecting away large amounts of solar radiation. At high altitudes the thinner atmosphere absorbs less heat and helps keep temperatures low. Alpine areas receive more precipitation than polar areas as they often lie in the path of depressions in the temperate zones of the world so there are regular new snowfalls. The direction in which a slope of a mountain faces is known as its aspect and in the northern hemisphere, northern-facing slopes have a lower snowline and are generally colder than slopes with a southerly aspect, which receive more insolation.

Below the snowline in mountain areas, there are the alpine versions of tundra, but they are often without permafrost. On the slopes of mountains, zones can be seen vertically that occur horizontally from the poles towards the Equator with the treeline on a mountain corresponding to the beginning of the boreal (northern coniferous) forests in the northern hemisphere, south of the tundra.

Periglacial areas lie on the edge of the polar zones, but albedo is less important as they are not snow-covered all year round. Coupled with the areas receiving more insolation, this means a short summer when plant growth can take place. Large areas of Siberia and Canada are far away from oceans; therefore continentality is an important factor in keeping temperatures low.

Looking briefly at two examples – one in Canada and one in Norway – we can see how climate in northern regions can be affected by more than just latitude.

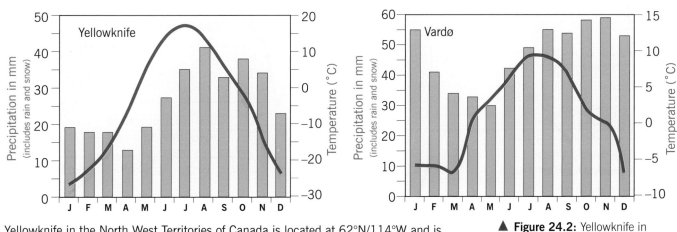

▲ **Figure 24.2:** Yellowknife in Canada and Vardø in Norway.

Yellowknife in the North West Territories of Canada is located at 62°N/114°W and is about 400 km south of the Arctic Circle. The average temperature in January is –27°C and in July it is 17°C. It receives 313 mm of precipitation annually. Vardø in northern Norway is located at 70°N/31°E and is about 400 km north of the Arctic Circle. Here the average temperature in January is –4°C and in July it is 9°C. Even though Vardø is much further north than Yellowknife, it does not become as cold, nor does it have such a large temperature range. Looking at an atlas, we can see that Yellowknife is located far away from any ocean and its modifying influence, so the temperatures are much harsher in winter and rise more in the summer months. In contrast, Vardø is located on the northern coast of Norway, adjacent to the Arctic Ocean. This modifies its climate, meaning it is less cold in winter, but also less warm in summer. This comparison illustrates the impact of continentality on cold climates.

Changing climate — why cold environments move

For much of the earth's existence, the climate has been warmer than it is now. Yet it only takes a 5°C drop in the global average temperature for an ice age to begin. The formation of the ice caps was linked to the changing position of the continents as they slowly moved across the surface of the earth according to the theory of plate tectonics.

Initially the oceans were able to transfer heat from the Equator to the higher latitudes. However, as land drifted into polar regions, some of this transfer was blocked and a larger temperature differential evolved between the two regions and ice caps began to form. It is thought that Antarctica has been covered by an ice cap for the last 38 million years, but the Arctic ice cap is more recent, about 2.5 million years old. It was created when the Isthmus of Panama joined North and South America together. This cut off the supply of warm water through the gap and reduced the amount of tropical water flowing northwards, allowing the Arctic to freeze over.

Milankovitch's Theory

You will remember Milankovitch's theory from your AS course, linking the changing movement of the earth in space to long-term climate changes. Milankovitch proposed that the glacial and interglacial periods were tied to changes in the amount of solar radiation that the earth received. These variations were linked to the sum of all the changes in orbit that the earth undergoes.

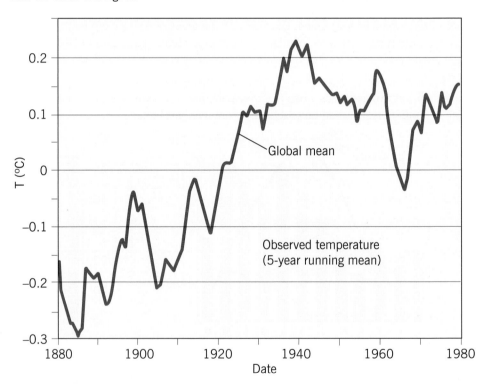

Other factors that affect long-term climate change include sunspot activity on the sun, which impacts on the amount of solar radiation emitted. Also, major volcanic eruptions can lead to more dust in the atmosphere allowing more solar radiation to be reflected, cooling the climate.

Examiners' tip

When carrying out research, especially on the world wide web, beware of bias. If the site is from a scientific site such as NOAA (National Oceanic and Atmospheric Administration), for example, it is a USA government-funded organisation and provides useful and reliable data. Take care when a site is run by an individual or an unknown organisation and try to find out some background before using its data.

Taking it further

Look at your Student CD-ROM, to see links to websites about climates and climate change.

Key term

Plate tectonics — the theory that the earth's lithosphere is divided into a number of major plates, which slowly move due to convection currents deep within the earth.

▶ **Figure 24.3:** Graph of global temperature changes over time.

Taking it further

To look at the impacts of climate change in Greenland read 'Land of ice goes green' on your Student CD-ROM.

Synoptic link

Look at Chapter 4 of Unit 1 Edexcel AS Geography.

How we know about the past

The table below summarises the sources of evidence available for past climates.

SOURCE	UTILISATION
Diaries, letters, stories and weather records. (Last 1500 years) Short- to medium-term changes.	Description of recent past climates.
Tree rings (dendrochronology) Medium-term changes.	Width of rings tells us whether climate was favourable for growth or not. Some preserved in peat bogs, 1000s of years old.
Radio carbon dating of wood. Medium-term changes.	Used for dating of tree remains.
Pollen analysis. Medium- to long-term changes.	Pollen grains preserved in peat analysed to show plants that were growing in area 1000s of years ago.
Sea-bed sediments. Long-term changes.	Cores taken to look for evidence of climate change.
Ice cores. Long-term changes.	Taken on Greenland and Antarctica. The atmospheres of past climates are preserved within the ice.

Future changes

▲ **Figure 24.4:** Climate data for three contrasting cold environments.

Scientists think we are in an interglacial, but what of the future? Levels of carbon dioxide are rising due, it is thought, to human industrial activity. This is leading to many changes:

- The breaking off and melting of Antarctic ice shelves, such as the Larsen B in 2002.
- Reduction of sea ice in the Arctic.
- Permafrost is decreasing in parts of Siberia and Canada, which is having an impact on natural ecosystems and human activity. As it thaws there is less ice and snow and so reduced albedo. This leads to more of the solar energy being absorbed, adding to the thawing.
- There is some evidence that the Gulf Stream/North Atlantic Drift is weakening (and it is the Gulf Stream that keeps western Europe warmer than it would otherwise be.) As the Arctic sea ice and ice from the Greenland ice sheet are melting, greater quantities of cold freshwater are entering the ocean. It is thought that the direction and strength of the Gulf Stream may change very suddenly.
- If a super-volcano, such as the one beneath Yellowstone National Park, were to erupt, the huge amounts of dust sent into the atmosphere would lead to a rapid cooling over much of the northern hemisphere for a period of up to five years.

Of course, instead of global warming, the natural 100,000 year glacial/interglacial cycle may dominate. If we are in an interglacial then we may be faced with another glacial period within the next 5,000–10,000 years. If this is the case, the human race would need to be ready to cope with the likely migration of millions of people away from the cold areas.

How fast can it change?

All over the world there is evidence of the retreat of glaciers and the melting of ice shelves. Using the website www.worldviewofglobalwarming.org, you can investigate the locations of many of these retreats in the 'Glaciers and Global Warming' section. One of the most famous glaciers that has suffered a massive retreat is the Rhône Glacier in the Swiss Alps. There are also many others in the Rockies of North America and in Greenland. Another problem is the thawing of the permafrost and some of the impacts are highlighted on this site. Other sections within the site will enable you to investigate the impact that these changes have on ecosystems, such as the problems faced by polar bears and the reduction of sea ice, from which they need to be able to hunt seals.

Synoptic link

Look at Chapters 4 and 5 of Unit 1 Edexcel AS Geography.

Taking it further

Use your Student CD-ROM and the website www.worldviewofglobalwarming.org to think about a rapid change in the climate of northern Europe and North America, investigating some of the possible outcomes for both the natural and human environments.

Weather processes in cold climates

We have looked at where cold climates exist and why, but local weather processes can lead to very different types of cold climate.

1. Vostok, Antarctica. 78°5'S / 106°9'E (Data BAS)

Month	J	F	M	A	M	J	J	A	S	O	N	D
Temp. °C	−32	−44	−58	−65	−66	−65	−67	−68	−66	−57	−43	−32
ppt mm	0.1	0	0.7	0.5	0.4	0.5	0.6	0.7	0.3	0.2	0.1	0

2. Verkhoyansk, Russia. 67°34'N / 133°51'E (Data Verkhoyansk page)

Month	J	F	M	A	M	J	J	A	S	O	N	D
Temp. °C	−51	−45	−32	−15	0	12	14	9	2	−13	−38	−47
ppt mm	5	5	3	5	8	23	28	25	13	8	8	5

3. Mount Pilatus, Switzerland. 46°59'N / 8°16'E – Altitude 2129 m (Data Swiss weather pages)

Month	J	F	M	A	M	J	J	A	S	O	N	D
Temp. °C	−4.9	−5	−4	−1.6	−2.5	5.7	8.2	7.8	5.7	1.9	−1.6	−3.5
ppt mm	125	110	130	170	169	219	218	200	155	121	105	115

Taking it further

Wind chill is how cold air actually feels to humans, based on air temperature and wind speed. Research the impact of wind chill in cold environments at www.bbc.co.uk/weather/.

▶ **Figure 24.5:** Examples of cold climates.
Source: British Antarctic Schools Pack 1999

▶ **Figures 24.6 and 24.7:** Showing the differences between cold landscapes.

Taking it further

To explore a case study of the meres of Shropshire – formed under periglacial conditions – read 'The meres of Shropshire' on your Student CD-ROM.

Key term

Kettle holes — depressions left by the melting of blocks of ice in deposits.

In Antarctica high latitude and altitude, plus albedo, keep temperatures low. The air is very dry and cold. There is negligible precipitation, often just a dusting of snow – Antarctica is really just a cold desert. The cold descending air can build up and flow outwards over the Antarctic Plateau at speeds of 18 km/h. However, when there are steeper slopes these winds, flowing down-slope, can reach speeds of 70 km/h and are known as katabatic winds. Outward-flowing winds mean that rain-bearing winds within depressions cannot flow in. Relief rain is experienced only on the Antarctic coasts. In places like Vostok, which are well away from the oceans and experience high wind speeds, extremely cold temperatures have been recorded such as −88°C in 1960. These cold temperatures allow very little evaporation or melting. Most precipitation over the Antarctic centre is in the form of 'diamond dust', ice crystals falling from a clear sky as the very limited moisture in the atmosphere is instantly frozen.

At Verkhoyansk in north-eastern Siberia, the lowest temperature outside the two polar regions has been recorded, a very chilly −68°C. For most of the year there is hardly any precipitation, but what falls, falls as snow. In June, July and August there is convectional rainfall, caused by the comparatively rapid heating of the land during Verkhoyansk's brief summer. During this time plants grow rapidly, but the precipitation levels are generally too low to support trees. Pools of water resting on the permafrost are ideal breeding grounds for biting insects such as mosquitoes and millions of insects hatch and fly, causing great discomfort to humans and animals.

The atmosphere in mountain regions, such as Mount Pilatus, Switzerland, has fewer dust particles and is thinner, so less heat is absorbed. Other factors also come into play, such as aspect. A location in the European Alps will enjoy higher temperatures if it is situated on south-facing slopes as it is able to receive more insolation than slopes with a northern aspect. For many mountain areas, the albedo will vary seasonally as snow melt will expose rock surfaces, which will heat up more quickly and absorb heat. This can lead to local temperature inversions, with warmer air being experienced higher up the mountain and colder air in the valley. This occurs when the air on the mountainside cools during the night and sinks into the valley, displacing warm air upwards, so a reversal of the normal situation is felt when moving from the valley upwards; therefore it becomes warmer with increasing altitude. Many alpine regions are at lower latitudes and therefore come under the influence of temperate depressions which, due to the high relief, bring more precipitation. Much of this will fall as snow, except during late spring and in summer months. Blizzards are common and snow depth can vary dramatically.

Changing cold environments of Britain

The dramatic scenery of northern and western Britain is closely linked to the periods of glaciation that we have already mentioned, but there is also evidence on much of lowland Britain of glacial retreat and former areas of periglaciation. There are areas of lowland in the Midlands and in the east of Great Britain covered with glacial deposits left by retreating ice sheets. Today areas which do not experience cold climates show the evidence of having been created by the action of ice. There are currently no glaciers in Britain and periglacial climates (alpine) are found only at areas of high altitude, especially in the Scottish Highlands.

▲ **Figure 24.8:** The attractive meres of the Shropshire Lake District which are relict kettle holes.

Taking it further

Find some information and good photos of knock and lochan landscapes at www.fettes.com/shetland/Knock%20and%20lochan.htm.

Taking it further

Visit your Student CD-ROM and read the case study 'The Cairngorms, north-eastern Scotland'.

Case study: Sutherland, Scotland – knock and lochan scenery

This case study shows the impact of glacial erosion in a lowland area.

Although lowland glaciated areas are usually associated with depositional landforms, there is evidence of erosion although often masked by later deposits. Near Lake Assynt in Sutherland, the Devensian ice sheet spread westwards over the lowlands and eroded material from its surface until only bare rock remained. When the ice sheet retreated it left a landscape of hills or knolls (knock) and small lakes (lochan). The lochan formed where the bedrock was less resistant or was more heavily jointed and, more susceptible to erosion by the ice, whereas the knocks are underlain by more resistant bedrock. In the present, this wild landscape is an important breeding area for wild birds but the thin soils on impermeable rock mean that very limited agriculture can take place here.

Taking it further

Look at your Student CD-ROM to explore the impact of a valley glacier within a highland area.

Summary

In this chapter you have learnt:
- about the link between levels of insolation and the location of cold environments.
- that the incidence of cold environments is also linked to very long cycles of the earth's orbit.
- that local weather systems will impact on cold climates.
- that Britain has evidence of very cold climates in the past and that some associated processes still continue in regions of high altitude.

MCQ

Taking it further

A useful site from NASA containing facts and figures and also a range of case study material on present day glaciated landscapes: disc8.sci.gsfc.nasa.gov/geomorphology/GEO_9.

CHAPTER 25 How do geomorphological processes produce distinctive landforms and landscapes in cold environments?

Key terms

Arête
Basal sliding
Corrie/cwm/cirque
Crevasses
Drumlin
Esker
Freeze-thaw
Glacial trough
Internal flow
Kame
Loess
Moraine
Nunataks
Pingo
Pyramidal peak
Roche moutonnée
Stone polygon
Stone stripe
Striations
Till
Truncated spurs
Uniformitarianism

Key terms

Basal sliding — the friction at the base of a glacier and pressure from the weight of ice above results in some melting, which lubricates the flow over the bed of the glacier.

Internal flow — that over time the ice crystals within an ice sheet align themselves parallel to the direction of flow due to pressure. This makes it easier for the crystals to move and slide past one another.

Nunataks — exposed peaks above an ice sheet.

Learning objectives

After studying this chapter, you will be able to discuss these ideas and concepts and provide located examples of them:

• The processes operating in glacial and periglacial environments.
• The landforms associated with glaciers, ice sheets and the areas adjacent to them.
• Relict landforms can tell us about past processes.

Geomorphological processes in glacial environments

The action of ice during the advance and retreat of glaciers and ice sheets is an important agent in creating landscapes through erosion, transportation and deposition. Glaciers move mainly by basal sliding and internal flow. The former is more prevalent in alpine glaciers because summer melting increases the availability of water as a lubricant, whereas the latter is more common in ice sheets as very little melting occurs, if any. In valley glaciers the differential movement of ice near the surface results in deep, vertical cracks called crevasses.

As glaciers move, landforms are created through erosion. Abrasion occurs during the glacier's movement across the landscape as sediment and rocks become embedded in the base of the glacier. As this material is dragged across rock surfaces, deep scratches called striations are caused, which can be seen thousands of years after they were formed. Plucking or rock quarrying occurs when the ice freezes in cracks and around small rocks. As the glacier moves, the material is dragged away inside it. Sub-aerial processes such as freeze-thaw operate on valley sides above the glacier or on nunataks. The shattered tors of the Stiperstones Ridge in Shropshire were once nunataks above an ice sheet.

As the glacier moves, the material it erodes is transported on (supraglacial), in (englacial) and under (sub-glacial) the glacier. When a glacier retreats/downwastes, this material is deposited and forms mounds of mixed angular rocks and clay called moraines. Sometimes huge boulders (called erratics) are entrained within the glacier and when retreat occurs they are left behind, often many kilometres from where they originated and on rock types that are completely different from their own origin.

▶ **Figure 25.1:** Cwm Idwal, Snowdonia – a good example of a corrie (cwm or cirque) showing the steep back wall and tarn (lake) in the foreground.

Melted water can surge out from beneath the glacier carrying large loads of sediment which, because they have undergone the processes of abrasion and attrition, are more rounded than true glacial deposits. As these streams lose energy, sediments are deposited with the heaviest particles being dropped first, thus sorting the load.

Taking it further

Find out more about glacial movement such as surges, compressing flow and rotational flow.

Case study: Cwm Idwal, Snowdonia

This case study illustrates the present situation of a relict landform left by the last glaciation. A cirque glacier (called a cwm in Wales and a corrie in Scotland) formed the cup shape of Cwm Idwal, with frost shattering above the glacier creating the steep back wall (the headwall). The aspect of the cirque is north-east, so the location is heavily shaded. During the last glaciation, this enabled snow to gather and gradually turn to ice in a hollow on the slopes of the mountain. Although the glacier is long gone, a lake (called a tarn) remains where the glacier once was. Mounds near the front of the lake are old glacial moraines and these held back meltwater to form the lake as the glacier retreated. Due to its aspect, Cwm Idwal still provides habitat for rare Arctic alpine plants, such as the Snowdon Lily, as temperatures are low. Today, Cwm Idwal is a National Nature Reserve and tourists come to view this reminder of an ice age.

Taking it further

To find out more about Snowdonia, access the following national park website and then go into Learning About and choose Geology: www.eryri-npa.co.uk.

Glacial landforms: upland areas

Glacial troughs are the steep-sided and flat-floored valleys that have been eroded by the action of valley glaciers, such as Yosemite Valley. They usually follow the route originally made by a river and in doing this they cut away the interlocking spurs of a river valley, leaving steep truncated spurs instead. As the glacier moves down the valley, the valley floor is eroded and over-deepened. Tributary valleys, even if glaciated themselves, cannot erode down to the level of the main valley. When the glaciers retreat, the exit of the tributary is above the level of the main valley and hanging valleys are formed, usually with waterfalls marking the point, such as Bridalveil Falls in Yosemite.

When ice collects in a large depression and builds up, frost shattering of the sides and abrasion of the floor due to rotational flow gradually deepen the hollow, forming corries. (See the case study: Cwm Idwal.) Eventually the ice can flow over the lip of the corrie and begin or contribute to a valley glacier. If two corries erode back towards one another, a narrow ridge can develop called an arête. If three or more corries cut back, then a distinctive pyramidal peak is formed such as the Matterhorn in Switzerland.

More resistant rock in the path of the glacier is smoothed and polished on the upstream side by the ice, but downstream there is frost shattering and plucking away of material, giving rise to a hummocky shaped landform, reminiscent of a sheep; hence its name, roche moutonnée or sheep rock.

▲ **Figure 25.2:** Yosemite Valley, showing the steep sides of a glacial trough caused by the erosive power of a valley glacier.

Glacial landforms: lowland areas

Drumlins are landforms created under ice and occur when there is so much material being carried that it is deposited and then shaped by the moving ice. They are egg-shaped mounds of eroded glacial material called till and have their steeper, blunter (stoss) end facing upstream. There are usually several together in a landscape and give rise to the term 'basket of eggs' topography or a swarm of drumlins. Relict drumlins can be found in the Ribble Valley as well as the Vale of Eden in Cumbria in the UK.

Examiners' tip

As you research the formation of landforms, make sure you can draw clear annotated diagrams to show your understanding of the landform itself and the processes that made it.

Key terms

Till — the material deposited by a glacier or ice sheet made up of clay, mud, gravel and unsorted boulders. Solifluction — the downward movement of saturated soil.

Moraines are mounds of unsorted debris left by retreating ice. They are a mix of till and boulders and can mark the furthest extent of a glacier. Another landform left by retreating ice is the kettle hole, which was referred to in the case study of the meres of Shropshire on your Student CD-ROM.

Landforms created by fluvioglacial processes include eskers, which are ridges of sorted material formed beneath a glacier and show the course of a sub-glacial stream. The sediments deposited began as angular debris as they were eroded by the glacier but are more rounded after they have undergone abrasion and attrition within the streams. When the streams have a high discharge, then the sediment load is high and much is washed out onto the outwash plain and deposited there. At times of low discharge, however, the tunnels cut by the sub-glacial streams fill with sediment. An example is the Dorrington esker near Lyth Hill in Shropshire. Kames, also formed through fluvioglacial processes, are mounds formed when material transported by meltwater is washed into crevasses or hollows in the glacier ice. Mainly comprising sands and gravels, they are sorted by the meltwater with the heavier gravels being deposited first and are often associated with the gradual break-up of the ice as a glacier retreats.

Geomorphological processes in periglacial environments

Processes operating around the edges of glaciers and ice sheets and also in very cold environments fall under the heading of periglacial. Permafrost typifies these areas, but is not always continuous across a region as local factors such as the microclimate and the presence of large rivers come into play.

Even in areas of permanent permafrost the upper few centimetres (known as the active layer) thaw in the brief summer. This means there is water available to plants, but the frozen ground below the active layer acts as an impermeable barrier and the ground becomes very boggy.

The action of freeze-thaw is very important in periglacial areas on bare rock surfaces, such as valley sides or on peaks above the ice sheet. Frost shattering is most noticeable in well-jointed rocks, including granite in certain circumstances. The gritstone tors of Derbyshire are the result of frost shattering, and weathering processes continue today. Below areas of frost shattering, rock debris gathers, forming scree slopes. The larger rocks are the furthest away from the base of the rock wall as they are the heaviest and therefore have the most momentum. Finer material settles nearer the rock face.

Solifluction is a very slow mass movement of particles of soil down-slope due to saturation and the impact of gravity. Although it does occur in other situations, it is most closely associated with periglacial areas. Two processes are involved – frost heave and gelifluction. Frost heave occurs when water in the ground freezes producing ice crystals, which then exert an upward pressure. This process causes soil particles to be lifted and moved down-slope under gravity. Gelifluction occurs when the upper layers of the permafrost (the active layer) thaw and there is an added down-slope movement. The combined movement produces solifluction and often takes the form of a tongue-like feature called a solifluction lobe.

Ice wedging occurs when water melts and flows into cracks in the soil opened up by freezing during periods of thaw. As evaporation rates are very low in periglacial areas, the water remains and freezes there during the next winter. This enlarges the crack further and more water will be taken in. Over many years a distinct ice wedge will form. This can be preserved in deposits as the gap is filled in with sediments when it finally thaws and this wedge of sediments cuts across layers in the surrounding material, giving humans clues as to what the landscape had been like in the past.

During winter, patches of snow in some places, such as those with a more northerly aspect, take longer to thaw. Beneath them freeze-thaw processes are occurring, weathering the rock, a process known as nivation. When the snow does thaw, the material is washed away, leaving a small hollow (nivation hollow) such as seen in the chalk valleys of Wiltshire. This process is repeated and the hollow grows; in some cases this is to such an extent that the snow does not thaw but remains and the beginning of a corrie is possible if this has occurred in an upland area.

Many periglacial areas are relatively flat and as there is little vegetation winds can have an impact on smaller sediments, removing them and leaving larger sediments behind. The sediment carried within the wind can help abrade surfaces within the periglacial environment. If there are large amounts of fine, wind-blown material (loess) that has come from periglacial areas it can often form deposits of fertile soil. The fertile soils of East Anglia are loess.

Periglacial landforms

We have already mentioned forms such as tors (Stiperstones, Shropshire), ice wedges and scree slopes. Other landforms associated with periglacial landscapes are pingos (see case study) and patterned ground.

PERIGLACIAL LANDFORM	PROCESSES
Tors (and nunataks)	Freeze-thaw processes in periglacial areas but can also be above an ice sheet.
Ice wedges	Contraction of soil as ground freezes, cracks open up. In warmer months water flows into cracks and then re-freezes, expanding and widening the crack.
Scree slopes	Freeze-thaw weathering of rocks in upland areas. Broken pieces fall away to collect at base of rock face.
Pingo	Interaction of lakes and surrounding permafrost.
Solifluction lobe	As a result of frost heave and gelifluction.
Patterned ground – stone polygons and stripes	Stripes form on gentle gradients, polygons on flat ground. Stones sorted by frost heave.
Permafrost	Very low temperatures for most of the year mean that lower levels of ground are frozen all year. Upper layer may thaw in summer.

◀ **Figure 25.3:** Table of periglacial landforms and associated processes.

▶ **Figure 25.4:** The characteristic shape of pingos, periglacial landforms, in the Mackenzie delta.

Case study: Mackenzie River delta, Canada

The Mackenzie River flows north to the Beaufort Sea, part of the Arctic Ocean, and is Canada's longest river. Most of the delta is a zone of discontinuous permafrost because the water acts as an insulator where the river channels flow. Away from the river channels, the permafrost can be up to 100 m deep. This area has the highest number of pingos in the world, almost 1,500 and of the closed system type. They take the form of almost circular hills and can be 50–70 m high and up to 300 m in diameter. At the heart of each hill there is a core of ice, which has formed as the permafrost has spread into an area of lakes. The water in the ground underneath the lake becomes trapped and freezes, eventually forcing the overlying sediments upwards to form circular hills. The pingos will gradually start to decay and collapse as the ice melts due to climate change or because the material covering the ice core cracks and the ice heart is breached and exposed.

Relict pingos can be seen in the UK at Thompson Common in Norfolk. By looking at present-day glaciated areas we can surmise what Norfolk would have been like at the time the relict pingos were formed. This idea of 'the present being the key to the past' is known as uniformitarianism.

Taking it further

Use the Open University Geological Society site below to find out more about pingos: ougseurope.org/rockon/surface/pingos.asp.

Patterned ground is a general term that covers stone stripes, polygons and circles that are associated with periglacial environments. Good examples can be seen on the slopes of the Stiperstones ridge in Shropshire, where the repeated freezing and thawing of the area after the retreat of the ice sheet caused polygonal patterns. As ice caused the upward lift of material, stones rolled to the edge and finer deposits were left at the centre. On steeper slopes stripes are formed rather than polygons. These processes can be seen in periglacial areas today, but are also useful evidence of former periglacial areas, such as East Anglia, where the patterns can be seen as crop marks. The climate of present-day East Anglia is far too warm for these features to have formed in recent times.

Another feature of formerly periglacial areas are dry valleys, such as found on the South Downs in Sussex. Although the chalk of which the Downs are largely formed is permeable, this area experienced periglacial conditions during the last glaciation. Permafrost formed, and this made the bedrock impermeable and rivers flowed over the land eroding river valleys. When the climate warmed, water could once again percolate underground and the valleys through the hills were left empty of rivers. These features are known as dry valleys and a well-known example is the Devil's Dyke near Brighton.

Summary

In this chapter you have learnt:
- how both erosional and sub-aerial processes operate in a glacial environment.
- that certain landforms are created in upland glaciated areas.
- that different landforms are created in areas of lowland glaciation.
- how processes operate in periglacial areas, including the impact of permafrost.
- that a range of landforms is created by periglacial processes and that evidence can be seen of active and relict landforms.

MCQ

CHAPTER 26 How are challenges and opportunities managed in cold environments?

Learning objectives

After studying this chapter, you will be able to discuss these ideas and concepts and provide located examples of them:

- The challenges and opportunities that cold environments present.
- That challenges and opportunities change over time.
- That changing demands and technology can lead to overcoming of challenges presented by cold environments.
- That different management approaches can lead to greater or lesser conflict.

Key terms

Challenge
Environmental Impact
  Assessment (EIA)
Opportunity
Thermokarst
Utilidor

Challenges and opportunities

Cold environments have presented challenges to humans throughout history. A challenge is created by the landscape and/or climate conditions that require a response; whereas an opportunity can be viewed as the human interpretation as to what the challenge has to offer. Past glaciations presented the challenge of extreme climate conditions, perhaps altering within quite a short timescale, and humans had to adapt or die. Today cold environments continue to throw up challenges and opportunities.

In alpine countries such as Switzerland, the challenge of the past was how to develop productive agriculture within a mountainous area with very cold winters. Steep slopes, cold temperatures and thin soils meant specialist agricultural systems developed. Difficult access also prevented full development until the 20th century.

Polar environments offer challenges to scientists in terms of access, viable transport, keeping equipment functioning at sub-zero temperatures and surviving some of the harshest conditions on earth. This is particularly true of the continent of Antarctica, which is uninhabited except for scientists. However, it offers opportunities for the study of unique land- and marine-based ecosystems and the chance to study past climates through sampling ice cores. In northern polar zones around the Arctic, there are indigenous peoples such as the Inuit of North America, who over the last thousand or so years have met the challenges of the extreme north and taken the opportunity to develop a sustainable lifestyle based on the Arctic ecosystem. New opportunities are now emerging for these people, as well as new challenges.

Challenges and opportunities in cold environments

The challenge offered by cold climates has only really been widely met during the late 20th century with the development of high-performance cold weather clothing. Before that, apart from a few hardy scientists and explorers, it was only the indigenous peoples of the north who had developed from the animals they hunted the clothing that could protect them from sub-zero temperatures. The wind chill factor and the problem of frostbite meant that accessing areas such as Antarctica was very limited until the latter half of the 20th century. Better cold weather gear also saw an increase in the number of people going skiing at higher altitudes.

Challenges in high altitude environments	Opportunities in high altitude environments
• Extreme climate. Sub-zero temperatures for much of the year. • Limited precipitation in high latitude areas. • Problems of access infrastructure in periglacial areas. • Permafrost in periglacial areas. • Low productivity. • Fragile ecosystem easily disturbed. • High relief in alpine zones and problems of access. • Harsh, cold climate for much of the year. • Thin soils in alpine areas. • Problems of avalanches in alpine areas having greater impact as people move into higher altitudes for winter sports recreation. • Low productivity because of thin soils, steep slopes and cool climate. • Fragile ecosystem easily disturbed. • Pressure from visitor numbers for sightseeing/walking.	• Large mineral deposits in several areas at high latitude. Oil, gas and diamonds. • The use of animals as resource: meat, skins/fur. • Accessing wilderness areas for recreation in areas of high latitude. • Wildlife watching particularly in areas of high latitude. • Opportunities for research into past climates. • Recreational development: skiing, trekking, mountaineering in alpine areas. • Use of HEP in alpine areas.

▲ Figure 26.1: Challenges and opportunities in cold environments.

Access to regions at high latitude was limited until the 20th century because for much of the year sea ice restricted access by ship. The cold climate and lack of precipitation meant that indigenous communities relied on animal and fish resources rather than agriculture in order to survive, a challenge to keep families fed. Sustainably using the resources of the polar regions can be a problem as the balance of the natural systems is easily disturbed. Increasing human population will inevitably place more pressures on the environment in terms of resource extraction, housing and waste disposal. Permafrost is a problem for permanent settlement as the active layer within it means it is difficult to maintain stable infrastructure. Heat from houses built in permafrost areas can melt the upper layers of the ground, depressions are formed and the building can collapse. Although this can occur naturally, permanent buildings accelerate this process. The resultant hummocky ground is known as thermokarst.

However, there are many opportunities within the polar regions. In the past these were mainly the extraction of natural resources such as seal skins and fur. Today the high latitude areas have important reserves of gas and oil and other minerals, not all of which have yet been exploited. The wilderness areas within the polar regions are now attractive as tourist destinations, especially for seeing wildlife such as polar bears in Churchill (Manitoba, Canada). The spectacular coastlines of locations such as Alaska and Antarctica with their calving icebergs are also a great attraction. The pristine continent of Antarctica offers humans the chance to investigate past climates via the analysis of ice cores and so help us understand our present situation.

Although high altitude areas offer many of the same challenges as polar regions there are some that are particular to these regions such as the problem of avalanches. These have always occurred in high mountain areas but the risks of death or injury are increasing because more people are choosing to live or to spend time in the mountains. Many high altitude areas (such as the European Alps) are within easy reach of very large populations and the demand for skiing and other winter sports, as well as for walking in the mountains, is creating challenges for management in terms of access, providing accommodation and also dealing with problems of path erosion. Yet these challenges are also opportunities for developing tourism in areas that 100 years ago would have had limited visitor numbers and whose economy would have been largely dependent on small-scale alpine farms.

A more recent development of an isolated alpine area for leisure and tourism is Queenstown in New Zealand where, since the late 1950s, winter sports and outdoor activities such as bungy jumping and paragliding have led to it being known as the 'Adventure Capital of the World'. Another opportunity in alpine areas is hydro-electric power (HEP). Glaciated valleys in upland regions with steep sides and a base of impermeable rock plus a high rainfall offer ideal locations for HEP dams.

It would seem that each challenge opens up new opportunities which can in turn lead to different challenges.

Case study: The Mackenzie River and delta

This case study looks at the challenges and opportunities presented by this area and how they have changed over time.

The Mackenzie River and delta is a largely untouched area. Until now, its huge expanse and the problems of permafrost have limited its development, except for sustainable use by indigenous people such as the Dene. The area has oil and gas reserves, which are now offering opportunities to the prospecting companies, but also to the indigenous peoples who are now fully involved in decisions as to their utilisation. The proposed 1,220 km Mackenzie Valley gas pipeline is controversial due to its impacts on this landscape. As other pipelines are likely to follow to form an energy corridor, it is important that the impacts are recognised and minimised in order for it to be sustainable. Several Environmental Impact Assessments have been carried out to assess the likely damage and what can be done to mitigate it. The idea is to protect the environment before the construction takes place.

◀ **Figure 26.2:** Utility pipelines (gas, water and sewage) run above ground in covered boxes called utilidors.

Overcoming challenges

Human beings are an adaptable species and we have managed to live in extreme conditions when it has been to our benefit to do so. New challenges mean that we must take great care of the cold yet fragile regions that we are making increasing use of in order for them to survive for future generations.

PROBLEM TO OVERCOME	HOW TECHNOLOGY OVERCOMES CHALLENGES
Keeping warm in extreme temperatures.	Late 20th century saw improvements in cold weather gear that was mass-produced. People could access extremely cold areas. Improved insulation, windproof and yet breathable.
Body detection in avalanches (alpine areas).	Skiers can wear electronic beacons which mean they can be found quickly if buried. Also can wear inflatable rucksack that helps carry them to surface if hit by avalanche.

▲ **Figure 26.3:** Examples of technology meeting the challenges of cold environments.

PROBLEM TO OVERCOME	HOW TECHNOLOGY OVERCOMES CHALLENGES
Protection from avalanches in alpine areas as more people live and play in these areas.	Advancements in avalanche protection. Snow fences, building design, understanding how avalanches move and research into the snowpack so that can assess when there is a danger of an event.
Keeping warm in houses and not melting the permafrost. A need for permanent settlement.	Houses are very well insulated. Often on stilts to keep warmth away from the ground. Utilities built within long, insulated, boxed structures called utilidors.
Accessing very cold seas, e.g. Southern Ocean around Antarctica.	Ice breaker ships which allowed access. Now used for tourism too.
Getting around on snow in areas of high latitude.	Previously only dog sled. Petrol-driven skidoos have made even herding animals much easier. Some areas like northern Canada, roads are created on the ice and trucks can now cope with the conditions.
Difficulty of accessing areas of high altitude.	Tunnelling technology has opened up much of the European Alps.
Difficult communication. Very limited infrastructure. Schooling often intermittent because of isolation and/or moving with the herds.	Use of satellites and IT for communication. Can also be used for schooling.
Knowing where you are.	Satellite Global Positioning Systems.

▲ **Figure 26.3:** continued.

▲ **Figure 26.4:** The Nenets are a nomadic reindeer-herding people whose way of life is under threat from oil and gas extraction on their traditional grazing lands.

▲ **Figure 26.5:** The Trans-Alaskan Pipeline showing where it has been raised to allow for the migrating herds of caribou to pass underneath.

The Nenets of the Yamal Peninsula are one example of how the challenges of a periglacial landscape were overcome to provide a strong, sustainable culture and how the challenges are now changing in the 21st century.

The Yamal Peninsula in north-west Siberia juts out into the Kara Sea and is a periglacial area with permafrost up to 300 m deep. The Nenets are a reindeer-herding people whose understanding of the harsh climate and fragile ecosystem has enabled them to live sustainably in this inhospitable land. The basis of their economy is the reindeer, which provides transport, clothing, skin for tents, meat and income. During the Soviet era, many of the Nenets were encouraged to settle and look after the reindeer in large state farms, which did not take into account their cultural and belief systems linked to the traditional herding. However, some families maintain the old ways, which do not harm the natural ecosystems that support them. The problem of the cold winters is solved by migrating south during the worst of the weather, down into where the forests begin.

Taking it further

Investigate the lives of another nomadic group and see what adaptations they have made to their lives in recent times.

Winter clothing includes wearing the reindeer fur next to the skin, which is a marvellous insulator. During summer, the herds move onto the coastal plain for new grazing, but also to be near the sea to try and control the biting insects that plague the reindeer during warm weather. The Nenets do not remain too long in one area, so that over-grazing of the fragile pastures does not occur.

In the 1980s the huge Bovanenkovo gas field was discovered in the Yamal and pipelines were built across the reindeer migration routes, causing the closure of traditional pasture areas. This led to conflict with the traditional Nenet herders. Reducing pasture led to over-grazing in some areas and settlements for gas workers were built on land that the Nenets had regarded as theirs to use for hundreds of years (although land ownership is not part of their culture). A lack of impact assessments of the gas and oil installations has led to a degradation of some environments.

At present there is further consultation with the Nenets about the growth of the oil and gas industries and some of their young people are being tempted to work within the industries, thus losing their links with the traditional culture. There is some trade in reindeer meat with the settlements, and other new markets have been found for the produce. There is a conflict between the traditional, sustainable lifestyle of the Nenets and the extractive oil and gas industries, the latter spurred on by the increasing demand for fossil fuels in Europe and beyond. Conservation bodies wish to create biosphere reserves within the area in order to protect fragile ecosystems from rampant and unregulated development. For the Nenets it will become harder to maintain their lifestyle with the temptation of well-paid jobs in the industry, increasing access such as the new railway and the lure of an easier life. However, without the Nenets, the Yamal ecosystems will have lost their main guardians.

Taking it further

Access the following National Geographic site to see how people adapt to living in the extreme climate of Siberia in order to extract oil and gas:

ngm.nationalgeographic.com/2008/06/siberian-oil/paul-starobin-text.

Case study: Alaska and the Trans-Alaskan Pipeline

This case study illustrates how the challenges of extracting resources were overcome by the application of technology.

The USA's largest oil reserves were discovered in northern Alaska in the late 1960s, but there was the challenge as to how to transport the oil to its market. The Beaufort Sea was frozen for much of the year, so the oil could not be taken out by tanker. Construction of the Trans-Alaskan Pipeline (TAP) began in 1973 and the first oil was pumped through four years later. The pipeline had to cross three mountain ranges with mountains up to 1,460 m high and more than 350 rivers, as well as an area prone to earthquakes. This table highlights the main problems and some of the solutions.

Problems	Solutions
• Ability to access pipeline	• Dalton Highway extended from Fairbanks to Prudhoe
• Extreme temperatures (down to −50°C)	• Oil warmed within pipeline to keep it flowing; also pumping stations used
• Unstable permafrost – problem of the active layer	• Pipeline built above ground – pilings have gravel pads to help resist frost heave
• Earthquake tremors might rupture pipeline	• The pilings supporting the pipeline allow some movement and the route taken is zigzagged to allow some flexibility in the event of an earthquake
• Avalanches and rock slides	• Pipeline placed in insulated boxes through vulnerable areas
• Caribou migration routes blocked	• Pipeline lifted higher than the standard 3 to 6 m to allow passage beneath of migrating herds
• Visual impact of pipeline	• Buried underground in insulated container pipe under some rivers and passes; insulated so warm oil does not thaw ground
• Fragile ecosystem easily damaged by construction and disturbance	• Despite care, some vegetation not fully recovered since disturbance
The future	• The pipeline is already in existence – as long as it is maintained to avoid all oil leaks, it would probably now be more sustainable.
• With the sea ice melting, will it be easier to transport the oil by tanker from Prudhoe?	

▲ **Figure 26.6:** The problems presented by the construction of the Trans-Alaskan Pipeline and how they were solved.

Managing cold environments

As we have already seen there are many people, groups or organisations that feel they have an involvement, a stake, in cold environments – these are known as stakeholders (see Figure 26.7). They are all likely to be affected by decisions made about the management of cold environments but in different ways.

Attitudes of the different stakeholders will vary – possible attitudes are summarised in Figure 26.7.

STAKEHOLDER	ATTITUDES
National government (e.g. Canada)	Will have country's balance of payments to weigh up and may well wish to extract high-demand resources such as oil. But also has responsibility for maintaining wilderness areas and supporting local communities. Conflict of interests. Tends to go for top-down approaches.
Local government (e.g. Iqaluit and Nunavut)	Needs to collect local taxes and so may wish to support new resource extraction but more answerable to local voters. Likely to understand local environments more than national governments. Mix of top-down and bottom-up approaches is likely.
Indigenous people (e.g. Inuit)	Have centuries of inherited understanding of their natural environment. Will wish to conserve but also to have the right to permit resource extraction under their supervision. Move towards sustainable resource extraction.
Other residents and businesses (e.g. local shopkeepers, snowmobile repairers, guides)	Will vary as to why living in the area. If working for extractive company, may support more consumption of landscape. Others may have moved there because of quality of the environment. Businesses may wish for further development to increase their customer base.
Tourism groups (cruise companies accessing Alaska)	Will want good infrastructure to get visitors into the area and likely to support national government strategies to build roads and airstrips but will want the environment maintained as it is the prime attraction for their clients.
Resource extraction companies (e.g. Exxon)	Pressure from shareholders and from national government (via public demand) to extract oil and gas. Legislation should reduce impact but often companies have to be closely supervised so that corners are not cut at the expense of the environment. Production is paramount and technology used to access and transport the resource.
Conservation groups (e.g. the Sierra Club)	The protection of the environment and its dependent species is paramount. May wish to oppose all development. Want to leave the cold environments in their natural state for future generations.

▲ **Figure 26.7:** A summary of stakeholders and their attitudes involved in the management of cold environments.

Taking it further

The Arctic (see AS work on climate change in the Arctic). Access the following two websites and decide on the differences between managing Antarctica and the present and future management of the Arctic: www.dailymail.co.uk/news/article-464921/Putins-Arctic-invasion-Russia-lays-claim-North-Pole-gas-oil-diamonds.html; www.pbs.org/wgbh/nova/arctic/passage.html.

In the summer of 2007 newspaper reports told of Russia's most recent 'land' grab as a Russian flag was planted on the floor of the Arctic Ocean, claiming that the underwater ridge of land was attached to Russia and was therefore part of the country. The area claimed is almost five times the size of Britain and contains huge reserves of oil and gas plus precious metals. As the Arctic ice melts and there is easier access to the reserves there will be arguments over to whom they belong. Denmark, the USA and Canada have already put in competing claims for the Arctic sea-bed although the area around the North Pole is assumed at present not to belong to any country and is administered by the International Seabed Authority.

Another problem for humans with the disappearing Arctic ice during summer months is who will control the possible opening up of the North West Passage, potentially the fastest route from Europe to Asia, cutting through the Canadian Arctic. Canada has said it will assume control over the Passage as it passes through its territory but this has been contested by the EU and USA. As yet, only very well-built ice breakers have managed to negotiate the Passage and at a very slow speed. The North East Passage is one that follows the Russian coastline and is already open for a few weeks a year with ships transporting goods to Asia and saving thousands of kilometres of travel.

Global warming is reducing permafrost beyond the Arctic Circle and, because most settlement in the High Arctic is coastal, it makes the sediments more susceptible to marine erosion. Another problem is the collapse of buildings and infrastructure as the permafrost melts. Other impacts on the lives of the people in this area include reduced hunting as there is not the thick ice for much of the year that they require to hunt seals and walrus from. The seals use ice floes on which to 'park' their pups whilst the adults go hunting but this ice is now much farther north and away from the animals' food source. This is leading to stress on the species. Polar bears also require sea ice from which to hunt seals. With this greatly reduced they are having to swim great distances looking for suitable ice floes and using up energy that is needed to see them through the bitterly cold Arctic winter. In Chapter 25 you have already seen the impacts of global warming on Greenland where much is positive for the people there but the challenge of global warming needs cooperative efforts from all those affected. One such organisation is the Circumpolar Conference which involves all indigenous people living around the Arctic in Canada, Greenland, Alaska and Russia. The biggest challenge for the peoples of the High North is to put aside territorial claims and look at what is best for their lives and the ecosystems upon which they depend as they face the impacts of global warming.

Summary

In this chapter you have learnt:
- how a challenge is different from an opportunity.
- that humans have managed to rise to the challenges and have used their understanding of the environment and/or technology to access the opportunities.
- that there are different management approaches, but that a sustainable approach is best for the economy, society and the environment.

MCQ

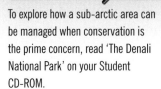

Taking it further

To explore how a sub-arctic area can be managed when conservation is the prime concern, read 'The Denali National Park' on your Student CD-ROM.

Taking it further

Find out how the authorities are managing this park for wildlife and for human recreation at: www.nps.gov/dena/.

Taking it further

The Arctic Wildlife National Refuge (ANWR) is also in Alaska and is coming under threat of development for oil extraction. Access the following two websites and weigh up the arguments for and against this development:
arctic.fws.gov/ – the website of the Fishing and Wildlife Service;
www.anwr.org – another viewpoint.

Taking it further

Access the website and find out what protection the Antarctic Treaty offered to Antarctica: www.antarctica.ac.uk. Visit your Student CD-ROM to read a case study on Antarctica.

Taking it further

Nunavut is a self-governing territory within the North West Territories of Canada. Use the website below to find out how and why the Inuit wanted this and what differences it has made in their lives:
www.gov.nu.ca/Nunavut/English/about.

CHAPTER 27 What are the characteristics of food supply and security?

Key terms

Famine
Food and Agriculture
  Organisation (FAO)
Food Availability Deficit (FAD)
Food insecurity
Food miles
Food security
Food supply
Globalisation
Hunger
Life expectancy
Margins
Nutrition transition
Obesity
Over-nutrition
Undernourished
Under-nutrition
Underweight

Learning objectives

After studying this chapter, you will be able to discuss these ideas and concepts and provide located examples of them:

- There are issues associated with food supply and food security. These include food miles, famine, globalisation of food tastes and under- and over-nutrition.
- Environmental issues result from food production due to inappropriate farming techniques.
- Food supply and food security vary spatially, with current patterns varying at different scales in rural and urban environments.
- Life on the margins means different things to different people and the role of food security affects the overall quality of life. This can include traditionally perceived areas of famine and the megacities in which poverty has an impact on quality and quantity of food supply.

Globally, 25,000 people perish every day due to hunger, which can be defined as a severe shortage of food. Our nutritional requirements vary with age, but can be summarised as being vital for the:

- adequate nourishment of pregnant mothers and their unborn child/children
- physical and mental development of children as they grow and develop through childhood and into adolescence
- prevention of the onset of diseases which affect the elderly
- general prevention of chronic diseases in all age groups.

Those people who are not able to access sufficient nutrients (based on their gender and age) are referred to as being undernourished. Most of the world's undernourished people live in less developed or developing countries, with nearly 90% of the world's hungry people living in Asia and the Pacific and sub-Saharan Africa. Almost unbelievably, 70% of all the underweight children (under the age of five) can be found in just 10 countries.

Key terms

Underweight — a condition in which one's weight is lower than the average weight that is expected. This calculation is based primarily on gender and age.

Food supply — the total amount of food that is available for distribution and consumption/storage in a given location.

▶ **Figure 27.1:** Demand and supply factors.

The demand for food

Before analysing the global situation in relation to food supply, it is worth considering a number of the factors that influence the demand and supply of food. These factors can vary from place to place, but can be generalised to include:

Demand factors	Supply factors
Demographic patterns State of the economy Consumer tastes/trends	Availability of resources Production costs Land use change Competition

Although the earth produces more than enough food to feed its population, which is now estimated to be in excess of 6.5 billion people, hunger and starvation remain pressing issues. This highlights the difference between food supply and food security. While the supply of food is great enough, not everyone lives with the security of knowing that they can access the food that they need.

Securing the supply of food

As seen in Figure 27.2, there are various dimensions to food security. In the first instance, an adequate supply of food must exist to service the nutritional needs of a given population. But, as you will see throughout this chapter, the added dimension of people's ability to access this food, and access it in a safe and healthy manner, are some of the greatest causes of global food insecurity.

There are many issues associated with food supply and food security. Over the following pages, we will consider the major themes which emerge from investigations into global hunger.

Famine

Generally, famines arise due to problems with the food supply, such as when a drought or another natural disaster places severe limits on the amount of food that can be produced in a given agricultural region. Outbreaks of pests and diseases are other 'natural causes' of famine. A Food Availability Deficit (FAD) is said to occur when there is not enough food to adequately supply the nutritional needs of a given population.

However, the failure of agricultural, economic and political systems to correctly manage the food supply chain can result in famine. Examples of this include:

- agricultural mismanagement
- armed conflict
- civil problems
- economic crisis
- refugee crisis.

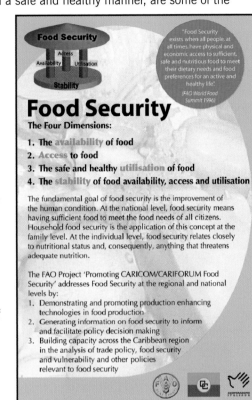

▲ **Figure 27.2:** The 'Four Dimensions' to food security, as published by the United Nation's Food and Agriculture Organisation.

Such events can lead to a widespread lack of food, or alternatively, to more localised problems of food insecurity based on barriers that prevent people from accessing the food that is available. In effect, famine can exist within pockets of a given population despite the fact that there is more than enough food to meet everyone's nutritional needs.

Under- and over-nutrition

Under-nutrition

The nutritional status of the world's less developed nations is most accurately described by the early stages of the process referred to as the 'nutrition transition'. The subsistence lifestyle of many people in the less developed world, especially those living in rural areas, means that the ability to process and store food is limited.

Sadly, under-nutrition strikes mothers, newborn babies and infants the hardest. Under-nutrition can result in an insufficient intake of essential nutrients, which are vital for pregnant or nursing mothers and in the earliest years of life, to assist in growth and development.

Case study: Emergency food assistance

With all the various causes, the onset of famine will mean that emergency food assistance may be required. This can be managed internally, if the affected nation has the means to organise, transport and distribute food reserves from within its borders to the affected region. However, if the means are not available or the effects of the famine are too extensive, outside assistance, in the form of UN-coordinated food aid, might be required. In late 2008, there were 36 nations that required such aid, with most of these based in the less developed or developing world.

▶ **Figure 27.3:** Some examples of regions and countries requiring emergency food assistance in late 2008. Note that causes of food shortage are highly varied.

Region	Number of countries affected	Examples	Cause of food shortage
Africa	21	Ethiopia	Crop failure
		Guinea	Refugees, conflict
		Kenya	Poor weather
		Sierra Leone	War damage
		Zimbabwe	Economic crisis
Asia	12	Afghanistan	Conflict
		China	Earthquake
		Myanmar	Cyclone
		Philippines	Typhoon
		Sri Lanka	Conflict
Latin America	3	Bolivia	Floods
		Cuba	Hurricane
		Haiti	Hurricane

▶ **Figure 27.4:** Sadly, under-nutrition strikes mothers, newborn babies and infants the hardest.

Key term

Under-nutrition — having less food (and nutrients) than is required to maintain a healthy diet.

Taking it further

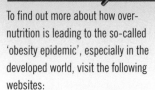

To find out more about how over-nutrition is leading to the so-called 'obesity epidemic', especially in the developed world, visit the following websites:
Department of Health (UK) www.dh.gov.uk/en/publichealth/ healthimprovement/obesity/index.htm
World Health Organisation www.who.int/dietphysicalactivity/ publications/facts/obesity/en/.

For those fortunate enough to survive childhood, an inadequate diet in the years between birth and five years can plague the developing child and result in some serious long-term consequences. Deficiencies in certain nutrients can result in physical and cognitive damage and, when these children reach child-bearing age, the effects of undernourishment in their early years can be passed on to their offspring.

Over-nutrition

At the other end of the scale, the nutritional profile of most of the world's more developed nations has allowed these economies to overcome the threat of famine. There is also a predominance of fat and sugar in the heavily processed foods of their diet.

People living in the developed world are generally living in a situation of food over-supply. That is, they have more than enough food to satisfy their nutritional needs. In fact, because of the high-energy nature of the foods that they consume, they are experiencing 'over-nutrition'.

Globalisation

As with many aspects of the economy, society and culture in the last few decades, the food industry has been influenced by globalisation. In a globalised system, there is freer movement in terms of:

- finance
- investment
- trade
- goods
- services.

In terms of the food industry, at the most basic level, globalisation has meant that countries have been freer than ever before to buy and sell produce. As a result, levels of food imports and exports have climbed markedly across the globe.

Large, Western-owned supermarket chains have found themselves at the centre of a new network of global distributors and receivers. The trend has moved away from small corner stores that have been operated as family-owned small businesses.

Whilst globalisation appears to have had many benefits for consumers, there have been some other less desirable effects. Just as food supply and distribution have been dominated by predominantly Western-owned corporations, so too have food tastes become increasingly 'Westernised'. In some places, traditional crops and plantings have been replaced by Western-style produce, which is not always ideally suited to the conditions that prevail in the local area.

Food miles

The globalisation of the food industry has meant an increase in food miles. The food that we purchase at our local supermarkets leaves a much bigger environmental footprint than ever before in terms of the distance travelled from point of origin (farm) to the point of consumption (our homes) and the production of greenhouse gases on this journey.

Inappropriate farming destroys environments

In the bid to increase the global supply of food and reduce food insecurity, it is tempting to think that humankind should just devote more effort to the establishment of farms, the planting of crops and the raising of animals.

The use of inappropriate farming techniques anywhere on earth, but especially in the margins, can create serious environmental concerns, including damage to the key elements of soil, water and air, in addition to flora and fauna. These will be further investigated later in this section, but in summary include:

- Soils:
  - Compaction by animals or machinery
  - Erosion by wind and water
  - Nutrient depletion
- Water:
  - Alteration of natural drainage patterns
  - Over-use of water in streams, rivers and reservoirs
  - Pollution of water sources by chemicals and nutrients

Key terms

Over-nutrition — having more food (and particularly the nutrients and energy in that food) than is actually needed to sustain a healthy diet. Globalisation — the breaking down of the traditional barriers to finance, investment and trade at an international level.

Synoptic link

Look at pages 75–76 of Edexcel AS Geography to consider the factors that accelerate globalisation. How have these factors played out in the food industry?

Taking it further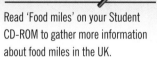

Read 'Food miles' on your Student CD-ROM to gather more information about food miles in the UK.

- Air:
  - Production of greenhouse gases
  - Creation of airborne pollutants, including dust and chemicals
- Flora:
  - Clearing of vegetation
  - Replacement of native species with exotic crops
- Fauna:
  - Destruction of habitats
  - Removal of natural vegetative food sources
  - Introduction of exotic species.

The global picture of food supply and food security

Whilst there is certainly enough food to feed the world, the spatial distribution of the food supply is such that some areas of the planet are over-supplied, while others are under-supplied. As a result, there are many areas of the world that are affected by food insecurity. One of the most effective ways to visualise the situation in relation to global food insecurity is through the use of the so-called 'Hunger map' (Figure 27.5).

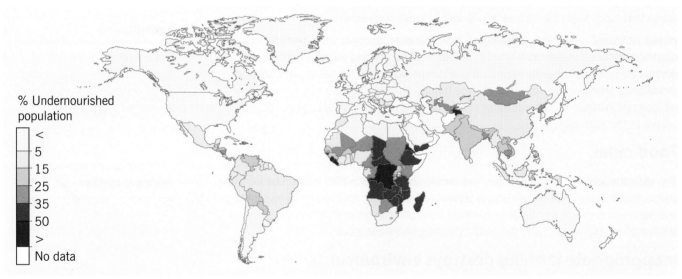

% Undernourished population

< 5
15
25
35
50
>
No data

▲ **Figure 27.5:** The FAO's global hunger map displays the percentage of the population which is undernourished in each nation. The map shows the situation in late 2008.

Taking it further

To find out more about the problems of distribution, read 'The supply of cereals' on your Student CD-ROM.

Africa is revealed as the worst affected continent. Food supply in places such as Somalia, Kenya, Uganda and Ethiopia has been limited by factors such as water shortage, conflict and civil unrest. In these places, food assistance will be needed for millions of people. However, the high variability that can exist within a continent is reflected in the fact that food security in western Africa has improved, with good yields expected to ease food supply problems that had occurred in the recent seasons.

Changes in the temperature of the oceans may also have an impact on the sustainability of the coastal fisheries. Fish consumption in these areas is high, by global standards, with the Pacific islanders, on average, consuming 70 kg of fish each year. The changed environmental conditions resulting from the warming oceans may disrupt current associations of plants and animals, altering the ecological balance and bringing significant change to food chains within marine ecosystems. With their diet so heavily dependent on the seas, such change could place serious stress on food security throughout the Pacific region.

The quality of life on the margins

Whilst the quality of a life is difficult to measure, it is apparent that under-nutrition has a severe impact on quality of life in the marginal areas of the world.

The net result of under-nutrition, especially at a young age, is the onset of physical and cognitive illnesses or disabilities. Such illnesses can have a direct impact on the ability of a child to receive an education and, ultimately, to participate productively in the local economy. Disabilities can also shorten the life span, resulting in a significant lowering of the average life expectancy. Additionally, the number of years that people live with a disability can severely affect the quality of their life. It can be seen that under-nutrition has a long-lasting effect on a community, one that journeys with children affected by poor nutrition as they develop into adulthood.

Within the marginal areas of the earth, there is also a disparity between the quality of life to be found in rural and urban areas. Overwhelmingly, it is the people in rural environments who are the 'poorest of the poor' within the earth's margins. The interplay of factors such as settlement patterns and demographic trends generally makes rural areas less of a priority in terms of government planning and policy-making. Notwithstanding their geographical isolation, as a result, rural locations are more likely to be beset by problems which have the potential to plunge the inhabitants into food insecurity, including fewer opportunities for work, lower income-earning capacity, relatively poor or non-existent systems of communication and transport and a lower level of service and amenity than that experienced by their urban counterparts. Environmental issues such as land degradation, desertification and climate change only serve to further weaken the capacity of rural communities to eke out an existence, and it is the marginal areas of the earth where these problems will strike hardest.

Urban environments, especially in the marginal areas of the earth, can have their own problems too, caused largely by the phenomenon of urbanisation. The problems that plague rural areas, as outlined above, as well as the promise of educational and employment opportunities, tend to push people to urban places, leading to problems of overcrowding and placing a drain on the services and amenities that are to be found in the cities and towns.

Synoptic link

Look at pages 208–10 of Edexcel AS Geography to find out more about unequal rural spaces. Pay particular attention to Cloke's Index and how it helps us to understand the changing features on the rural–urban continuum.

Synoptic link

Look at page 115 of Edexcel AS Geography to find out more about the causes of rural-to-urban migration.

Key term

Life expectancy — the average number of years that a person is expected to live. Life expectancies vary with gender, location and socio-economic circumstance.

Summary

In this chapter you have learnt:

- to explain the difference between food supply and food security, and identify issues that are associated with both.
- to describe a range of environmental issues that arise during food production, making the link between these and inappropriate farming techniques.
- to understand that food supply and food security vary around the world.
- to demonstrate how food security affects the quality of life for people around the world, but especially in the more marginal areas, with the knowledge that those living in the rural parts of these environments are the worst affected.

MCQ

CHAPTER 28 What has caused global inequalities in food supply and food security?

Key terms

Absolute poverty
Biofuels
Commodity prices
Dryland agriculture
Famine
Food Entitlement Deficit (FED)
Food surplus
Integrated Farm Management
International Food Policy Research Institute (IFPRI)
Linking Environment and Farming (LEAF)
Marginal areas
Neo-Malthusianism
Organisation for Economic and Community Development (OECD)
Organic farming
Relative poverty
Technocentric

Learning objectives

After studying this chapter, you will be able to discuss these ideas and concepts and provide located examples of them:
- There are complex interlinking and overlapping causes of famine and food surpluses.
- The classification of environmental, social and economic factors, both short- and long-term, direct and indirect.
- Population pressures also create food insecurity, with viewpoints highlighted by neo-Malthusians versus technocentric followers of Boserup.
- There are impacts of attempting to increase the global food supply, including damage to the environment. LEAF and organic schemes are preferentially used in a range of locations.
- The groups of people that are most vulnerable to the effects of food insecurity and why.

Famine

According to the International Food Policy Research Institute, a famine can be defined as 'a catastrophic disruption of the social, economic and institutional systems that provide for food production, distribution and consumption'.

A famine is much more than a crop failure that results in a lack of food. The underlying causes of famine are much harder to define as they are complex and overlapping.

Population pressures

Short-term effects

One of the greatest contributors to famine is the pressure exerted by population. Put in simple terms, more people means more mouths to feed. In the last four decades, the global population has doubled. Growth will continue to be focused in the less developed world, including the regions of Asia, Africa and Latin America (Figure 28.1). Continued population growth has placed incredible stress on our agricultural systems (and, in turn, on the natural environment, as we will see later), making it more and more difficult to meet the food needs of a hungry global population.

The largest demands on agricultural systems of production come from a dual source – the need to produce food for humans and feed for livestock. As populations of both humankind and their flocks and herds continue to grow, so too does the demand for food stocks to nourish both.

In recent years, with increased consciousness about the use of fossil fuels and their impact on the earth's climatic system, a third area of demand has emerged. This is the production of crops to be used as biofuels, which have been proclaimed in some quarters as an alternative to our heavy dependence on fossil fuels. Whilst not yet rivalling food or stockfeed in terms of the level of demand, the advent of biofuel technology and its impact on crop production has been one of the factors behind a general rise in the price of commodities in the short term.

Key term

Biofuels — a source of energy that is derived from plants. At the present time, most biofuels are generated from crops such as sugar cane, corn, wheat and sugar beet. Ethanol, an alcohol-based energy source, is the world's most common biofuel. Biodiesel, which is made from vegetable oil, has been known to power round-the-world holiday-makers who have collected 'fuel' for their cars and vans from the leftover cooking oil used in fish and chip shops!

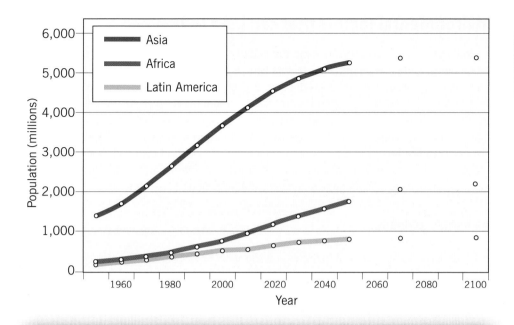

◄ **Figure 28.1:** Estimates of population growth towards the end of this century reveal that growth will continue strongly in Asia and Africa: two of the world's most underdeveloped regions.

Case study: Playing catch-up

The earth's population has risen steadily since the Industrial Revolution. This trend is set to continue, with research by the United Nations indicating that the global population will increase by 2.5 billion people by 2050. Estimates from the International Food Policy Research Institute (IFPRI) indicate that in order to meet this demand in the short term (that is, the next two decades), the production of cereal crops will need to increase by 35%, while meat production needs to increase by 55%. How this can be achieved, without serious damage to the natural environment, is the next big question.

A longer-term view of population: the ideas of Malthus

What will be the ultimate effect of the exploding global population on the ability of humankind to feed itself? Many philosophers have contemplated the answer to this question. In 1798, Thomas Malthus argued that while the human population could be expected to increase exponentially, its ability to produce food progressed in a linear pattern.

An alternative view of population: the ideas of Boserup

It can be said that Malthus's view of the global population tended to be fairly pessimistic in its outlook. A different view was expressed by Ester Boserup, a Danish economist. Boserup's more optimistic view of population argued that population growth was actually the stimulus for the development of innovative thought and ideas, especially with respect to agriculture (the technocentric view).

Principal among these would be the technological advances that would help propel food production to new levels.

Neo-Malthusianism

Coming to the fore in recent years has been a new school of thought, called Neo-Malthusianism.

Neo-Malthusians see the need for the human population to be kept in check in order to address the issue of global poverty. Poverty is seen as the underlying cause of many of the world's other pressing social and economic issues, including conflict and disease. By extension, poverty is also one of the factors contributing to the development of food insecurity across the globe, including famine.

Key terms

Technocentric — of, or pertaining to, ideas and belief systems that have a strong focus on the development of technology, especially to the betterment of humankind.

Absolute poverty — an economic indicator which measures, for a given area, the number of people who live below a certain level of income.

Relative poverty — an economic indicator which is used to measure the number of households whose level of income is less than an amount designated as the 'threshold' income level. It is a useful indicator for analysing the way that wealth is distributed within a region or nation.

Key term

Resource base — used to describe the foundations upon which the economic strength of a community is built. A narrow resource base exposes a community to fluctuations within the natural environment or commodity markets.

Environmental factors that can lead to famine

In addition to population pressures and the underlying and intrinsic poverty of some communities, certain environmental factors can also produce famine. Famines have been known to occur when systems of production, especially agricultural systems, fail. Some of these factors, but not all, are often beyond the control of the local population. Examples include the failure of crops due to the onset of a poor season, the impact of a natural disaster, or an outbreak of a pest or diseases. Good farm management practices, including selective breeding and crop rotation, can reduce the likelihood of pest and disease outbreaks. However, the underlying poverty that exists in many parts of the less developed world makes these types of practice and preparation difficult to achieve.

Case Study: The vulnerability of the earth's drylands

The communities that live in the earth's dryland regions are entirely dependent on rainfall to supply water for their agriculture and livestock, usually in addition to domestic use. By their very nature, drylands tend to have highly variable patterns of rainfall, meaning that drought is an ever-present threat.

The Sahel, in Africa, is a well-known example. Stretching 6,000 km from the west coast to the east coast of the continent, the Sahel forms the boundary between the Sahara Desert and the savannah lands found to the south. As such, it is a zone of transition, where rainfall is variable. The countries which lie within this region are among the poorest nations on earth, and when periods of drought are severe or extend over more than one growing season, famine can result. Famines throughout the Sahel, in places such as Ethiopia, Somalia and Sudan, have been all too common. Millions are estimated to have died in the Sahel as a result of famine in the last three decades.

Taking it further

There are some excellent sites that you can use as a starting point for researching drylands in more detail. These include:
United Nations Dryland Development Centre
www.undp.org/drylands;
Land Degradation Assessment in Drylands Project – search for this at www.fao.org.

Synoptic link

Look at page 23 of Edexcel AS Geography where the impact of climate change on different environments is considered. How are drylands and areas prone to drought likely to be affected by the changing climate?

Other factors causing famine

Famines rarely affect the entire population of a country. More often, they affect communities or regions. Sometimes, rather than experiencing a Food Availability Deficit (FAD), people in these places may be subject to a Food Entitlement Deficit (FED). This occurs because the access of people to food supplies is not always even; some people receive less food than that to which they are entitled, which equates to the amount that is required to sustain growth and/or health. Those affected by FED tend to be the most vulnerable, which in practice usually visits food insecurity on the poorest people living in rural areas. It is worth remembering that famines have a definite social, and often political, context.

Systems of production can also be disrupted by other events. Changes of government, oppressive regimes, or the development of armed conflict can lead to famine. During the course of such events, labourers may be drawn into events and away from their food production roles. Alternatively, these events can see land and infrastructure becoming damaged or falling into disrepair, placing the food supply in jeopardy.

Food surpluses

As opposed to famine, food surpluses are not a humanitarian disaster. Food surpluses can result from a number of factors, which can include:

- supportive government policies
- increased agricultural plantings
- economic incentives provided by government
- the promise of good yields and good financial returns.

It is apparent that the factors that result in food surplus occur more frequently in the developed world. Here, where the inputs into the agricultural system are greater, bumper crops and record harvests are more regularly achieved.

Environmental impacts of increasing the global food supply

Taking it further

To look at how Australia has been affected by agricultural systems of production, read 'The Australian example' on your Student CD-ROM.

Increasingly, it is the developing countries which are becoming the focus of global agriculture. Current trends reveal that both the production of agricultural commodities and the consumption of these products are increasing most rapidly in the developing nations.

According to the OECD-FAO Agricultural Outlook for 2008–2017, 'by 2017, these (the developing) countries are expected to dominate production and consumption of most commodities, with the exception of coarse grains, cheese and skim-milk powder'.

This would appear to be good news as it suggests a chance to even out some of the global inequalities that currently exist in terms of food supply and food security. It is important to bear in mind that in the rush to produce more from our global systems of agriculture and to do so in a more equitable way, there may be some impacts, especially for the environment.

Mostly, the best agricultural land is already being utilised, which means that we are turning to the more marginal areas of the earth in our hunt for more farmland. In these places, farming is very difficult to sustain, due to the poor quality of the nutrient-deficient soils, lack of water and highly variable patterns of rainfall. Clearing marginal areas for farming effectively removes any of the buffers which exist in the natural environment. This exposes the soils to erosion by wind and water and increases the likelihood of problems such as salinity and desertification.

Organic farming – reducing the impacts

Organic farming has long been recognised as helping to reduce the environmental impact of farming, though debate still rages over its ability to produce yields that are higher or even equivalent to conventional methods. According to the UK's Department for Environment, Food and Rural Affairs (DEFRA), the main focus of organic farming systems, for crops and livestock, is on:

Crops	Livestock
Soil fertility	Feeding
Crop rotation	Housing
Crop protection	Health management
Organic seed	Use of manures
Organic crop storage	

◀ **Figure 28.2:** Focus of organic farming systems.

In order to lessen the impact of agriculture on the environment, organic farmers reject a majority of the conventional farming methods. Instead, they employ techniques which have a higher degree of sustainability, and which work to restore and protect the natural balance of the ecosystem. Included among these methods are:

* composting
* planting of fertility-building crops
* green manuring and livestock manuring
* maintenance of ground cover
* biological pest control
* selection of pest- / disease-resistant crops
* minimum tillage of the soil
* encouragement of native species
* the use of animal health plans
* strict monitoring and certification for organic compliance.

Taking it further

There is a wealth of information on organic farming on the internet, with many excellent examples of what is happening in the UK and around the world. Using these websites as a starting point, research more about the philosophy behind the concept of organic farming.

For overviews of organic farming principles and priorities, visit: www.defra.gov.uk/farm/organic/systems/method.htm.

To find out more about the number of farmers who are utilising organic methods, consider: www.ukagriculture.com/farming_today/organic_farming.cfm www.organicfarmers.org.uk.

In the developed world, consumers have been willing to pay more for goods that are certified as organic, convinced of the health and environmental benefits of doing so.

The debate over organic farming is in relation to the yields that it can achieve in comparison with conventional farming techniques. In the developed world, there is a consensus that the yield from an organic farm would be lower, but exactly how great a difference between this and the yield from a conventional farm is still being debated.

▲ **Figure 28.3:** A farmer in India ploughs a pasture into his fields in an organic practice known as green manuring.

The LEAF Organisation

LEAF stands for Linking Environment and Farming. The LEAF organisation was created in 1991 with the aim of bringing together farmers, consumers, scientists, environmentalists and government representatives to work towards the improvement of the farming industry. This was to be achieved following the principles of Integrated Farm Management (IFM), which took a holistic view of agriculture, encouraging farmers to combine the best of their conventional farming methods with modern technology in order to farm in a responsible and environmentally friendly manner.

According to the website of LEAF UK, the focus of their organisation is to instil:

> 'a whole farm policy providing the basis for efficient and profitable production which is economically viable and environmentally responsible. IFM integrates beneficial natural processes into modern farming practices using advanced technology. It aims to minimise environmental risks while conserving, enhancing and recreating that which is of environmental importance.'
>
> Source: LEAF UK website
> http://www.leafuk.org/leafuk/organisation/ifm.asp

LEAF schemes now connect a huge network of farmers across the UK, providing an important link between the industry and consumers. The principles of Integrated Farm Management help to ensure that the health and wellbeing of the environment remain a top priority.

The poor and young remain the most vulnerable

Whilst the developing nations might be taking a larger proportion of the global trade in commodities, there is little doubt that the world's most vulnerable people will continue to be at the mercy of food insecurity for the foreseeable future.

Current trends in commodity markets reflect increases in the prices of most items, and especially foodstuffs. For the poorest people living in the less developed world, this means that it will be even more difficult to sustain a living. Most nations that face food insecurity are net importers of foodstuffs. The OECD and FAO estimate that families in these communities allocate as much as 50% of their household income to food. Higher prices for commodities severely impact upon families who are in this situation, with the net result of increasing food insecurity for many millions of people globally.

Children are especially vulnerable to food insecurity. Globally, 10.9 million children die in the nations of the less developed world every year. Hunger and malnutrition, the results of food insecurity, account for 60% of these deaths, with a lack of essential vitamins and minerals as a root cause of the problems.

Research also shows that there are longer-term effects of poor childhood nutrition. These include:

• the completion of fewer years of schooling
• lower levels of cognitive growth
• lower income-earning ability in adult life.

Synoptic link

Look at page 81 of Edexcel AS Geography and investigate why there are such marked disparities in global wealth. What impact does this have on food security?

Taking it further

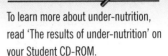

To learn more about under-nutrition, read 'The results of under-nutrition' on your Student CD-ROM.

Summary

In this chapter you have learnt:

• to explain some of the causes of famine and food surpluses.

• to appreciate that the causes of famine can be classified as being environmental, social and/or economic, and that these causes are linked in complex ways.

• to demonstrate the role that population plays in creating food insecurity.

• to use the theories of Malthus and Boserup to discuss the interplay between population and resources.

• to show that there are impacts of attempting to produce more food, and that these impacts can be limited by techniques such as organic farming.

• to account for the vulnerability of the poor and especially pregnant/nursing mothers and young children to the effects of food insecurity.

MCQ

CHAPTER 29 What is the role of desertification in threatening life at the margins?

Key terms

Arable
Climate change
Compaction
Deforestation
Desertification
Drylands
Earth Summit
Ecological balance
Erosion
Land degradation
Natural buffers
Over-cultivation
Over-grazing
Topsoil
United Nations Convention
  to Combat Desertification
  (UNCCD)

Synoptic link

Look at pages 45–6 of Edexcel AS Geography which consider the economic impact of climate change on the African continent. What does this passage suggest about the future of food security in this part of the world?

Learning objectives

After studying this chapter, you will be able to discuss these ideas and concepts and provide located examples of them:
- The scale and impact of desertification and its causes (climatic and human activities).
- The scale, characteristics and vulnerability of dryland ecosystems, in order to establish the physical causes of risk and vulnerability.
- Understand why drylands are extremely vulnerable to over-exploitation and inappropriate land use by categorising and investigating the human factors causing vulnerability (socio-political and economic).
- The relationship between food production and supply in desertified regions.

Desertification is one of the major threats to food supply and security.

At the 'Earth Summit' held in Rio de Janeiro in 1992, the gathered nations recognised that more needed to be done in the fight against desertification, and work began on the formulation of a United Nations Convention that would herald a new, integrated approach to tackling this issue. On 26 December 1996 the United Nations Convention to Combat Desertification (UNCCD) came into effect. The Conference of Parties (COP), the governing body of the convention, now meets on a biennial basis to continue to fight against desertification.

The onset of desertification

One of the first signs of desertification is the loss of topsoil from farmlands. Topsoils represent the nutrient-rich layer which gives fertility to soils; hence their loss can be devastating. This can lead to the onset of other warning signs, including the loss of natural vegetation and the failure of crops. Once desertification has taken hold, people begin to suffer from food and water insecurity. At its worst, desertification can result in famine and the resultant migration of population to areas that are less marginal.

Some places are more vulnerable to desertification than others (Figure 29.2). As we will see in this chapter, areas of high vulnerability tend to be the earth's drylands. As the UNCCD definition suggests, the 'factors' which cause desertification, and which are particularly destructive in dryland environments, include both human activities and climatic variations such as:
- drought
- soil erosion
- over-farming
- deterioration of the soil
- loss of natural vegetation.

The impacts of desertification

Soils, vegetation and animals can recover quickly from periods of drought. But when environments become degraded, the natural buffers that exist in the ecosystem are removed, meaning that the entire ecosystem is more susceptible to degradation and, consequently in many parts of the world, desertification.

Soils

Land degradation can expose the valuable layer of topsoil to erosion by wind and water. Increased erosion can result in the formation of channels and gullies through the landscape, which in turn can alter patterns of drainage. If the land is overworked by humans, machinery or animals, layers within the soil profile can be compacted into one another. This prevents air and water penetrating into the lower layers, and can lead to an increase in surface runoff, which in turn can result in more erosion.

The effects of land degradation are not only felt in the immediate area. Soil can be transported from a degraded area by fluvial processes. Large quantities of loosened soil flowing downstream can cause the sedimentation of rivers, lakes and estuaries. This can also have serious effects for water supplies, which become silted, and navigation channels, which become blocked.

Vegetation

The removal of vegetation from the landscape is one of the main causes of land degradation. The roots of plants help to stabilise soils and their foliage helps to reduce the erosive power of winds as they move across the landscape. Loss of vegetative cover exposes more soil to erosion by wind and water. Winds can scour soil away from the roots of remaining plants, leaving them exposed at the surface. The removal of trees, often in wholesale ways, in a process known as deforestation, is particularly destructive. Once large drifts of soil are on the move, other environments are threatened with burial. Establishing crops in such 'dust bowl' conditions is virtually impossible.

Key terms

Desertification — according to Article 1 of the UNCCD, desertification can be defined as 'land degradation in arid, semi-arid and dry sub-humid regions resulting from a variety of factors, including climatic variations and human activities'.

Erosion — the wearing away of rocks and soils by the action of water, ice and wind.

Topsoil — the uppermost layer of the soil which usually contains the most nutrients in the entire soil profile.

Deforestation — the clearance of trees.

Case study: The US Dust Bowl of the 1930s

In 1862, the United States Congress passed a piece of legislation that would have a significant impact on the nation's Great Plains area. The so-called 'Homestead Act' encouraged settlement on the Great Plains, a region of vast prairie lands. Settlers brought with them grazing cattle and planted crops such as wheat in what were essentially dryland conditions. Inappropriate farming techniques, including extensive over-grazing, combined with the onset of drought in the 1930s, turned huge tracts of the region into the infamous 'Dust Bowl' (Figure 29.1). When crops failed due to drought, the winds of the plains transported soils in huge dust clouds; darkening the sky and partially burying fences, machinery and homes. The farms of the Dust Bowl became unworkable and thousands of farming families migrated away from the region to find work in other places.

▲ **Figure 29.1:** The US 'Dust Bowl' of the 1930s was a precursor to the type of environmental degradation that would occur in other parts of the world with increasing frequency over the course of the 20th century.

Environments at risk – the drylands

Land degradation can take hold in almost any environment, but it appears to have its greatest impact in the earth's dryland regions. According to the United Nations Environment Programme, the Millennium Ecosystem Assessment revealed that drylands, which are predominantly found in the interiors of the continental areas, account for 40% of the earth's land surfaces. They are also characterised by large fluctuations in precipitation and high levels of seasonal variability.

Although they are marginal, drylands are extremely significant areas. They have an amazing biodiversity and are home to plants and animals that are not found in any other regions. Crops such as barley and sorghum came from the drylands, and the remaining endemic species of these crops are of great importance because they tend to be disease-resistant. In addition, dryland plants are widely used in drugs, resins, waxes and oils. It is estimated that dryland plants provide the basis for one-third of all the plant-derived drugs in the United States. Drylands are also home to large mammals, while also being an important habitat for migratory birds.

Key term

Drylands — as the name suggests, drylands are areas with limited supplies of freshwater. Communities living in these areas are almost totally dependent on rainfall for their water needs.

Global Desertification Vulnerability

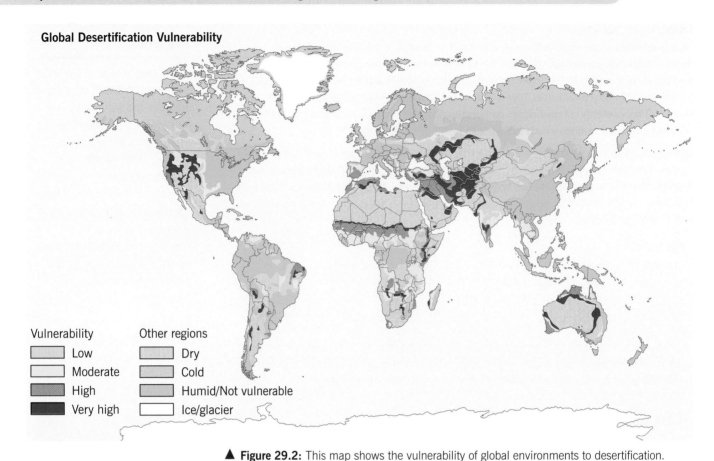

Vulnerability	Other regions
Low	Dry
Moderate	Cold
High	Humid/Not vulnerable
Very high	Ice/glacier

▲ **Figure 29.2:** This map shows the vulnerability of global environments to desertification.

Drylands are particularly vulnerable to desertification because their soils tend to be more fragile and their coverage of vegetation is sparser than other areas of the planet. Additionally, climatic conditions are generally harsher in the dryland regions.

The scale of desertification

It is estimated that 10–20% of the earth's drylands are already significantly degraded. Globally, 250 million people live in areas that suffer from land degradation and desertification. Some parts of the world are more affected than others (see Figure 29.2). In Africa, for example, it is estimated that almost 50% of the continent is degraded to some extent.

Human causes: inappropriate land use practices

Among the human causes of desertification is the application of land use practices that are unsuited to particular environments. Some of these, such as over-grazing or over-cultivation, exploit the resources of the environment for short-term gain and do permanent damage to topsoils. The soil profile can also become compacted by the repetitive movement of livestock and machinery across paddocks that are farmed in conventional ways. This has the result of making the soils virtually impenetrable to both air and water, and can seriously reduce the health of the soils and the productive capacity of the land.

Deforestation is another practice that can destroy the ecological balance that exists in an ecosystem. Removing natural vegetation upsets the equilibrium that exists in the environment by destroying habitats and interrupting nutrient cycles. Shallow-rooted exotic crops such as cereals do not bind the soil as effectively as the natural vegetation did, and topsoils, in particular, can become exposed to erosion by wind and water.

Taking it further

To learn more about the different dryland definitions that exist, read 'The earth's drylands' on your Student CD-ROM.

Examiners' tip

Under the right circumstances, desertification can take place almost anywhere. It is important to stress to your examiner that you understand the earth's dryland regions to be the places most vulnerable to desertification, due to the environmental conditions that are found there. Inappropriate farming in the drylands simply increases their vulnerability.

Other human factors, such as poverty, can also lead to the degradation of the land. In the face of poverty, communities that cannot afford to work the best agricultural lands may be reduced to making a living from the more marginal areas. The intensity of their poverty may well mean that people living in these communities have no choice but to extract as much as they can from their already tired and worn-out soils, leading to the further degradation of land that is already under stress. Population pressures that characterise many of the less developed parts of the world only add further stress to the environment.

Ignorance can also play a role in the degradation of formerly fertile lands. During times of war, the ecological and productive value of land can be overlooked or forgotten. Armed conflict, in particular, can bring significant levels of destruction to the environment, especially in situations of total war.

Key term

Over-cultivation — to exhaust the soil or the land through excessive tilling of the soil.

Case study: Addressing the human causes of desertification in Uganda

Uganda has experienced massive migration of people away from its rural areas in the face of land degradation, drought and desertification. It is evident that women and children make up the bulk of the displaced people and, even within the cities, they still face poverty and hunger. In response, Uganda's Agricultural Advisory Service has helped to select what it describes as 'lead farmers' within the villages of the nation. The country has been 'zoned' according to the strength of the soils and rainfall that exist in each region, as well as for the potential markets for agricultural produce. The government is devoting resources to improving productivity, whilst also encouraging the planting of cash crops which will help to address underlying poverty by providing local communities with much-needed funds. Agro-forestry is being encouraged as a means of strengthening the resource base, as well as growing fruits such as oranges, avocados and mangos. Accompanying this has been training in picking, packing and storage techniques, which will help farmers to achieve the standards needed for their fruit produce to enter the US and European markets.

Climatic factors

Links also exist between desertification and climate. Intense periods of drought can result in the loss of vegetative cover, again exposing soils to the damaging effects of the wind. Many of the world's drylands, which are among the regions worst affected by desertification, experience high rainfall variability, meaning that drought is an all-too-common reality.

Climate change is likely to bring more prolonged droughts, which will lead to an increase in land degradation and, consequently, desertification. As vegetative cover is lost to the encroaching desert-like sands, the carbon that was sequestered in the plants and the soil is released into the atmosphere. This serves to further enhance global warming and climate change, which, in turn, will see the cycle repeat.

Recent research indicates that desertification is one of the biggest environmental challenges facing humankind. As arable lands are lost to desertification, food security is threatened and the livelihoods and lifestyles of communities are placed at risk. It is estimated that if desertification continues unabated, 50 million people could become displaced by its onslaught in the next 10 years.

Key terms

Ecological balance — the equilibrium that exists between living organisms and their environment.
Arable — refers to land which can be used for the growing of crops.

Case study: Climate change and food production in Africa

According to figures released by the FAO, improved agricultural technology and practice will mean that levels of agricultural production will increase by 50% by the year 2030. However, at the same time, land degradation, drought and desertification are reducing the availability of arable land across the face of the globe. In the face of a changing climate, this situation could be particularly serious within the drylands of Africa. Some estimates put the loss of arable farmland within the Sahara and sub-Sahara as high as 75%. The net result is likely to be increased levels of poverty, migration, famine and hunger.

Examiners' tip

Whilst the climate and environmental conditions of the drylands make them vulnerable, human factors play a much larger role in bringing about desertification. Emphasise this in your explanation of the role that communities play in this issue.

▶ **Figure 29.3:** Desertification is one of the biggest environmental issues facing humankind, with direct impacts on food supply and food security.

Food supply and food security in desertified regions

In the longer term, the increasing level of desertification of many of the world's dryland areas may have serious consequences for global food production. It is estimated that in the next 50 years we will need to triple the production of food in order to be able to meet the nutritional requirements of the expanding global population. If left unchecked, desertification may lead to an increase first in malnutrition, then famine and finally starvation.

At the same time, desertification has the potential to create instability in affected regions. By plunging an area into food and water insecurity, desertification can lead to mass migration away from rural areas and the breakdown of communities and their social fabrics. All of this is likely to destabilise a region, in a civil and political sense, making food production in the future even more difficult.

Case study: Desertification in the developing world

Recently, Alejandra Sobenes, the Vice-Minister of Environment and Natural Resources in Guatemala, indicated that 12% of this developing nation was already in the grips of desertification. According to the minister, 45.4% of the entire land area of Guatemala is susceptible to drought. This raises fears for the safety of food production and security in Guatemala with the onset of climate change. Already, 13% of the indigenous population lives below the poverty line and has major issues with food security. In a statement the minister outlined her thoughts about how these issues should be addressed: 'We the developing countries, those who are most gravely affected, cannot go on ignoring the degradation of the land. Our demand to developed countries is that we address these problems, systemically, together.'

The wider effects of desertification

Putting a figure on the cost of desertification is a difficult task. Its cost in terms of 'lost production' is estimated to be somewhere in the region of $US 42 billion each year. But this is purely an economic cost.

Desertification also has a range of other social impacts. In the face of badly degraded environments, many people living in areas affected by desertification simply choose to leave and try their luck elsewhere. Typically, this draws people to the larger towns and the cities where these migrant populations become a social and economic burden for other communities to support. In some places, shanty towns develop, where populations are high and living conditions are appalling.

It is now apparent that food security is dependent on three main factors:
• Health of the soil
• Availability of water
• Methods of food production.

The importance and value of soil, in particular, and its protection against desertification, is paramount. Whilst these factors will vary from region to region, in the globalised world of today, food production levels can also be influenced by the nature of the international marketplace. With the freeing up of trade has come the widespread use of chemicals, fertilisers and pesticides, which would seem to be an advantage for farmers in the less developed world. But unless these are used in a sustainable way, the degradation of the land can result, increasing the likelihood of desertification. Additionally, the export subsidies that are applied in some countries of the developed world can have a direct effect on commodity prices, with the effect of undermining the ability of farmers in the less developed world to make their living from the land.

Summary

In this chapter you have learnt:

• to describe the scale and impact of desertification.

• to explain the human and climatic causes of desertification.

• to establish the scale and characteristics of the earth's dryland regions and, in so doing, demonstrate the highly vulnerable nature of these regions.

• to describe the nature of the inappropriate land use and farming techniques which expose drylands to the effects of land degradation and desertification.

• to demonstrate how desertification affects the ability of dryland regions to produce food and leads to food insecurity, especially for poor communities living in the most marginal areas.

MCQ

CHAPTER 30 How effective can management strategies be in sustaining life at the margins?

Key terms

Capacity building
Commodity prices
Fair trade
Genetically modified (GM)
International Coffee
  Organisation (ICO)
Intervention
Millennium Development
  Goals (MDGs)
Non-governmental
  organisation (NGO)
Partnership for Enhancing
  Agriculture in Rwanda
  through Linkages (PEARL)
Resource base
Sustainability

Learning objectives

After studying this chapter, you will be able to discuss these ideas and concepts and provide located examples of them:

• Management techniques and strategies attempt to increase global food supply and food security, including fair trade and distribution. The politics and general stability of an area are also relevant factors.
• Why greater international efforts are increasingly needed to secure global food supplies, including technological, low-cost and environmental solutions.
• Initiatives that have been most effective in sustaining life at the margins, including organisations involved in the marginal food supply areas.
• The role of sustainable strategies in food supply and food security.

In 1970, the United Nations passed a resolution relating to international aid. The world's industrialised nations committed to devoting 0.7% of their GNP to aid-related projects. These funds were intended to help address issues such as poverty and hunger and the figure has remained as a benchmark ever since. Very few countries, other than the Scandinavian nations, have regularly met the target.

Humanitarian aid certainly helps to address issues such as food supply and food security but what else is being done to improve the quality of life at the margins? In recent years, it has become evident that more must be done to address the underlying causes of the inequalities that exist in terms of food supply and food insecurity.

Synoptic link

Look at page 227 of Edexcel AS Geography to find out about international measures of inequality. Fair trade schemes aim to redress some of the imbalance in the Human Development Index.

▲ **Figure 30.1:** Eye-catching advertisements, such as this one, help to raise awareness about the responsibility of those living in the developed world to ensure fair trade.

Fair trade

One of the strategies designed to improve the economic circumstances of communities in some of the more marginal areas of the earth is the concept of fair trade. Under fair trade schemes, a 'fair share' of the profits generated by the sale of goods is distributed between all those who participated in the production process. A fair share is one that reflects the time and effort invested at each stage of the production process, as opposed to the largest share of the profits being claimed by the eventual seller, who did the least to actually produce the item. Sadly, this has been the case for far too long, and has prevented profits from being utilised where they would do the most to address the underlying poverty – at the level of the farm and the local community.

Case study: Why coffee?

Certain commodities, most notably coffee and chocolate, were identified as requiring a fair trade intervention. Why these products? The answer has a lot to do with geography. Coffee and the ingredients for chocolate are generally produced on small, independently operated farms that are based in the less developed world, especially throughout South and Central America. Additionally, the coffee trade is a massive market, worth an estimated $80 billion annually, second only to oil as the highest traded commodities. Furthermore, world coffee prices took a tumble in the early part of this decade, as a result of an over-supply of coffee on the world market. Prices reached their lowest level in 30 years. Globally, this directly affected 25 million people who were reliant on the coffee trade for their livelihood. So, it would seem that globally the time was right for coffee to be traded fairly. More importantly, the political will necessary to establish fair trade schemes existed in the developed world.

There are wider benefits that emerge from the establishment of fair trade systems and schemes. With more money in the pockets of local farmers, there is an increased likelihood that they will be able to invest in improving their agricultural lands and their farming practices, which will mean a positive outcome for the environment. This is especially important in the more marginal areas of the earth. The community also benefits from increased employment opportunities and the positive social effects that flow from this.

The stabilising role of the NGOs

Additionally, the work of non-governmental organisations within the agricultural regions of the less developed world has been vitally important in helping to ensure sustainability. In Africa, the wonderfully named Partnership for Enhancing Agriculture in Rwanda through Linkages (PEARL) has focused on helping agricultural producers to develop their products and to connect better with their markets. By giving farmers the equipment and know-how they need to improve their products, NGOs play a key role in helping to strengthen the resource base of producers. In so doing, they help to bring stability to an area.

Examiners' tip

The role of NGOs in addressing global under-nutrition should not be underestimated. Because they operate at a grassroots level and have a high degree of involvement in local communities, NGOs bring practical solutions to food supply problems and provide the tools that communities need to become self-sufficient. Make sure that you emphasise this with strong examples in your exam.

Case study: Providing a political voice for the disenfranchised

Fair trade schemes are a way of giving farmers the recognition they deserve in an economic sense. In the same way, farmers in the less developed world also need a political voice that can represent their interests at an intergovernmental level, in the absence of any support from within their government. The International Coffee Organisation (ICO) is one such group. By being the intermediary between governments in various nations, the ICO brings a collective voice to coffee growers across a range of locations. With the support of the United Nations, the ICO has been able to help regulate the coffee industry and to create standards in terms of trade practices, which has ultimately been to the benefit of coffee growers. The ICO has also been an advocate for farmers in the face of falling global coffee prices, encouraging the concept of fair trade and wealth distribution.

Greater international efforts needed

Whilst the work of community and non-governmental organisations has made inroads into addressing the inequalities that exist in food supply and security, more needs to be done on an international scale to help sustain life in the earth's most marginal regions.

Attempting to increase the global food supply by conventional methods, which include the opening up of new farmlands, the use of heavy cultivation regimes, chemical fertilisers and pesticides, will undoubtedly come at the cost of the natural environment. Recent debate has focused on ways to achieve better yields from the land that is already being farmed.

The intensification of our farming endeavours would see humankind trying to 'make more out of' its areas of agricultural production. In some areas, additional inputs into the farming system, including fertilisers, labour or machinery may result in substantially better levels of production.

Key term

Fair trade — the idea that all stages in the production process should receive a fair share of the profits that are generated from the sale of an item.

▲ **Figure 30.2:** The holistic approach of the UN's Food and Agriculture Organisation to building capacity within communities is reflected in this image.

For this strategy to be sustainable, making these inputs must lie within the capacity of communities, and must not result in the degradation of the natural environment. Significant research would be needed to identify the inputs that would be most effective in the incredible variety of global environments and agricultural contexts.

Intensifying our efforts can also result from re-examining our agricultural practices and finding new approaches to old problems. The development of a global industry in aquaculture in the last two decades serves as an excellent example. Aquaculture is the practice of intensively raising fish in tanks, reservoirs and now, specially designed floating pens in the open sea. Through research, trial and error, and experience, aquaculture has developed to the point where it may well replace traditional methods of fishing for certain species of fish.

Some argue that technology will provide a solution to the world's food supply problems. Much controversy has surrounded the concept of genetically modified (GM) crops, which have the potential to significantly increase yields. Whilst the use of GM crops does not reduce the environmental impact of agricultural practices, it does suggest the potential to produce higher yields, reducing the need to establish new areas of farmland. For some time, GM crops were touted as the solution to the world's hunger woes, but doubts remain as to the impact that GM crops could have on existing species if cross-pollination between the strains was to occur. While this debate continues to rage, trials of GM crops continue in various locations around the globe, with their use relatively widespread in the United States and Brazil.

Towards the end of the last century, the United Nations developed a series of Millennium Development Goals (MDGs) for the 21st century. The MDGs were end-dated to 2015, with the aim being to achieve key targets in relation to each goal by this point in time. The first and arguably most important of these goals was to 'eradicate extreme poverty and hunger'. Two targets were attached to this goal:

• Target 1: Reduce by half the proportion of people living on less than a dollar a day.
• Target 2: Reduce by half the proportion of people who suffer from hunger.

The UN's Food and Agriculture Organisation is an international body dedicated to helping reduce the world's problems with hunger, and as such, helps to make significant progress towards the MDGs. The FAO focuses on building capacity within nations so that they can better manage their food supply and security.

The capacity of a community can be built in many different areas (Figure 30.2) and involves much more than agriculture. It takes a holistic approach to strengthening the community through health, education and social welfare, whilst also giving due attention to its economic, cultural and political context.

Case study: The FAO in Mozambique

Between 2002 and 2007, the FAO ran a project in Manica Province, Mozambique, which was aimed at improving nutrition and household food security. Working with a number of government ministries and provincial directorates, the FAO aimed to increase the ability of the local population to access nutritional food on a year-round basis. Primarily, this was achieved by:

• promoting the use of specially adapted crops
• using simple labour-saving techniques, low-cost technology and sustainable practices to improve crop productivity
• introducing livestock farming, where appropriate
• improving the technology used after the harvest of crops.

In this way, the FAO was able to build the capacity of the community to provide for their nutritional needs, while at the same time increasing food security by diversifying the diets of the local people. Working with NGOs such as Helen Keller International (HKI), the project was able to improve awareness of good nutritional practices by providing educational resources for use in local schools. Additionally, District Nutrition Facilitators were appointed and trained to provide nutrition education programmes for the community which would help to ensure the long-term success of the intervention.

The current global situation

Recent figures released by the FAO indicate that although current progress towards achieving the MDGs is slow, a better situation will exist by 2015, when the results of the sustainable strategies that are being put in place now will bear fruit. By 2015, the overall number of undernourished people in the developing nations is expected to reduce by half (refer to final row of the table in Figure 30.3), when compared with the baseline rate (which is set at the number of undernourished people in 1990–1992).

Region	Percentage of undernourishment		
	1990–1992 (baseline)	2015	MDG target
Sub-Saharan Africa	35.7	21.1	17.9
Near East/North Africa	7.6	7.0	3.8
Latin America/Caribbean	13.4	6.6	6.7
South Asia	25.9	12.1	13.0
East Asia	16.5	5.8	8.3
All developing nations	20.3	10.1	10.2

Figure 30.3: The expected percentage of undernourished people in the various regions of the developing world by 2015, along with a comparison with the targets set by the Millennium Development Goals.

Case study: Sub-Saharan Africa – an area of need

One of the greatest marginal areas of need in terms of undernourishment is sub-Saharan Africa. Even though FAO projections show that the percentage of hungry people in this region will decline by 2015, levels of undernourishment will still be high. This will mean that Sub-Saharan Africa will continue to be one of the most undernourished regions on earth.

The problem facing this region, often beset by natural disaster or human conflict, is that even in the absence of these monumental issues, the resource base is so narrow that agriculture remains highly vulnerable to climate change and fluctuating commodity prices. In addition, the underlying poverty found in these regions makes addressing food insecurity in a real or long-term manner very difficult. The problems within this region tend to be greatest in rural areas, which are the poorest in terms of their economic resources and also food supply. However, migration from rural areas to urban centres creates pressure there too, by placing additional strain on resources and facilities that are often already stretched to the limit. The development of shanty towns on the fringes of urban centres is one of the effects of the process of urbanisation in the developing world.

Sustainability: the way forward

The global population now has the knowledge and the power to move forward in the area of food supply and food security in a sustainable way.

According the World Health Organisation (WHO):

'Eliminating hunger and malnutrition is technically feasible. The means are there. The challenge lies in generating the requisite political will, developing realistic policies and taking concerted actions nationally and internationally.

During the last decade, there have been a number of attempts to set specific goals and targets for eliminating or reducing various kinds of food and nutrition insecurity and all the major forms of malnutrition. However, progress towards these targets has been lagging far behind what was intended and a continuation of present trends would leave millions of people undernourished and suffering from all the major forms of malnutrition in the next millennium.'

Source: WHO, 2009: http://www.who.int/.

Synoptic link

Look at page 94 of Edexcel AS Geography to see how the limited resource base of Gambia has seen it remain poorly connected to the international community.

Examiners' tip

You can use progress toward the Millennium Development Goals at both the macro (global picture) and micro (regional picture) levels to draw out the marginal areas of the earth that should be the focus of our efforts to redress issues with food security.

Knowledge

With knowledge of the importance of nutritional health, especially for mothers and children, and with the assistance of agencies such as WHO, nations have been able to commit to national nutrition plans of action. Principally, these plans cover nine areas of sustainability:

- Incorporating nutrition goals into development policies and programmes
- Improving household food and nutrition security
- Protecting consumers through improved food quality and safety
- Prevention and management of infectious diseases
- Promotion of breastfeeding
- Care for the socio-economically deprived and nutritionally vulnerable
- Prevention and control of specific micro-nutrient deficiencies
- Promotion of appropriate diets and healthy lifestyles
- A commitment to assess, analyse and monitor nutrition situations.

Interventions

With the support of national government, there are many simple interventions that can be made to help address the problems caused by under-nourishment. In spite of their simplicity, these programmes have been found to be very effective, and the measures involved include:

Maternal interventions:
- providing supplements of iron during pregnancy
- providing supplements of micro-nutrients during pregnancy
- reduction of tobacco and alcohol use during pregnancy.

Newborn babies:
- promoting breastfeeding in general and exclusive breastfeeding for the first 6 months.

Infants and children:
- zinc supplements
- vitamin A supplements
- promoting the use of iodised salt
- the promotion of hand-washing and general hygiene
- treating severe malnutrition as soon as it occurs.

Assessing scale and level of need

To effectively address issues of under-nutrition, interventions are needed at all of the levels listed previously – for mothers, newborn babies, infants and children. However, the scale of the intervention is also important. All areas must be addressed at the same time and to an adequate extent if the problem is to be addressed in a long-term, sustainable way. It is also important that the quality of the intervention is able to be maintained over time.

Whilst all of these interventions are helpful in addressing food-related issues, immediate help must be given to those most in need. Research indicates that efforts should be concentrated on women and children aged under two, as this is where the greatest impact on the cycle of malnutrition can be made.

Strengthening the resource base

By now, it should be clear that poverty and hunger are inextricably linked. It is evident that life on the margins, and especially in the world's dryland regions, is dangerously over-dependent on agriculture. Up to 70% of the people living in the developing world are either directly or indirectly reliant on agricultural production for their livelihood. This increases the vulnerability of these regions to famine and food insecurity (Figure 30.4). As the dependence on agriculture grows, so too does the percentage of the population exposed to undernourishment.

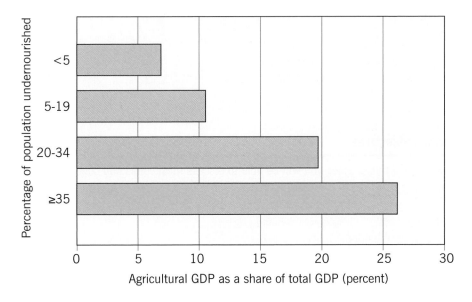

Souce: FAO

◀ **Figure 30.4:** A heavy dependence on a narrow agricultural resource base, as reflected in agricultural GDP as a share of total GDP, exposes communities to food insecurity and undernourishment.

One way to address the dependence on agriculture is to broaden the community's resource base. This may involve diversifying production by introducing new crop varieties or livestock. It can be through on-farm interventions, such as the introduction of new management techniques or technology, as long as these are appropriate to the context of the local environment and its people. It may also involve the creation of alternative sources of non-farm income, to help insulate against bad seasons or downturns in the agricultural sector.

Only through effective management techniques and sustainable strategies can we hope to sustain life in the most marginal areas of our planet.

Summary

In this chapter you have learnt:

- to describe some of the techniques and strategies that are being used to increase the global food supply and to improve food security.

- to demonstrate that, despite some progress towards the Millennium Development Goals, greater international efforts are needed in relation to global food issues.

- about examples of initiatives that have been effective in improving the food supply and food security in the marginal areas of the earth, including the work of non-governmental organisations.

- to identify sustainability as the key strategy in addressing food supply and food security, citing examples of sustainable strategies that will address the issues that underlie these concerns.

MCQ

CHAPTER 31 What is the nature and value of culture in terms of peoples and places?

Learning objectives

After studying this chapter, you will be able to discuss these ideas and concepts and provide located examples of them:
• Defining culture in terms of human cultures (ethnicities, beliefs, histories) and places (the production of cultural landscapes).
• The origins of the term 'culture'.
• The range of human cultures and a variety of cultural landscapes linked to these, which continually evolve and change.
• Some cultures and landscapes are more vulnerable than others to environmental, socio-economic and political pressures.
• The cultural diversity of people and places is valued and protected to different degrees by different players.

Culture is a complicated concept with a range of meanings and it is important to all human populations. Culture varies from region to region with some areas being relatively similar, whereas others offer greater diversity. Cities are often culturally diverse, which is reflected in the population, services and built environment.

Globalisation is regarded as a key process in driving culture towards a global model. Media TNCs and communications technology aid this process. In spite of this, localised cultures survive and new cultures can still be generated. Culture can determine our attitude to the wider world in terms of consumption, exploitation, conservation and protection. Attitudes to the environment differ between cultures.

Defining culture

Culture is the way of life of a particular society or group of people. Among other factors, it includes beliefs, behaviours, customs, traditions, rituals, dress, language, art, music, sport and literature. It is a complex and increasingly important concept within geography.

The meaning of the word 'culture' has changed over time. Originally from the Latin *cultura*, it referred to cultivation as in farming, hence the terms agriculture (farming), horticulture (fruit crops), viticulture (vines) and apiculture (bees). Later, with European colonisation overseas, culture was used to describe the way of life of human groups, such as the Caribbean culture. Culture is now applied to the activities that produce distinctive systems of knowledge and expression, such as the art, music, literature, dance and sport of a people.

Key term

Indigenous people — an ethnic group inhabiting a geographic region that has the earliest historical association with that area.

Synoptic link

See pages 80 and 83–6 on McDonald's in the Edexcel AS Geography book.

Early studies of cultural geography looked at the relationship between folkways and the physical environment and the generation of cultural landscapes. Modern cultural geography looks at global commercialised consumption, such as Disney, Coca-Cola, McDonald's and Levi Strauss. Culture is increasingly important in developed countries and developing countries for a variety of reasons.

Cultural landscapes are defined as areas which have a distinct geographical expression resulting from the interaction of people and nature. Such landscapes include cultural and natural features associated with an event, activity, person or population (Figures 31.1 and 31.2). They are important as they reflect a region's origin and/or development, and the interaction of people and the environment.

They can provide scenic, economic, environmental, social and educational benefits, and they help a population to develop an understanding of themselves. Examples of cultural landscapes include Uluru (Ayers Rock) and the Amish communities in Pennsylvania and Ohio (USA).

▲ **Figure 31.1:** Mosque at Bandar Seri Banawar, Brunei.

▲ **Figure 31.2:** The Statue of Liberty. What culture does this suggest?

Taking it further

Identify the main aspects of culture that influence your lifestyle.

Examiners' tip

Investigate local cultural landscapes in your home area. Cultural globalisation can be investigated in large cities such as London, Birmingham and Manchester.

The range of human cultures

Cultural influences

Language

Some languages have over 100 million native speakers. These include English, Mandarin, Spanish, Portuguese, Hindi, Arabic, Russian and Bengali. English is one of the dominant world languages, but there are major variations in vocabulary and accents from country to country and also from region to region. The United Nations has six official languages – Arabic, Chinese, English, French, Russian and Spanish. Language evolves over time and certain words have crept into use just as others have disappeared. Some languages such as Cornish are almost extinct whilst others, such as Irish, have undergone a major revival since the 1970s linked with an increased interest in Irish cultural activities. New variations, such as SMS language, have also developed.

Religion

According to the 2005 survey in the Encyclopaedia Britannica, there are five major global religions: Christianity, Islam, Hinduism, Chinese folk religion and Buddhism. While Christianity and Islam can claim to be truly global, the remaining three are more regional in their distribution (Figure 31.3). Christianity and Islam have both used political networks and military strength to expand their spheres of influence. The spread of Christianity across the globe can be linked with the expansion of European colonies throughout Africa, Asia and the Americas. The spread of Christianity gave a shared culture in areas which were linked by colonial powers, therefore economic and political integration (domination) coincided with cultural integration (domination). In the case of the British Empire, improvements in communications, such as telegraph and submarine cables, allowed more rapid communications than had been previously possible, and this enabled the transmission of cultural information. The development of an education system based on British curricula and textbooks further helped the British culture spread, into its colonies.

Other religions have faded over time. Zoroastrianism is the philosophy and religion based on the teachings of the prophet Zoroaster. It was once the dominant religion in Persia. It may have been the world's first monotheistic (one God) religion and religious historians believe that many Jewish, Christian and Muslim beliefs derive from Zoroastrianism. There are probably fewer than 200,000 followers of Zoroastrianism, mostly located in parts of India.

In other areas, notably China, there are many folk religions which draw on aspects of mythology. There are believed to be nearly 400 million followers of Chinese folk religion, which is a combination of religious practices, worship of ancestors, Taoism and Buddhism. There are also remnants of Neolithic religions such as the worship of the sun, moon, earth and stars.

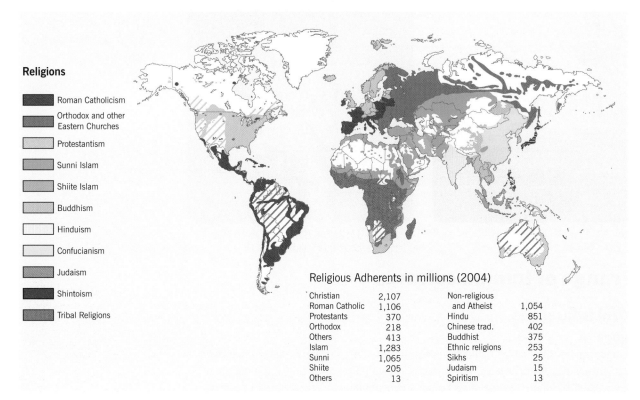

Religions

- Roman Catholicism
- Orthodox and other Eastern Churches
- Protestantism
- Sunni Islam
- Shiite Islam
- Buddhism
- Hinduism
- Confucianism
- Judaism
- Shintoism
- Tribal Religions

Religious Adherents in millions (2004)

Christian	2,107	Non-religious	
Roman Catholic	1,106	and Atheist	1,054
Protestants	370	Hindu	851
Orthodox	218	Chinese trad.	402
Others	413	Buddhist	375
Islam	1,283	Ethnic religions	253
Sunni	1,065	Sikhs	25
Shiite	205	Judaism	15
Others	13	Spiritism	13

▲ **Figure 31.3:** Map of global religions.

Key term

Glocalisation — a localised form of globalisation. For example, a global firm like Nissan or McDonald's develops a local variant of a mass-produced product, such as vegetarian burgers in India.

Synoptic link

See pages 93 and 124–5 in the AS book to revisit China.

Global brands

Despite globalisation and the rise of global brands, glocalisation often occurs in a local market. In India mutton is used in Big Macs and vegetable oil is used for frying. Barbie dolls are available in over 30 national varieties. Although there are global media corporations such as CNN there are also important local newspapers and radio stations. Some small-scale news companies may become well known on the international stage. For example, during the armed conflicts in Afghanistan and Iraq, the Arabic news agency al-Jazeera was often the main source of information about groups at war with American and British troops.

Political systems

There is also a range of political systems. Much of the Western world is characterised by democratically elected governments, but there are other variations. In New Zealand seats are reserved for Maori representatives. In China an authoritarian socialist government stands alongside a capitalist economy. Other socialist countries, such as Cuba, Vietnam and North Korea, have different degrees of openness.

Links between culture and landscape

Traditional cultural landscapes and postmodern technoscapes and ethnoscapes

Traditional cultural landscapes suggest a shared lifestyle with a common religion, economy, values and attitudes. These are often more manifest in rural areas (Figure 31.4). Often production and consumption of goods are localised and there is less contact with outside forces. In traditional rural areas, people were more likely to work, socialise and worship in locally based activities and buildings. As communications increase, there is increased contact with other geographic regions, an increase in trade, a diversity of employment and alternative forms of entertainment. Society becomes less influenced by people and places, but more affected by technology. People are less bound by locally based activities and are increasingly globalised in their interactions. Even the food people now eat is more likely to come from a wider area than in traditional communities. A good example is the rise of internet cafes, which have allowed people to work or communicate from almost any part of the world (Figure 31.5). Although there is a great digital divide, for people in developed countries the IT revolution has permitted them to be part of the worldwide postmodern technoscape.

▲ **Figure 31.4:** A traditional cultural landscape.

Taking it further

Suggest ways in which cultural diversity has changed in the UK in the last 20 years.

Case study: Cultural change in Tibet

Tibet's population believes that the Chinese invasion of Tibet has imposed colonial rule on their country and eroded part of their culture. They desire the right to political self-determination and an end to over 50 years of Chinese rule.

Tibet is one of the most remote and isolated parts of the world. It is often described as 'the roof of the world', being located high up in the Himalayas. For much of the early 20th century (1911–49) it functioned like an independent country. However, following the 1949 Chinese Revolution and the creation of the People's Republic of China, Tibet's independence largely vanished. China attacked Tibet in 1950, and in 1951 Tibet signed an agreement giving China control over Tibet's external relations and the establishment of the Chinese military in Tibet in return for guaranteeing Tibet's political system.

During an uprising in 1959, Tibet's spiritual leader, the Dalai Lama, fled and sought refuge in northern India. About 80,000 Tibetans followed. In 1965 the Chinese government created the Tibetan Autonomous Region (TAR).

Tibetan culture is changing. The Chinese government has encouraged migration of the ethnic Han population into the region. The building of the China–Tibet railway was finished in 2005 and this has speeded up the migration of Han people. Many Tibetans claim that the ethnic Han are given more of the better-paid jobs in the area. The railway was almost exclusively built using Han labour. Many see the building of the railway as a political tool: not only does it allow for increased migration of the Han into Tibet, it also allows China to increase its military presence in the area. It lets China exploit Tibet's resources and move them to China's urban–industrial complex.

The main religion in Tibet is Buddhism and this has become highly politicised. In 2008 protests by monks in Lhasa led to riots in which about 100 people were killed. The Chinese government claimed that only 13 were killed. Businesses belonging to Han migrants were attacked and burnt during the riots.

▲ **Figure 31.5:** A technoscape – internet café.

Cultural diversity in Ireland

In Northern Ireland, Irish culture is associated with traditional Irish music and song, dance (e.g. Riverdance, a modern version of Irish dance), sports (Gaelic football and hurling), the arts (drama, poetry, literature, carvings and metal working, such as Celtic crosses), the Irish language (Gaelic) and traditional Irish dress and food. In contrast, loyalist or unionist culture finds expression in the parades and marches held every summer. Parades fulfil a social, economic and religious function.

Culture is valued as a source of national and personal identity. Owing to the conflict between Protestant and Catholic populations, members valued their own culture and identity with a sense of pride. In the Republic of Ireland cultural identity has been developed through the education system. The teaching of Irish, and to an extent English and history, in schools makes use of Irish myths and legends, as well as historical events, to develop literacy as well as a sense of cultural identity.

Nowhere are variations in cultural participation in sport more complex than in Ireland. For example, Gaelic football and hurling are played throughout the Republic of Ireland, but only among the Catholic communities of Northern Ireland. Until 2007 the national stadium at Croke Park could be used only for Gaelic games and not for rugby or football. Football is played in the Republic of Ireland and Northern Ireland. The national teams for rugby and cricket, however, represent the whole of the island of Ireland, i.e. both the Republic and Northern Ireland. Cricket is mainly played in Northern Ireland and around Dublin, mainly among those of British origin.

The Gaeltacht are found mainly in the peripheral western counties of Donegal, Mayo, Galway and Kerry, together with parts of counties Cork, Meath and Waterford (Figure 31.6). About 86,000 live in Gaeltacht areas. The Gaeltacht are areas where the Irish tradition and culture are maintained and allowed to evolve naturally in a modern setting.

Taking it further

Visit http://en.wikipedia.org/wiki/Scottish_Gaelic_language to find out about the distribution of Scottish speakers and Gaelic culture in Scotland, and http://en.wikipedia.org/wiki/Welsh_language for Welsh.

Examiners' tip

Make sure you refer to named examples. Cultural diversity may sound very vague if factors and processes are over-generalised.

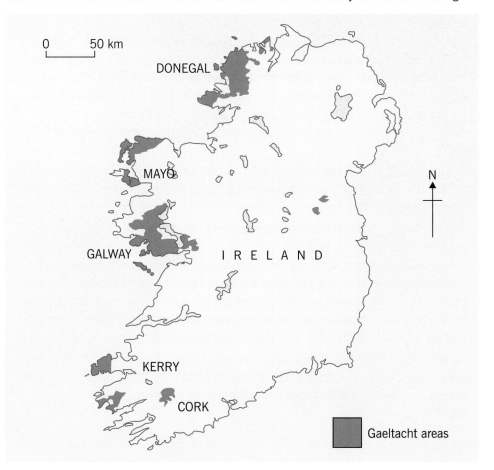

▶ **Figure 31.6:** The Gaeltacht areas of Ireland.

Udaras na Gaeltachta is a government agency responsible for promoting the economic and social development of the Gaeltacht in order to preserve and extend the Irish language as the principal language of the region. It was established in 1980.

In addition, the Irish language is taught in all schools in Ireland, and many Irish myths and legends (Fionn MacCool, Cuchullain) feature in primary school books.

◄ **Figure 31.7:** A Gaeltacht area in Kerry, South West Ireland.

Summary

In this chapter you have learnt:

• how to define culture in terms of human cultures and places.

• about the origins of the term 'culture'.

• about the range and variety of human cultures and cultural landscapes.

  • that some cultures and landscapes are more vulnerable than others.

  • that the cultural diversity of people and places is valued and protected to different degrees.

MCQ

CHAPTER 32 How and why does culture vary spatially?

Learning objectives

After studying this chapter, you will be able to discuss these ideas and concepts and provide located examples of them:

• How some countries and regions are culturally more homogeneous than others.
• How cultural diversity is greater in urban areas than in rural areas.
• How governments and other bodies may promote diversity or homogeneity.
• How cultural imperialism creates cultural homogeneity, but has also caused a cultural backlash.

Key term

Homogeneity — a situation in which there is a lack of variation.

Cultural homogeneity

Some countries and regions are more culturally homogeneous than others. Some countries where immigration is very common are very mixed and diverse, such as in the USA. On the other hand, Australia has experienced much in-migration but its isolation has led to a greater degree of cultural homogeneity. Countries which have received little in-migration, such as Japan, tend to be culturally homogeneous. In some cases the political process can influence cultural homogeneity at a local or regional level. The apartheid policy in South Africa led to racial segregation and so at a local scale there was increased homogeneity with a patchwork of cultural heterogeneity at a larger, regional scale. Similarities between cultures depend on factors such as geographical isolation, communications and rates of social and economic development. For example, in geographical terms, the UK is a fairly densely populated country with a long history of in-migration. This helps to explain its cultural heterogeneity. On the other hand, while Japan is mainly culturally homogeneous, there are regional variations.

Urban–rural contrasts

Cultural diversity is much greater in urban areas than in rural areas. This is because there are more job opportunities, more varied housing and more services (health, education, retail) than there are in rural areas. Thus more migrants from a wide variety of cultures are attracted to large urban areas, thereby increasing the cultural mix. In contrast, the opportunities in rural areas are limited, both in type and number. Likewise the number of services to be found there are more limited so rural areas attract fewer people. Often they may attract similar types of people – such as the elderly, who may wish to retire to a quieter location, or those with young families, who desire a safer location for their children. As rural areas are less accessible to public transport, it is only the wealthier who can afford the private transport needed in rural areas who move there. Thus the areas are not as diverse as urban areas. In the UK, the most diverse areas are within cities, whereas rural areas are much more homogeneous. This is largely the result of migration. Large cities such as London offer many job opportunities and attract migrants from all over the world. In contrast, most rural areas experience net out-migration as there are few jobs available. Consequently they are far more homogeneous than their urban counterparts. Urban areas with a significant number of a particular cultural group may be able to support a range of facilities for that group. For example, a large number of Jewish people in a region may be able to sustain a synagogue. The presence of a synagogue in an area may attract further Jewish people. There may also be the threshold population so that other services could be supported too.

Taking it further

Visit www.korea.net/korea/G08.asp for an excellent starting place for finding out about all aspects of Korea.

Case study: Korea

Despite foreign invasions, occupation, division and the Korean War, South Korea has a strong sense of national identity and culture. It could be argued that Korea's strong sense of cultural identity is precisely because it has had to fight to retain its independence and cultural identity.

Korea existed as a distinct and united kingdom for almost 1,300 years. This ended only in 1910 when the country became a Japanese colony. Korea became independent after the defeat of Japan in World War II. The Republic of Korea was founded in 1948 along with the Democratic People's Republic of (North) Korea. Despite invasions and dominance by neighbouring countries, Korea remains culturally homogeneous and with a clear sense of national identity. That national identity has been fostered in recent years by events as divese as the World Cup (jointly hosted with Japan in 2002) and the restoration of the Cheong Gye Cheon stream in downtown Seoul, a symbol of Korea's past as well as its future, and its natural environment.

The Cheong Gye Cheon (Clean Stream) was a natural river flowing through the centre of Seoul, which became Korea's capital in 1392. The stream flooded in the rainy season and experienced low flows for much of the year, causing widespread pollution when it was not in flood.

The Cheong Gye Cheon Restoration Project is of environmental, historical and cultural significance and has allowed Seoul to popularise its historical and cultural traditions (Figure 32.1). Five ancient bridges have been excavated and some of the stones used in the construction of the new levees. Traditional cultural activities such as a lantern festival and bridge stepping have been re-established.

▲ **Figure 32.1:** Cheong Gye Cheon.

The project is much more than merely the environmental restoration of a stream. It has given the people of Seoul a new identity based on their history and culture. It is part of a symbolic project to revive part of Korea's historic, cultural and natural heritage. It may well prove to be the prototype for future redevelopment schemes elsewhere.

Korea's population of 48 million includes about 530,000 foreigners, about 1.1% of the population. Although a relatively small percentage of the total population, it is increasing steadily. Nevertheless, Korea has remained a homogeneous state for a long time, although there is some evidence of change (Figure 32.2).

One aspect of Korean culture is the company town. In Pohang, the steel company Posco, employs 17,200 workers and houses for 5,000 families. The plant includes a 25,000-seater stadium and the company sponsors two football teams, the choir and the orchestra. Another aspect of Korean culture (similar to Japan) is the extremely competitive academic environment. Entry to prestigious universities is the key to career success. Many parents send their children to private schools and crammer schools.

Case study: Iceland

Icelandic culture is varied and renowned for its literary heritage (myths and sagas), silver and wood carvings and weaving. Sagas include the kings' sagas and the Icelanders' sagas. The Icelandic language is close to the Old Norse spoken by the Vikings and still contains words such as Fos (meaning waterfall), which have parallels in Britain such as Skelwith Force in the Lake District. Iceland has a number of religions, although Lutheran is the most important. One of the most important cultural landscapes in Iceland is to be found at Thingvellir (Figure 32.3). This was the site of the original Icelandic parliament and has recently been reconstructed. It is now an important cultural and tourist attraction. In Iceland outdoor sports are very popular, especially skiing and swimming in geothermal spas and pools. Iceland's harsh physical environment has led to a low population density. This, coupled with geographic isolation, has led to a very homogeneous culture.

▲ **Figure 32.3:** Parliament at Thingvellir.

▲ **Figure 32.2:** McDonald's in Korea.

Taking it further

Visit http://www.iceland.is/history-and-culture/isit to find out about Icelandic culture.

Within urban areas there are very different cultural groupings (Figure 32.4). In London, for example, the white British population generally live in the outer boroughs. In contrast, the Afro–Caribbean concentrations in Clapham (south London), Notting Hill and Hackney relate back to cheap housing districts and air-raid shelters that were available around the time of the first labour migration in 1948. The Bangladeshis are concentrated in the east end of London, whereas the Chinese population is extremely dispersed, depending on where they have set up their businesses.

The role of government and other players

Government and other players' attitudes, both positive and negative, towards human diversity and landscape diversity, are important in preserving diversity or moving towards cultural homogeneity. UNESCO believes that cultural diversity is the common heritage of humanity. It believes that it is important for economic growth, intellectual development and social, moral and educational quality. It recognises that there are many inappropriate developments which threaten cultural diversity. Consequently, UNESCO's focus is on developing countries and those in which there is conflict. It tries to preserve cultural diversity through an education programme and training activities which improve knowledge and awareness of the value of cultural diversity, and the economic benefits of preserving it.

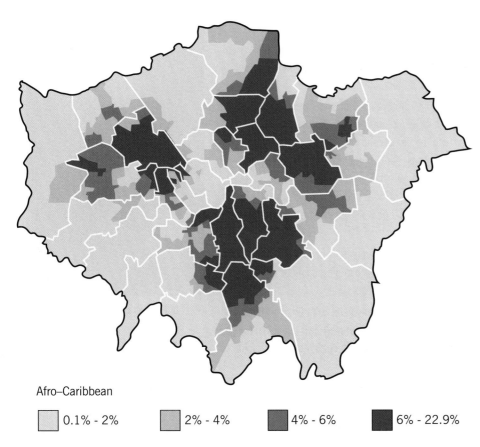

Afro–Caribbean

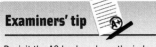

| 0.1% - 2% | 2% - 4% | 4% - 6% | 6% - 22.9% |

▲ **Figure 32.4:** Map of distribution of whites and Afro-Caribbeans in London.

Examiners' tip

Revisit the AS book and use the index to look up cities, London, segregation (including spatial segregation) and assimilation.

Key term

Cultural imperialism — the practice of promoting the culture or language of one nation in another. It is usually the case that the former is a large nation that is powerful in economic and military terms and the latter is a smaller, less affluent one.

Cultural imperialism and anti-globalisation

The world is becoming more uniform and standardised through a technological, commercial and cultural synchronisation emanating from the West, thereby implying that globalisation is tied up with modernity.

Aspects of colonial imperialism

Cultural imperialism occurs when a large, strong economic or political power imposes its culture on a smaller, weaker country. There is a long history of cultural imperialism going back as far as the Greek and Roman Empires, and including the European colonies in the Americas, and the carving up of Africa. Much of this extension of colonial power was in the search for raw materials and wealth to help run the Empire (see also Chapters 10–12 on superpowers). Modern-day cultural imperialism is not necessarily carried out by countries but could be carried out by multinational companies. Moreover, the spread of consumerism, and so-called Western values, could be described as a form of consumerist colonialism. Electronic colonialism refers to the spread and influence of electronic giants such as Google, Time Warner, Microsoft and Disney. Cultural colonialism can be manifest through changes in language, tourism, the growth of the media and fashion, for example.

Case study: Israel

Following the Second World War, Britain withdrew from Palestine and the UN divided the area into Arab and Jewish states. The Arabs rejected this policy. Subsequently the Israelis defeated the Arabs in a series of wars, but this failed to solve the situation. In 1982 Israel withdrew from the Sinai. Outstanding territorial disputes with Jordan were resolved in the 1994 Israel–Jordan Treaty of Peace. In 2000 Israel withdrew from southern Lebanon, which it had occupied since 1982. In 2003 the USA, EU, UN and Russia set out a road map to a final settlement of Israel and a democratic Palestine. However, progress was undermined by violence between 2003 and 2005. An agreement in 2005 significantly reduced the violence. In 2005 Israel unilaterally disengaged from the Gaza Strip, but retained control over most of the points of entry. However, the election of Hamas in 2006 to head the Palestinian Legislative Council froze relations between Israel and the Palestinian Authority.

▲ **Figure 32.5:** Israel and disputed territories.

Settlement policy and cultural landscape

In Israel, as well as their use for residential and agricultural purposes, rural settlements have had important ideological (cultural and political) influences. The use of civilian, especially agricultural, settlement plays a unique role in the Arab–Israeli conflict. Settlement has been a key element (Figure 32.5):

- in the expansion of Jewish control over Palestine (pre-1948)
- the consolidation of that control throughout Israel (1948–67)
- in more recent attempts to establish long-term control over the West Bank and the Gaza Strip (post-1967).

The creation of a civilian presence can therefore be an important means of ensuring long-term control in circumstances where the land cannot be purchased legally.

The functional nature of the settlements is even more important. An agricultural village brings far more land under control than a commuter or dormitory village. Also farming creates a strong bond between the settler and the land, hence a sense of belonging to the area.

A major component of Zionism (the movement to restore a Jewish nation in Palestine) was the desire to return to the land and to the agricultural origins of the Jewish people. Settlement dispersal was also a major factor in determining the ultimate borders of the state of Israel in 1948–9. The vast, empty Negev Desert region was included within the state's boundaries because it was perceived as constituting the future development region for new settlement projects.

During December 2008 and January 2009 Israel launched an offensive at Hamas in the Gaza Strip, killing 1,300 Palestinians. The offensive did much to damage the opinion of Israel worldwide.

According to Palestinian sources, one in seven buildings was completely or partially destroyed, and losses were valued at $2 billion. The political impacts of the attacks may go further than the physical damage. Old divisions between Israelis and Arabs deepened. Saudi Arabia warned Palestinians that their internal rifts were more dangerous than Israel aggression. Hamas, the Islamist resistance party, accused Fatah, the peace-talking party, of colluding with Israel. Fatah blamed Hamas for provoking the Israeli attack. The influence of foreign countries was varied. Western countries, Egypt, Saudi Arabia and Jordan favour Fatah and shun Hamas. In contrast, Iran, Syria and Qatar favour Hamas.

There are around 6,000 languages in the world and this may drop to 3,000 by 2100. English is becoming the world language. Two-thirds of all scientists write in English and 80% of the information stored in computers is in English. It is an official language in much of Africa, the Pacific, and South and South-east Asia. Tourism is now the world's largest industry. Tourism can lead to a spread of culture, which may be undesirable.

The growth in the influence of TNCs is reflected in the rise of global consumer culture built around world brands (see page 251 on McDonald's, Coca-Cola and Starbucks). National media systems are being superseded by global media complexes (see Chapter 33).

Taking it further

To see an example of how Israeli settlement policy has changed in recent years, read 'Israeli settlement policy' on your Student CD-ROM.

Case study: Tibet

Tibet was controlled by the Chinese People's Liberation Army between 1951 and 1959. The Tibetan rebellion of 1959 saw the Dalai Lama and 9,000 followers flee into India. Tibet became an autonomous region of China in 1965. However, Chinese rule was unpopular among Tibetans and the economy stagnated.

From 1979, however, the Chinese government took a more sympathetic and pragmatic approach to Tibet. Traditional farming and trading patterns were reintroduced and some former political leaders (and rebel leaders) were given a political role in the running of Tibet. There were even attempts to encourage the Dalai Lama to return. On the other hand, pro-independence demonstrations between 1987 and 1989 met with a violent response.

Taking it further

Visit the website www.tibetanculture. org to find out how Tibetan culture is being preserved. Compare this with Chinese websites where the protection and development of Tibetan culture is the focus.

▲ **Figure 32.6:** Tourism and the spread of British culture.

The spread of liberal democracy has been profound and is now practised in the vast majority of nation-states around the world. Underlying this diffusion is the Western belief that it is the most desirable form of governance.

Anti-globalisation

After the emergence of the anti-globalisation movement in Seattle in December 1999, increasing numbers of protests were raised against the Western economic model. The anti-globalisation organisation originated from the 1994 Zapatista uprising in Mexico and the 1997 global economic crisis. Critics denounced the 'single-mindedness' or exclusivity which favoured the economic growth of Western countries at the expense of others, and called for a 'more human face of globalisation'.

Initially the authorities labelled the demonstrators as 'troublemakers' but Joseph Stiglitz, a former chief economist of the World Bank, offered support for the protesters. He won the Nobel Prize for Economics in 2001 and called for greater state controls and regulation. The financial crisis that emerged in 2008 shows some support for his views. He questioned the practices of the World Bank and the International Monetary Fund (IMF).

The economic crises affecting most developing countries, notably in Asia and Latin America, showed that the critics were right and that the Western model had failed.

Ethics versus economics

The Western economic model has produced huge inequalities in wealth. For example:

- the ten richest people in the world have more than 1.5 times the income of all the developing countries put together
- 4% of the income of the 360 richest people, who own more than 50% of the world's wealth, could solve the problems of the world's poor
- the three wealthiest people have assets equalling the GDP of the 48 poorest countries.

For most religious, spiritual or 'humanitarian' institutions these discrepancies carry a moral contradiction that has led them to call for a revision of the situation generated by this economic model.

Examiners' tip

Make sure your essays have a structure: an introduction, main body and conclusion. The introduction should set the scene and identify the case studies that you intend to use.

Summary

In this chapter you have learnt:

- how some regions and nations are culturally homogeneous, such as Korea and Iceland.
- why urban areas are more culturally diverse than rural areas.
- how governments and other agencies promote cultural diversity or homogeneity.
- how cultural imperialism has created a backlash. Some examples include Coca-Cola and KFC.

MCQ

CHAPTER 33 How is globalisation impacting on culture?

Key terms

Blog
Bollywood
Hyper-individual

Learning objectives

After studying this chapter, you will be able to discuss these ideas and concepts and provide located examples of them:
- The different views on the significance of globalisation in cultural diversity.
- The role of global media corporations in the spread of cultural values and attitudes.
- The development of local hybrid versions of globalisation.
- The opposing opinions on the impact of globalised consumerist societies on people and the landscape.

Synoptic link

Visit the Edexcel AS Geography book and revise Globalisation on pages 72–9, 81–6 and 123–7.

The impact of globalisation on cultural diversity

There are many different views on globalisation (Figure 33.1). The most common are the hyperglobalist, the sceptical and the transformationalist views. Each takes a different slant on the significance of globalisation and its impact on cultural diversity.

Hyperglobalist view

Hyperglobalists believe that this is a new geographical era in which globalisation processes dominate. They argue that the nation-state is no longer important; instead there is a single global market supported by a transnational network of production, trade and finance. They believe that forms of government above the level of the state – such as trading blocs like the European Union – are increasingly important.

Some scholars see in this the erosion of the power of the state, and thus the victory of capitalism over socialism. This view was widely supported following the collapse of the former Soviet Union. Socialist hyperglobalist writers see globalisation as aggressive and regressive. Both believe that economic forces are dominant in an integrated global economy.

Hyperglobalists suggest that there is a new world order based on consumerism. They believe that this is leading to a spread of liberal democracy. Hyperglobalists take the line that globalisation leads to homogeneity of culture: the Westernisation or Americanisation of the world economy and culture.

However, the financial crisis of 2008 and the involvement of national governments in an attempt to support their economies suggest that the nation-state is not yet dead, and that hyperglobalists may have to modify their view.

Sceptical view

Sceptics question whether globalisation is anything new. They believe that the world was just as integrated in the 19th century. They also claim that if the hyperglobalists were correct, then there would be uninterrupted flows of labour, trade and capital. However, labour is relatively immobile and protectionist policies limit the amount of free trade. Sceptics believe that national governments are still the most important players. The rise of China, India and Iran as emerging powers is due, in large part, to government policies. In addition, they argue that trade blocs promote regionalism rather than globalisation.

Sceptics believe that the hyperglobalists are only interested in increasing their market share in the new global economy. This leads to the marginalisation of the poor. The sceptics' view would result in cultural heterogeneity, although homogeneity of culture may occur within a single nation, such as China or Iran.

Transformationalist view

The hyperglobalists and the sceptics represent two extremes on the globalisation continuum. The transformationalists lie somewhere in between. These academics believe that globalisation is real and is changing society. They consider that such change is merely an extension of colonial relations. They also believe that the role of national governments is changing rather than being made redundant.

They argue that cultural exchanges lead to hybrids. According to transformationalists, the state is actively engaged in economic and cultural issues. This produces a diversity and increased unevenness. There is an increase in the differentiation of global society, politics and economy.

	Hyperglobalist	Sceptical	Transformationalist
What is happening?	The global era	Increased regionalism	Unprecedented interconnectedness
Main features	Global civilisation based on global capitalism and governance	Core-led regionalism makes globe less interconnected than in late 19th century	'Thick globalisation'. High intensity, extensity and velocity of globalisation
Main forces at work	Technology, capitalism and human ingenuity	Nation-states and the market	'Modern' forces in unison
Views on globalisation	Borderless world and perfect markets	Regionalisation, internationalisation and imperfect markets	Time–space compression
Implications for the nation-state	Eroded or made irrelevant	Strengthened and made more relevant	Transformed governance patterns and new state imperatives
Historical path	Global civilisation based on new transnational elite	Clashes through actions of regional blocs	Indeterminate: depends on type and action of nation-states and civil society
Core position	Triumph of capitalism and the market over nation-states	Powerful states create globalisation agenda to perpetuate their dominant position	Transformation of governance at all levels and new networks of power

▲ **Figure 33.1:** Three theses of globalisation – a schema.

The media

Global media corporations are increasingly replacing national media companies. With global deregulation some media companies have expanded into the international market. The industry has become increasingly concentrated. About 20–30 large transnational companies dominate the world's global entertainment and media industry. The majority of these are from the USA, for example, Time Warner AOL and Disney. Most right-wing media support the view that the spread of market economies, capitalism, competition, free trade and democracy is a progressive trend. Capitalism is seen as promoting economic growth, which in turn leads to improvements in human welfare.

In the news media, CNN, the BBC and ABC provide a similar style of presentation, often focusing on the human interest story. Moreover, there is often a Western bias. The Arab station al-Jazeera offers non-Western and sometimes anti-Western alternatives.

In some instances, hybrids might be an alternative outcome of cultural globalisation/ Westernisation. Thus cultural globalisation could produce a mixed outcome rather than a Western outcome. The adaptation of McDonald's restaurants to fit local dietary patterns is a good example (see Chapter 11, page 95).

Taking it further

Comment on the arguments of the hyperglobalists, sceptics and transformationalists. Which do you think provides the best summary of the significance of globalisation on cultural diversity?

Case study: Viacom

Viacom is short for Video and Audio Communications. It is an American media multinational company with global satellite and cable television networks (e.g. MTV Network and BET) and movie production and distribution (e.g. Paramount and DreamWorks). In 2007 Viacom came to an agreement with the Indian company Global Broadcast News and formed Viacom-18. This carries Viacom's channels in India and there are plans for Hindi entertainment and movie channels to be delivered by Viacom. In the same year Viacom made a $500 million deal with Microsoft to share content and advertising.

Case study: The Disney Corporation

The Disney Corporation wields tremendous power and influence. It has dealings in films, videos, theme parks, television, retail stores, cruise ships and clothing (Figure 33.2). It is the world's second largest global media giant after Time Warner AOL.

The corporation has its critics. In the past it was criticised for Cold War propaganda and currently it is criticised for its use of cheap labour in sweatshops. There are others who criticise the cultural messages that are evident in Disney films. Nevertheless, it is still perceived as 'wholesome' family entertainment.

Animation is the key to Disney's economic strength and cultural influence. Seven of the world's top 10 selling videos are Disney cartoons, and *The Lion King* alone has earned over $1 billion. One of the reasons for its success is that animated films cross political borders easily. The distribution and redubbing costs are low, but the potential profits are

▲ **Figure 33.2:** Disney – wholesome family entertainment or hyper-individualistic culture?

great. Critics argue that the animations help promote a capitalist ideology. They see elements of patriarchy (monarchy) and racism in many of the films.

For example, Disney's individual heroes and heroines generally come from a background of economic and cultural privilege. Social inequalities are rarely mentioned. Critics claim that the film assumes class hierarchies and denigrates democracy, promotes hyper-individualism and condones the use of force, coercion and underhand ways to achieve their goals.

Key terms

Hyper-individual — a person who is only concerned about their own wellbeing and self-fulfilment, showing little or no regard for others.
Bollywood — general term given to the Indian film industry.

Local cultural globalisation

Case study: Bollywood

Bollywood is the term given to the Mumbai-based Hindi-language film industry in India. Unlike Hollywood, there is no actual place called Bollywood. The type of films produced in Bollywood reflect aspects of Indian culture. In the 1950s romantic musicals and drama were prominent. In the 1970s films became more violent. Since the mid-1990s there has been a return for more family-friendly romantic musicals.

There are many influences on Indian cinema, including ancient Indian epics, ancient Sanskrit drama, traditional folk theatre, Parsi theatre, Hollywood and Western musical theatre.

Bollywood films are popular in India and among the Indian diaspora worldwide, especially in North America and Europe. This is especially true where there is a large Indian community such as in Toronto, Chicago and New York. They are also popular in southern Asia, Afghanistan, Pakistan, Bangladesh, Nepal and Sri Lanka. Surprisingly, they are also enjoyed in West Africa. Despite featuring a different culture, religion and language, there appear to be enough similarities to render them popular. The clothing is similar; men often wear turbans, porters carrying large loads are common, and markets teeming with animals often feature. Given the strict Muslim culture, the films show more respect towards women. For example, they are fully clothed and on-screen kissing is rare.

Music

Globally the music industry is dominated by a small number of very large TNCs, such as Sony, Universal, EMI, Warner and BMG. These are mainly based in the USA and have been responsible for the diffusion of music from the USA and UK to other parts of the world.

Many forms of music have become globalised and rock and roll, blues and soul were early examples. More recently, punk, rap, hip-hop and boy/girl bands have all become globalised. Rap/hip-hop originated in the ghettoes of US cities as a political protest movement against mainstream US culture. It has since become part of the capitalist culture. Indeed, many forms of music, such as blues and punk, began as protest or counter-culture, only to be endorsed by cultural TNCs and become part of the consumer culture.

There are examples of local hybrids. For example, Latin American rock contains elements of Latino rhythm and flamenco style. New Zealand hip-hop blends US and Polynesian cultures.

Taking it further

To learn about the different types of music in the Caribbean, read 'Music in the Caribbean' on your Student CD-ROM.

Fashion

Clothing is an important part of culture. It can represent culture and beliefs. The kimono is associated with Japanese culture just as the toga was with the Romans. Clothing is also affected by environment and gender; therefore there as many regional variations as there are cultural variations.

For example, clothing styles in the USA have evolved considerably since 1945. The 1950s saw the rise of the leather jacket, associated with rebel figureheads like James Dean and Elvis Presley. In the 1960s, hippie culture led to the development of jeans with flowers and bright-coloured shirts. Many of the changes are seen among teenagers and young adults. In the 1980s hip-hop and punk became more common. Punks frequently wore ripped jeans, heavy boots such as Doc Martens, chains and black clothing. Goths tended to wear dark clothing. In contrast, urban cultures such as hip-hop fashion include baggy jeans, brand name T-shirts and Timberland boots or Converse shoes. Trousers are worn low on the hips and baseball caps are a common sight.

Regional variations can also be seen. On the west coast of the USA, beachwear, shorts and T-shirts are very common. This is hardly surprising, given the warm climate. In contrast, Inuit populations in Alaska wear parkas, hats and gloves made from furs. This helps them to cope with the cold Arctic climate.

Elsewhere, major sports teams are an important form of global branding, and their replica kits can be found in the most unlikely places (Figure 33.3).

▲ **Figure 33.3:** Sports fashion in the Tumburong rainforest.

New forms of expression

Blog is an abbreviation of the term web log. Blogs are websites normally developed or maintained by one person and containing regular inputs of texts, images and references to other blogs. Many blogs are written about specific events, whereas others are more of a diary format.

Texting means sending short text messages on mobile phones using the Short Message Service (SMS). Many of the words used are abbreviated or use acronyms, for example, AFAIK As far as I know; CID Consider it done; CUL8R See you later; OTOH On the other hand; CU 2MORO See you tomorrow; and TWIMC To whom it may concern.

In the book *Language and the Internet*, David Crystal examines the widespread view that the internet is bad for language, that technospeak will rule, standards drop and creativity decline as globalisation creates homogeneity. He argues the reverse: that the internet allows an expansion in the range and variety of language and is providing opportunities for personal creativity.

Taking it further

To find out about the different types of Japanese kimono, visit the Student CD-ROM and read 'Variations in Japanese kimonos'.

▲ **Figure 33.4:** Ethnic foods.

▲ **Figure 33.5:** Adidas shoes.

Globalised consumerist societies

Consumption refers to more than just an economic transaction. Some items have a symbolic value and the consumption of these items can help to create a cultural or symbolic identity such as the wearing of sports tops of a favourite team. Certain brands are associated with particular cultures, e.g. the US hip-hop culture is associated with Adidas shoes, therefore consumption may lead to social and cultural differentiation. Whether this is occurring to a large enough scale to create one global culture is debatable.

Cultural consumerism occurs when the objects, ideas and/or traits of a culture are bought and sold. This is most noticeable in the tourist sector where authentic and exotic cultural experiences are part of the tourist experience. On another scale, the development of ethnic foods (Figure 33.4) in supermarkets reflects a growing demand for a greater variety of foods. In many world cities the promotion of ethnic enclaves, such as Chinatown in Soho in London, is a form of cultural consumerism, allowing Western residents to experience a non-Western culture.

For some, cultural capitalism is a form of economic elitism. The group buying into the culture, whether it's music, clothing (Figure 33.5), food or furnishings, is setting itself apart from mainstream society. The so-called cosmopolitan consumer is generally found in rich countries. In developing countries cosmopolitan consumerism occurs, but is the preserve of wealthy minorities.

In some cases, cultural consumerism can improve livelihoods and preserve cultural traditions. This may be the case with cultural tourism. Some, however, see this as the prostitution of culture. As such, culture is at the mercy of market forces and cultural consumerism may create damaging stereotypes.

Examiners' tip

Try to have balance in your arguments – show both sides of the argument and evaluate their claims and counter-claims before you reach your final judgement.

Case study: Fiji

In Fiji mainstream tourism was based on beaches and sunshine. Some operators began to introduce the Fijian experience with kava drinking welcome ceremonies and meke (dances) for authentic visits. However, these ceremonies are rare outside the tourist enclaves. The Fiji Visitors Bureau provides a great deal of detail on its website about traditional Fijian beliefs, social structures and ceremonies. In reality, these characteristics are changing rapidly as Fijians become increasingly an urbanised and Westernised population. However, for the tourist sector a fossilised version of Fijian culture is helping to market the country to Western tourists.

There are different interpretations:
- Cultural commodification has helped to preserve culture which would otherwise have disappeared.
- The new forms of culture are new variants imposed from above, creating a false culture.

Summary

In this chapter you have learnt:

- that there is a variety of views, from the hyperglobalists to the sceptics, as to the significance of globalisation in cultural diversity.
- that global media corporations, such as Disney, wield great power in terms of cultural globalisation.
- that local hybrids, such as Bollywood, and new forms of fashion and language produce new and alternative cultures.
- that there are different opinions on the impact of a globalised consumerist society on culture.

MCQ

CHAPTER 34 How do cultural values impact on our relationship with the environment?

Key terms

Commodities
Market exchange

Synoptic link

Visit the Edexcel AS Geography book and revise Globalisation on pages 72–9, 81–6 and 123–7.

Learning objectives

After studying this chapter, you will be able to discuss these ideas and concepts and provide located examples of them:
- Different cultures have different attitudes towards the environment.
- Different attitudes affect how the landscape is exploited and/or protected.
- Anthropocentric (human-focused) values are necessary in justifying consumer cultures.
- There is a clear conflict between environmentalism and consumer capitalism. In addition, different movements, such as the green movement, have developed to try to resolve this conflict.

Different cultures and their attitudes towards the environment

In the history of the earth it is only recently that humans have stopped being a part of the physical environment and have formed cultural environments instead. Many definitions of the natural environment leave humans completely out of the equation, although some imply the importance of humans, either directly or indirectly. Human societies vary in terms of their culture, social organisation, level of technology and resources.

Defining the natural environment
Biology Online – an academic–educational organisation

'All living and non-living things that occur naturally in a particular region. A natural environment is one in which human impact is kept under a certain limited level.'

Business dictionary – an economic–educational organisation

'Climate, weather and natural resources that affect human survival and economic activity.'

Somerset County Council – a political organisation

'A common definition of "the natural environment" is "the Earth's surface and atmosphere, including all living organisms as well as the air, water, soil and other resources necessary to sustain life."'

The geographer Parker argued that culture (C) = society (S) and technology (T) multiplied by the environmental resources (R) and anti-resources (AR). Countries could be great or small, weak or poor with respect to society, technology, resources and anti-resources. He therefore believed that Russia was characterised by C = (S + t) × (R + AR), whereas the USA was C = (s + T) × (r + ar).

According to the Soviet view, man was a distinct yet integral part of the environment. The socialist philosophy was that humans should master the environment. In contrast, the US capitalist view was that the environment was there to be exploited and to create wealth. These two views were not so very different in practice.

In some societies, such as the USA and Russia between the 1930s and 1970s, there was a clear attempt to show human triumph over nature. Both countries acted in a highly anti-environmentalist way. Stalin's plan for the transformation of nature argued that a vigorously controlled society could conquer the physical environment. Large-scale schemes such as the diversion of the Syr Darya and the Amu Darya and the planned diversion of the river Ob away from the Arctic to Soviet Asia were designed to use nature to benefit humankind. The same could be said of the damming of the Colorado by the US government and the Dust Bowl of the 1930s.

It could be argued that in the early to mid-20th century every society did to the environment what it thought it should do. At the other extreme, small groups of environmentalists were seen as denying the role of technology and society. Nevertheless, the environmentalists' side was helped by the pictures sent back by the space programmes of the 1960s and 1970s. Increased awareness of the fragility of the earth and its finite resources caused many organisations and nations to think again. The images showed that people are part of a physical environment, as well as a cultural environment, and that there are differences in the human–environment relationship between different places. Society cannot operate without an understanding of the geographical basis of its human affairs.

In many countries, such as Germany and New Zealand, the Green Party has a significant representation in parliament. The anti-environmentalists, or those who deny environmental problems exist and/or technology and human ingenuity will always solve the problems, are isolated in the present climate.

The industrial revolution in the West accelerated the consumption of natural resources. When these resources became scarce the West turned to its various colonies and trading partners. Agricultural development in the colonies led to widespread deforestation for the development of plantations. Similarly, socialist industrialisation, such as in Russia and China, led to massive environmental degradation, at first at home and, increasingly, abroad.

Emerging superpowers, such as Brazil, India and China, wish to use natural resources to further their economic development (Figure 34.1). Countries that are already rich, such as the UK and Germany, can argue for the conservation of resources, even though they did not conserve their resources in the pursuit of wealth and development.

Arguably the environment was, and still is, managed in a sustainable way among the indigenous hunter-gatherers and subsistence farmers, such as the Penan of Borneo and the Kalahari bushmen. Nevertheless, even among these peoples, anthropologists suggest that infanticide rates may be as high as 15–50% of all births in order to permit the survival of the tribe.

The state of play

Most nations are technocratic. They believe science and technology will find ways of using the earth more sustainably and are likely to be hyperglobalists or transformationalists. Many NGOs are ecocentrics, meaning that they are of the opinion that people must learn to live with the earth. They are more likely to be sceptics or radical transformationalists.

Different attitudes, different uses

Defining sustainability

DEFRA, UK

'development which meets the needs of the present without compromising the ability of future generations to meet their own needs…'

US Department of Energy

'…developing the built environment while considering environmental responsiveness, resource efficiency, and community sensitivity'

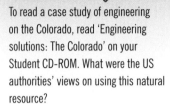

Taking it further

For a case study on the Aral Sea read 'Changing hydrology of the Aral Sea' on your Student CD-ROM. How did this disaster happen? What does it tell us about the views of the Soviet government?

Taking it further

To read a case study of engineering on the Colorado, read 'Engineering solutions: The Colorado' on your Student CD-ROM. What were the US authorities' views on using this natural resource?

▲ **Figure 34.1:** HEP scheme in China, part of the Chinese attempt to control and harness nature.

Taking it further

Visit the National Development and Reform Commission of the People's Republic of China and read their report on the Program of Action for Sustainable Development in China in the Early 21st Century. Go to www. acca21.org.cn/ca21pa.html for *China's White Paper on China's Population, Environment and Development in the 21st Century.*

Taking it further

For other definitions of sustainable development visit the Student CD-ROM.

India

The idea of sustainable development has evolved as an attempt to deal with the environmental problems caused by economic growth in contemporary India. There are various interpretations of the theory of sustainable development, but its main objective is to achieve a process of economic development without an indiscriminate destruction of our environment.

China

'For a developing country like China, however, the precondition for sustainable development is development. The path of relatively rapid economic growth and gradual improvements in the quality of development must be taken in order to meet the Chinese people's current and future needs for basic necessities and their desires for higher living standards, and in order to consolidate the nation's strength. Only when the economic growth rate reaches and is sustained at a certain level can poverty be eradicated, people's livelihoods improved and the necessary forces and conditions for supporting sustainable development be provided.'

(China's White Paper on *China's Population, Environment and Development in the 21st Century*)

Environmental sustainability

Environmental sustainability is one of the Millennium Development Goals (MDGs). Target 9 aims to reverse the loss of environmental resources. The MDGs state that environmental resources have a crucial role to play in helping economic development and reducing poverty. Environmental sustainability is particularly important in developing countries as many of the world's poorest people depend on natural resources for food, water, fuel, shelter and medicine. These people are also most vulnerable to natural disasters. In addition, the MDGs state that developed countries have a role to play in environmental sustainability by reducing their consumption of resources and pollution of the natural environment.

Since 2006 Yale University has produced an Environmental Performance Index (EPI) (which replaced its Environmental Sustainability Index) based on environmental risks (such as disease), pollution, productive natural resources and climate change. In 2008, Switzerland, Norway and Sweden had the highest EPIs.

Dealing with climate change

The Kyoto Protocol was an agreement made to cut greenhouse gas emissions across developed countries by about 5% compared with emissions in 1990. It became legal in 2005, following ratification by Russia. However, it is due to be replaced in 2012 and nations are trying to agree a post-Kyoto treaty. It is proving difficult as different countries with different attitudes want different plans of action.

Figures from the UN released in 2008 suggest that the world is on track to meet these targets. Emissions by the 40 developed countries fell by 5% compared with 1990. Developed countries that are on target include France, the UK, Greece and Hungary. In contrast, Canada, Japan and Germany are set to miss their targets. However, the reason for the drop is less to do with climate policy and more to do with the collapse of the former Soviet Union, and the subsequent economic decline in eastern Europe. Without this, emissions of greenhouse gases would have increased by about 10%. Newly industrialised countries (NICs) witnessed an increase of greenhouse gas emissions by over 7% between 2000 and 2006.

A number of stances are taken on the emission of greenhouse gases. For example, the European Union sees itself as the world leader in the reduction of greenhouse gas emissions and wants to limit climate change to 2°C above pre-industrial levels. In contrast, the USA has not made its position clear, but is likely to demand mandatory emissions commitments from developing nations such as Brazil, India and China.

China and the USA, the world's two largest carbon emitters, are playing a political cat and mouse game. China intends to resist internationally binding goals for emission reductions. Nevertheless, it has set non-binding national goals on renewable energy, energy efficiency and decreased emissions of greenhouse gases. It wants its economy to grow before setting binding targets. China has also requested that developed countries should contribute at least 0.7% of their GDP to help developing countries develop clean technology and deal with climate change.

Similarly, India is opposed to legally binding targets. India aims to bring 500 million people out of 'energy poverty'. It has suggested it would work to keep its per capita emissions to below those of developed countries.

Anthropocentric cultural values and consumer societies

The study of consumer culture is a relatively recent phenomenon in human geography. In the 1970s and 1980s studies focused on the housing market, but in the 1990s the geography of consumerism began to look in detail at other services, e.g. food, clothing, recreational landscapes, consumer goods, theme parks and so on. This late development is somewhat surprising given the ubiquity of consumer goods in everyday life and their huge economic importance.

The geography of consumption includes the way in which commodities have certain messages. (Figure 34.2) Sometimes this message may be created through advertisers, producers, retailers or the consumers themselves. Other studies of consumption have focused on the ways in which commodities are sold: in hypermarkets, rural stores and at markets and car boot sales (Figure 34.3–34.5). Another issue is the globalisation of commodification, i.e. the transfer of items from one part of the world to another. This may be from developing countries to developed countries, as in the case of exotic flowers, or from developed countries to developing countries, as in the case of certain multinational corporations (MNCs), such as Coca-Cola, Starbucks (Figure 34.6) and McDonald's. Another issue is that of new forms of commodities being produced and marketed. The commodification of knowledge, as in the case of genetic material, is a good example.

▲ **Figure 34.2:** Halal food.

Consumerism has reached almost all areas of modern life. It has also reached most areas of non-Western society, leading to the idea of a global culture. Most activities, from birth to death, have commodities associated with them, as do natural disasters, Christmas (Figure 34.7), wars, education, leisure time, health and so on.

Consumerism is in part the result of basic human needs for food, clothing, shelter and medicines. It has existed since the rise of the Sumerian people in Mesopotamia between 5000 and 3500BC. Consumerism is increasingly influenced by marketing, advertising, special deals, promotions, loyalty cards, availability of free parking, shopping under one roof, shopping centres with play areas and crèches and so on. Clearly, human values are influencing consumer cultures rather than just basic human needs.

Growing consumption

The pace of economic change in China and India is remarkable. India's economic growth is somewhat behind China's and its gross national income is about $2,500 per capita compared with $4,600 in China. However, both are growing and both countries are becoming increasingly important consumer societies (Figure 34.8). The economic success of China is not based on natural resources, but on decades of investment in people at the upper end of the educational system. These are now China's emerging middle classes. However, in becoming major consumers they have also become major polluters.

In 2005 China had over 350 million mobile phone users, compared with 7 million in 1996. The number of people living in extreme poverty fell from 66% in China and over 50% in India in 1980, to 17% and 35% respectively in 2001. China and India are largely self-sufficient in food production.

Key terms

Commodities — the goods that are produced for the purpose of sale or exchange. This is at the other end of the scale to subsistence production, which is for one's own consumption (within the household).

Market exchange — matches the search by commodity producers to make a profit with consumers.

▲ **Figures: 34.3, 34.4 and 34.5:** Hypermarket, rural store and market in Bandar seri Begawan, Brunei.

▲ **Figure 34.6:** Starbucks – part of the global consumer culture.

▲ **Figure 34.7:** The commodification of Christmas.

Country	Grain consumption kg/person/ year
China	292
India	173
Europe	561
Japan	354
USA	918

▲ **Figure 34.8:** Grain consumption in selected countries, 2005.

▶ **Figure 34.9:** Ecological footprints for selected countries, 2002.

Since 1985 India has not had to import more than 3% of its grain and China no more than 6%. However, the change from grain-based to a meat- and dairy-based diet is causing problems for countries elsewhere in the world and to the environment. More land is needed for the production of 1 kg of meat compared with 1 kg of grain. Coupled to this, some land is being used to produce biofuels rather than to produce food. This leads to one of two likely scenarios: there is less land available for grain production and therefore more people will go hungry; or more land needs to come into production, therefore habitats are destroyed and biodiversity is reduced.

	Total footprint (million hectares)*	Footprint/ person	Footprint as a share of the nation's biocapacity	Footprint as a share of global biocapacity	Growth in footprint, 1992–2002 (%)
China	2,049	1.6	201	18	24
India	784	0.8	210	7	17
Europe	2,164	4.7	207	19	14
Japan	544	4.8	569	5	6
USA	2,810	9.7	205	25	21

*Biological productive space

Conflict between environmentalism and consumer culture

The rise of consumer cultures comes at a price. An increase in life expectancy and economic prosperity occurs alongside the increased use of natural resources. This has been especially marked in the developed countries, but is growing in NICs.

For example, the UK consumes more resources than it can produce sustainably. This way of life is maintained by importing and using resources from other countries.

According to the World Wildlife Fund, humankind is using about 20% more resources than the planet can sustain in the long term and the world's ecological footprint has tripled since 1961 (Figure 34.9).

The UK is consuming approximately three times more resources than its fair share and displays characteristics of a materialistic, consumer culture. Although the UK is small in geographical terms it contains about 1% of the world's population. If everyone in the world consumed at the average rate of the UK, we would require three planets. Nearly two-thirds of the services provided by nature to humankind are in decline.

The concentration of populations in set locations, e.g. large cities, means that populations are less mobile and adaptable, and potentially more vulnerable to environmental change, some of which may be exacerbated by humankind's resource use and pollution. The use of fossil fuels and the risk of global warming is a case in point. Globally, low-lying coastal areas are most at risk.

In the UK, attention has recently been focused on the proportion of the population at risk of flooding either on river floodplains or from coastal erosion and sea-level rise.

Similarly, in China, economic growth has led to major environmental problems. China contains just 8% of the world's freshwater, but 22% of the world's population. In India, only about 10% of sewage is treated. Air quality in both countries is poor; 16 of the world's 20 worst polluted cities are in China. The demand for forest products is leading to deforestation. China banned forest cutting in 1998 and now looks overseas for its supplies.

The way forward

There have to be concerted efforts to significantly increase resource efficiency, particularly in areas such as transport, energy (heating and electricity) and water. Recycling of materials also saves energy and uses fewer raw materials. Public attitudes towards consumption must be modified so that there is less glamour attached to materialistic and highly consumptive lifestyles, with greater value attached to a more needs-based approach to living. This is a significant challenge and it is likely that one of the most effective ways of engendering more responsible attitudes is to include education on this issue.

▲ **Figure 34.10:** Japanese fish market.

Taking it further

Visit the Student CD-ROM to find out about Christmas lunch and food miles.

Examiners' tip

Keep abreast of political initiatives, whether international, national or local. There are many policies regarding sustainability and climate change. These can be used to add detail to your answers.

Summary

In this chapter you have learnt:

- how different cultures have different attitudes to the environment. This was shown by an examination of US and Russian attempts to master the environment.

- how different attitudes affect how the landscape is exploited and/or protected. This was illustrated with respect to sustainable development and climate change.

- how anthropocentric (human-focused) values are necessary to justify consumer cultures, as in the case of China and India.

- how there is a clear conflict between environmentalism and consumer capitalism. Again, this was clearly the case in China. In addition, different movements, such as the green movement, have developed to try to resolve this conflict.

MCQ

CHAPTER 35 Defining risks and exploring patterns

Key terms

Disease
Epidemic
Epidemiological transition
Focus
Health inequality
Human health risk
Infection rate
Malaria
Malnutrition
Morbidity
Pandemic
Quality of life
Recovery rate
Vector

Taking it further

Look at the UK Department of Health website – www.dh.gov.uk – to see what the government is doing to try to improve health in the most socially deprived areas of the country. For example, in November 2008 the Department of Health announced a package of £13.5 million to improve health in disadvantaged areas.

Key term

Human health risk — the likelihood that a given exposure or series of exposures may have damaged or will damage the health of individuals.

Learning objectives

After studying this chapter, you will be able to discuss these ideas and concepts and provide located examples of them:
• The range of human health risks.
• Patterns of health risk at different scales.
• How health risks may alter over time.
• The importance of health to both the quality of life and economic development.

Human health

Defining human health

The *World Health Organisation (WHO)* has defined human health as

'A state of complete physical, mental and social wellbeing, and not merely the absence of disease or infirmity.'

The WHO maintains that good health is a fundamental human right.

Health is arguably the most important factor in the quality of life of an individual person. To have and maintain good health an individual needs proper shelter, nutrition, clothing, exercise, sleep and rest. Good hygiene is also essential to reduce the chances of infection, while access to medical care allows health to be monitored and illnesses treated.

Health is closely connected to other major aspects of the quality of life, particularly the income of the individual and the level of economic development of a country as a whole. A high level of economic development can help significantly in the avoidance of many health risks, although affluence can bring new health risks of its own such as those associated with obesity, smoking and drinking alcohol. Conversely, relatively poor countries such as Cuba can prioritise health to produce very good healthcare systems even though per capita income is low.

Studying health patterns

Geographers have been studying the spatial patterns of diseases and their causes and consequences for some time. Here there is a clear overlap with epidemiology. This is the branch of medical science concerned with the occurrence, transmission and control of epidemic diseases. It was epidemiologists who first identified the link between smoking and lung cancer in the 1950s.

Exposure to risk

Risk is the possibility of suffering harm or loss. Doctors and scientists use the term risk when assessing human health threats from exposure to disease and to chemicals or pollutants in the environment.

Risk is equivalent to a person's exposure multiplied by the virulence of the disease or the toxicity of the pollutant in the environment.

Exposure is a combination of the virulence of the disease/concentration of the pollutant and the length of time people are exposed to the potential threat.

The range of health risks

Health risks have been defined as the probabilities of death and incidence and remission of non-fatal health outcomes of differing severities that individuals face at each age. There is an extremely wide range of health risks. Figure 35.1 distinguishes between short-term and long-term exposure to contaminants, and identifies some of the health consequences that can result. Symptoms or illnesses occurring from short-term exposure are called acute effects. Effects resulting from long-term exposure are known as chronic effects. Figure 35.2 illustrates the considerable differences in type of disease between less and more developed countries.

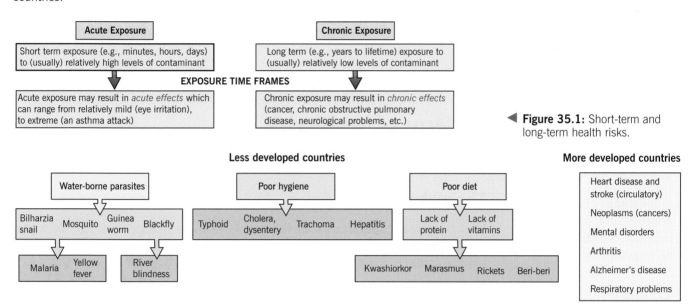

Figure 35.1: Short-term and long-term health risks.

Figure 35.2: Differences in type of disease between less and more developed countries.

The incidence and spread of disease

Disease is usually a disorder of a specific tissue or organ due to a single cause. However, some diseases may have a number of causes and are said to be multifactorial. Disease can be classified in different ways. Figure 35.4 recognises nine broad categories, although some diseases are classified into more than one category.

The number of people in a population who are affected by a disease depends on the infection rate and the recovery rate. When the former is greater than the latter it is likely that a large number of people will be affected. Such a level of infection is termed an epidemic or pandemic. The spread of epidemics is very strongly related to:

- the size of a population
- the rate of mixing in a population. This is the rate of face-to-face contacts between members of a population. The rate of mixing is particularly high in the overcrowded, densely populated slums of large developing world cities.

The rate of mixing of the global population has increased greatly over the last half a century or so, particularly due to advances in transportation. Populations with a large number of susceptible people invariably have high infection rates. 'Susceptibles' are people at risk of catching a disease. More than half of all deaths worldwide are due to four chronic diseases: heart disease, diabetes, lung diseases and some cancers.

Key terms

Disease — any impairment of normal physiological function, especially a specific pathological change caused by infection, stress, etc., producing characteristic symptoms.

Infection rate — the number of people infected by a disease in a given time.

Recovery rate — the number of people recovering from infection during that time.

Figure 35.3: Sleeping with mosquito nets in a tropical area: a major precaution in reducing the spread of malaria.

Category of disease	Cause of disease	Examples
physical	permanent or temporary damage to any part of the body	leprosy, multiple sclerosis
infectious	organisms which invade the body	measles, malaria
non-infectious	any cause other than invasion by an organism	stroke, sickle cell disease
deficiency	poor diet	scurvy, night blindness
inherited	an inherited genetic fault	cystic fibrosis, haemophilia
degenerative	gradual decline in body functions	coronary heart disease, Huntingdon's disease
mental	changes to the mind, which may or may not have a physical cause	schizophrenia, claustrophobia
social	social behaviour, such as drug misuse	drug dependence, e.g. dependence on alcohol
self-inflicted	wilful damage to the body by a person's own actions or behaviour	attempted suicide, lung cancer

▲ **Figure 35.4:** Different categories of disease.

Examiners' tip

Be clear about the distinction between an epidemic and a pandemic. Examination candidates often confuse these important terms.

Key terms

Epidemic — where the number of people infected with a disease is measurable at the national or regional scale.

Pandemic — where the number of people infected by a disease is measurable at an international scale.

Taking it further

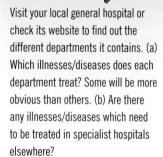

Visit your local general hospital or check its website to find out the different departments it contains. (a) Which illnesses/diseases does each department treat? Some will be more obvious than others. (b) Are there any illnesses/diseases which need to be treated in specialist hospitals elsewhere?

Taking it further

To see a table showing the methods of transmission of some infectious diseases, go to your Student CD-ROM.

Patterns of health risk

Patterns of health risk can be recognised at different scales: global, national and local, and can change over time.

The global scale

Most transmissible diseases such as malaria and TB have a clear global pattern which can be explained by one or a number of distinct causal factors. Such factors may be primarily physical or mainly human, but are usually to some degree a combination of the two.

Figure 35.5 shows the geographical incidence of malaria: 40% of the global population is at risk from malaria, which kills over 1.3 million people a year. Most deaths are of children under five years old. This disease affects up to 500 million people. Sub-Saharan Africa accounts for 59% of all global cases and 88% of all global deaths from malaria.

Malaria is common in tropical areas where the anopheles mosquito (the vector) is able to survive and multiply. The malarial parasite requires a temperature of over 20°C to complete its life-cycle and it thrives in humid conditions. Malaria brings fever and flu-like conditions. If it is untreated it can cause convulsions, coma and death. Surviving children may suffer learning impairment and brain damage. Repeated episodes of malaria can result in anaemia and general lethargy. This can have a significant impact on the efficiency of a country's workforce.

The key question is 'Will there ever be a malaria vaccine?' It has proved much harder to produce a vaccine for malaria than for many other diseases. The best way to prevent malaria is not to get bitten. The main precautions are:

- Cover up in terms of clothing.
- Use an insect repellent.
- Always use a bed net.
- Stay indoors at dawn and dusk. These are the times some mosquitoes are most active.
- Take anti-malarial pills.

Research has shown that countries with malaria have (a) incomes 33% below those without it, and (b) economic growth 1.3% per person per year less.

National and local scales

All countries show some degree of variation in health risk by region. Even in a relatively affluent country such as the UK spatial variations can be substantial. For example, the risk of heart disease is considerably higher in Scotland and the North of England than it is in the South of England, reflecting the higher average incomes and better living standards of the South. In the latter, knowledge and understanding of health matters is also higher, with people in general adopting a healthier lifestyle.

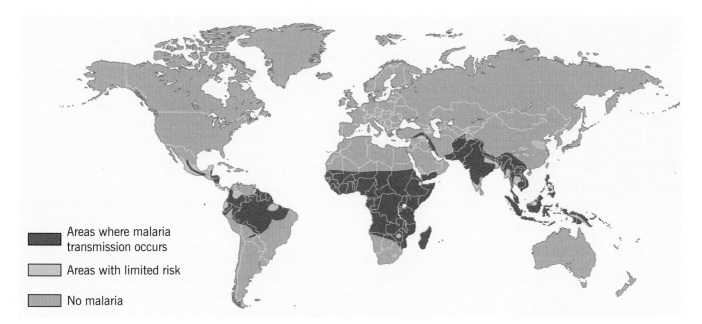

Areas where malaria transmission occurs

Areas with limited risk

No malaria

Such contrasts in health risk can result in very significant differences in life expectancy. In the UK, for the period 2001–3, the lowest male life expectancy of 69.1 years was in Glasgow City while the highest of 80.1 years was in East Dorset.

Even at a smaller scale, significant differences can be observed. Within London the poorest wards (subdivisions of boroughs) have infant mortality rates double those of the richest wards. Likewise, there is a clear contrast in a range of morbidity (disease) rates between the poorer inner London boroughs and the more affluent outer boroughs.

Temporal changes

Health risks can change substantially over time, particularly in the light of significant socio-economic progress. The epidemiological transition model is a useful aid in describing the typical changes that take place.

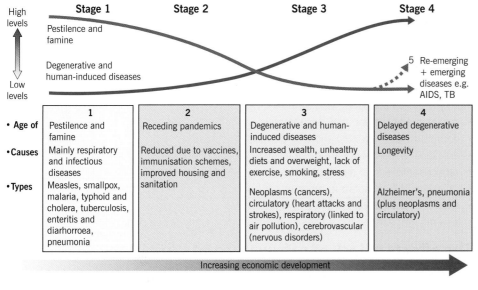

▲ **Figure 35.6:** The epidemiological transition.

Figure 35.6 shows the stages of the epidemiological transition, which has clear links with the model of demographic transition:

▲ **Figure 35.5:** World map showing the areas affected by malaria.

Synoptic link

Look at Figure 7, page 243 of Edexcel AS Geography to see the big contrast in the top ten causes of death in developing and developed countries.

Key terms

Malaria — a parasitic, mosquito-borne disease which is common in tropical areas where the anopheles mosquito can survive and multiply.

Vector — the method by which a disease is transmitted.

Focus — the area where epidemics appear to originate.

Epidemiological transition — the change from mainly infectious diseases, still common in poor countries, to the degenerative diseases, which have become the main cause of death in richer nations.

▲ **Figure 35.7:** Cholera in London in the 19th century.

Taking it further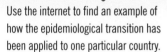

Use the internet to find an example of how the epidemiological transition has been applied to one particular country.

Synoptic link

Look at page 74 of Edexcel AS Geography to remind yourself of the stages of the model of demographic transition.

Synoptic link

Look at pages 220–1 of Edexcel AS Geography for a discussion of Unhealthy places.

Key terms

Quality of life — this term sums up all the factors that affect a person's general wellbeing and happiness.
Malnutrition — insufficiency of one or more nutritional elements necessary for health and wellbeing.

- In countries with very low levels of economic development respiratory and infectious diseases have a major impact on the health of the population. As a result morbidity rates and age-specific mortality rates are high.
- Economic development, often including health-related aid programmes, leads to a significant reduction in the traditional causes of morbidity and mortality.
- As average incomes rise further, the changes in lifestyle generally associated with increasing affluence come into play. At this stage, degenerative and human-induced diseases dominate. The original model did not go beyond this stage.
- Considerably higher life expectancy necessitated the addition of a new fourth stage to the model where delayed degenerative diseases such as Alzheimer's, osteoporosis and prostate cancer become much more common.
- However, in recent years there has been growing concern about re-emerging (MRSA and drug-resistant TB) and emerging (HIV/AIDS) diseases that might mark a fifth stage in the model.

The epidemiological transition has been linked to urbanisation, with the greater concentration of people in urban areas increasing exposure to communicable diseases and adding new hazards such as pollution. The model can be used to provide a framework for healthcare strategies over the medium to long term.

How health affects both quality of life and economic development

Health is of vital importance to the overall quality of life of individuals, households and communities, and to the economic development of the regions and countries in which they live. Poor health can cause a chain reaction that severely inhibits the development process. This is particularly severe in LEDCs where major health issues are associated with malnutrition, lack of safe drinking water and sanitation, and poor access to health facilities. Tackling these problems is fundamental to ending poverty. Although the higher proportion of deaths in developing countries occurs as a result of infectious diseases, the mortality rate from degenerative diseases is also high. Poor health intensifies in poor areas in both LEDCs and MEDCs.

The major global measure of quality of life differentials is the human development index which is updated each year. Two of the indicators used to calculate the human development index – life expectancy and infant mortality – are health indicators.

The impact of malnutrition

Over 800 million people worldwide are malnourished. Three-quarters live in rural areas, mainly in Africa and Asia. Malnutrition:
- makes medical treatment less effective
- compromises immunity, allowing diseases to spread
- weakens mothers who are more likely to die in childbirth or produce stillborn babies
- reduces intellectual development
- increases the school drop-out rate
- results in poor physical health and disability
- severely impacts on the efficiency of the economically active population.

The effects of lack of safe water and sanitation

More than two million people, many of them children, die each year from diarrhoea and a range of other conditions associated with poor water and sanitation. These factors remain one of the biggest threats to health globally. Over one billion people in Africa and Asia lack safe drinking water and nearly 40% of the global population lacks access to toilets. The UN World Water Development Report stated: 'The real tragedy is the effect it has on the everyday lives of poor people, who are blighted by the burden of water-related disease, living in degraded and often dangerous environments, struggling to get an education for their children and to earn a living, and to get enough to eat. The brutal truth is that the really poor suffer a combination of most, and sometimes all, of the problems in the water sector.'

The economic cost

Chronic diseases have significant economic consequences for individuals, families and the general economy. Such diseases affect consumption and performance in the labour market. This can severely restrict the growth of an economy.

The World Bank estimates that AIDS may now be costing 24 African countries 0.5% to 1.2% of per capita growth each year. A vicious cycle exists between poor health and poverty. Poor health prevents development and increases the impact of poverty. Poverty worsens the health situation due to economic burdens such as debt repayments and medical/drug costs. Figure 35.8 shows the direct and indirect costs of malaria to LEDCs.

Direct costs	Indirect costs
Individual medical costs which often account for a quarter of the annual income of African families affected.	Loss of productivity in the workplace.
The cost of preventative measures.	Lack of continuity in education due to significant periods of absence.
Loss of earnings as sufferers cannot work during attacks of malaria.	Reduced investment in affected areas – tourists may avoid some high-risk areas and TNCs may not want to do business in such an area.
Public health spending which can account for up to 40% of total government expenditure.	Growing subsistence crops rather than cash crops due to the impact of the disease on labour supply during harvest.

Conversely, economic development can finance good environmental health, sanitation and public health campaigns and provide broader-based social care. Development can provide the money necessary to improve housing and other key services. In such ways the cycle of poverty can be broken by development. However, much depends on how equitably the benefits of development are spread throughout the population. Sometimes policies designed to enhance economic growth may actually increase poverty and the maldistribution of resources.

The cycle of deprivation in MEDC inner cities

Ill-health figures prominently in the cycle of deprivation (Figure 35.10) which is frequently used to explain the socio-economic problems of inner cities in the UK and other MEDCs. In the late 1990s the new Labour Government set up a number of health action zones in an effort to tackle this aspect of inner city deprivation. One health action zone is the Lambeth, Southwark and Lewisham health authority in south London where the hospitals, social services departments, police and probation services discovered they were all dealing with problems from the same families.

Recent figures for the UK show that over half of men and two-thirds of women are overweight. It is estimated that 50% of children in the UK will be obese by 2020. Obesity costs the UK £8.2 billion each year in sickness absence, premature death and NHS treatment. The rise in obesity is directly linked to unhealthy diets and inactivity, causing a range of chronic diseases and lower life expectancy. The positive side of this situation is that diet-related illness is almost entirely preventable.

Summary

In this chapter you have learnt:

- that human health risks range from short-term to chronic.
- that patterns of health risk exist at global, national and local scales.
- about the epidemiology model, showing how health risk patterns change over time.
- how health affects quality of life and economic development.

MCQ

◀ **Figure 35.8:** The direct and indirect costs of malaria.

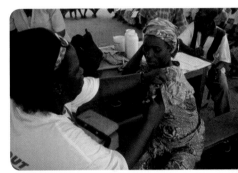

▲ **Figure 35.9:** A clinic in a poor LEDC with patients queuing for immunisation.

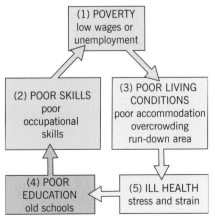

▲ **Figure 35.10:** The cycle of deprivation.

CHAPTER 36 What are the causes of health risks?

Key terms

Accessibility
Connectivity
Core
Diet
Diffusion
Infant mortality rate
Model
Periphery
Pollution
Socio-economic status

Learning objectives

After studying this chapter, you will be able to discuss these ideas and concepts and provide located examples of them:
- The complex causes of health risks.
- The relationship between socio-economic status and health.
- The links between some diseases and geographical features.
- The role of models in helping to understand health risk causes and patterns.

The complex causes of health risks

The causes of health risks are complex with pollution being a significant factor in an increasing number of places around the world.

A number of environmental and human factors can be identified as significant health risks. The characteristics of the environment can influence the spread of both infectious and non-infectious diseases. The main influential environmental factors are discussed in Figure 36.1.

▶ **Figure 36.1:** Environmental factors contributing to significant health risks.

Factor	Comment
Water	Dirty water is the main cause of disease in the developing world. Improving sanitation and water supply has been shown to cut the infant mortality rate by an average of 55%. Standing pools of water are particularly significant in disease transmission, harbouring vectors and parasites.
Geology	In the UK about 2,000 deaths a year are attributed to lung cancer caused by radon gas produced from the decay of uranium. This is naturally present in many rock types.
Ecology	Ecological systems can be viewed as life support systems. When ecosystems are placed under considerable stress, their ability to support a healthy population can be compromised.
Insect and animal vectors	Natural and human-induced changes in the habitat of disease-carrying insects will alter the disease incidence pattern.
Ozone depletion	The health risk here is related to damage to DNA caused by UV-B radiation. As a result the incidence of melanomas (skin cancers) has risen considerably in many countries.
Weather	Weather patterns have both direct and indirect effects on mortality and morbidity rates. Within the EU, winter-related illness is especially linked to mortality in the UK due to inadequate heating and clothing.
Climate change	It is expected that climate change will have the following types of impact on health: (1) direct, such as higher mortality from extreme climatic events such as storms, (2) secondary, such as tropical disease becoming more common in higher latitudes, and (3) tertiary, such as conflict over freshwater supplies.

Human factors which increase health risk can be subdivided into (a) personal lifestyle choices and (b) factors external to individual decision-making. Personal lifestyle choices relate mainly to smoking, alcohol consumption, diet and exercise. External factors include pollution, quality of housing, the safety of residential and work environments and road safety levels. Modern society, with its emphasis on consumerism, has fostered a range of health risks including obesity, diabetes and depression. A report produced by the Population Health Research Institute in Ontario, Canada found that Western diets caused a third of all heart attacks worldwide. They identified three global dietary patterns:
* 'oriental', marked by high consumption of tofu and soy
* 'prudent', characterised by a high intake of fruits and vegetables
* 'Western' typified by relatively large amounts of fried foods, salty snacks, eggs and meat.

The oriental dietary pattern made no difference to heart attack risk. This is because its healthy foods like tofu were cancelled out by unhealthy ones such as soy sauce which has a high salt content. However, 'prudent' eaters were 30% less likely to suffer heart attacks than people who consume few fruit and vegetables.

Diabetes has been linked mainly to poor diet and lack of exercise, but new research is focusing on the role of a family of toxic chemicals known as persistent organic pollutants (POPs). People with high levels of POPs in their bloodstream are much more likely to have type 2 diabetes than those with none.

Pollution

Figure 36.2 shows how people are exposed to chemicals and how exposure to these chemicals can affect human health. The methods of exposure to pollutants are:
* Breathing in chemical vapours and dust (inhalation)
* Drinking or eating the chemical (ingestion)
* Absorbing the chemical through the skin (absorption).

Of all types of pollution, air pollution has the most widespread effects on human health. Air pollution impacts on people at a range of scales from local to global. In many parts of the developing world indoor air pollution is more severe than that experienced outdoors. This is the result of the use of biomass fuels for cooking and heating.

In November 2008, a High Court judge in the UK ruled that people in rural communities have suffered damage to their health from long-term exposure to pesticides. The judge stated that there was solid evidence that residents had suffered harm to their health from crop spraying close to their homes. He also criticised the current model for assessing the impact of crop spraying on humans.

Taking it further

To look at the most hazardous persistent organic pollutants go to your Student CD-ROM.

Key terms

Diet — the food that a person usually consumes.
Pollution — contamination of the environment. It can take many forms — air, water, soil, noise, visual and others.

Taking it further

'The biggest pollution problem is global warming.' Discuss this assertion.

▼ **Figure 36.2:** How exposure to pollution can affect human health.

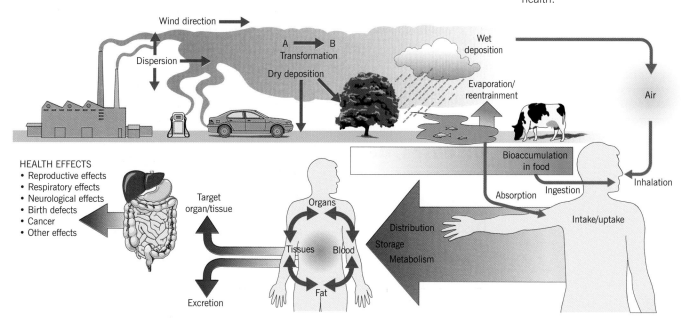

The relationship between socio-economic status and health

There is a strong correlation between health patterns and spatial variations in economic standards of living. Socio-economic status is a strong predictor of health. Better health is associated with:

- higher incomes
- higher levels of education
- more prestigious employment
- living in neighbourhoods where a higher ratio of people have high incomes and levels of education.

According to research, people in lower socio-economic groups are biologically older than those in higher groups. Lower socio-economic status can accelerate the ageing process by about seven years. Living in deprived areas has been found to be associated with increased prevalence of:

- mental health problems
- behavioural problems
- physical abuse among children and adolescents.

Infant mortality is one of the most sensitive indicators of socio-economic status (Figure 36.3). All causes of neonatal mortality in England and Wales show a socio-economic gradient and all except one cause of postnatal deaths (diseases of the nervous system and sense organs) show a socio-economic gradient. For example, research has shown that there are substantial social and cultural inequalities in knowledge about antenatal screening.

Health inequalities in China

A study of China's health system published by *The Lancet* in 2008 noted that children born in some rural areas are six times more likely to die by the age of five as children in the booming cities. Many rural areas remain in desperate poverty in contrast to the growing number of people classified as 'middle class' in the main cities. The study focused on the social costs of rapid economic growth with investment disproportionately targeted on major urban areas. One result is that life expectancy in Shanghai is 11 years more than in the poor western province of Gansu. Infant mortality ranged from 26/1,000 in the richest parts of the country to 123/1,000 in the poorest areas. 96% of the population of large cities have safe drinking water, but this declines to less than 30% in poor areas. The government has been criticised for such an unfair distribution of wealth and health services.

The government has published proposals to extend health insurance to all in China by 2020. At present it is largely urban-based. Thus, most people living in rural areas have to pay doctors and hospitals directly. The study also noted that:

- doctors often prescribed the most profitable rather than the most useful drugs
- the care of migrant workers, who had come from poor rural areas to find work in the booming cities, was particularly inadequate
- literacy rates were actually falling in some rural areas.

Diseases, geographical features and models

The development and spread of infection are often linked to geographical features and may follow geographical pathways and patterns.

Distance

Distance is a major factor affecting access to healthcare. In LEDCs in particular the health investment gap between urban and rural areas is often very large indeed.

Key terms

Socio-economic status — a combined measure of an individual's or family's economic and social position relative to others, based on income, education and occupation.

Infant mortality rate — the number of deaths of children under one year of age per 1,000 live births per year.

Synoptic link

Look at pages 220–1 of Edexcel AS Geography for a brief discussion of health as an indicator of inequality.

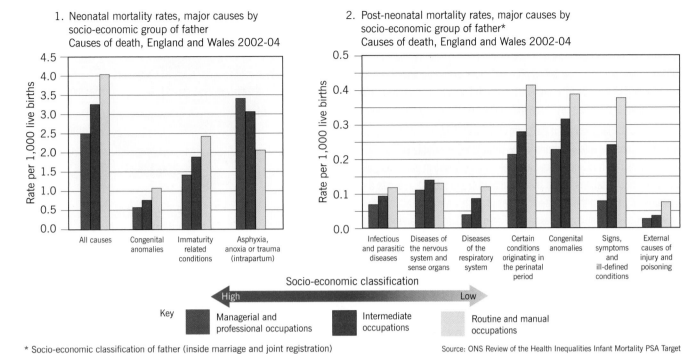

1. Neonatal mortality rates, major causes by socio-economic group of father
   Causes of death, England and Wales 2002-04

2. Post-neonatal mortality rates, major causes by socio-economic group of father*
   Causes of death, England and Wales 2002-04

* Socio-economic classification of father (inside marriage and joint registration)

Source: ONS Review of the Health Inequalities Infant Mortality PSA Target

▲ **Figure 36.3:** Major causes of infant mortality by socio-economic group of the father.

This impacts on both medical emergencies and routine/longer-term care. Even in MEDCs distance can be a significant influence. This affects the elderly in particular if they lack personal mobility. The decline in public transport services in many rural areas in the UK has contributed to the 'isolation' many elderly people feel in relation to key services.

Transport routes and accessibility

As people and goods move along clearly defined transport routes they can carry diseases with them. Each stage of transport innovation has increased the mixing of populations, resulting in changing patterns of disease spread and distribution. The rapid increase in air travel in recent decades has had a particular impact. The global spread of cholera, from its focus in India, has been directly linked to changes in international trade patterns. Three phases have been recognised:

- Until 1816, the first six epidemics were confined to India. Cholera then became a pandemic, moving slowly across Asia with traders travelling on foot, horseback or by sailing boat.
- In the seventh outbreak from 1965 the disease was mainly transmitted by sea. Pilgrims travelling to and from the Muslim shrine at Mecca were the main carriers.
- Air travel spread the eighth outbreak much more rapidly than previous pandemics.

Patterns of disease and illness may follow natural routeways such as rivers which (a) harbour vectors such as blackfly which cause river blindness and (b) carry high levels of pollution.

Improvements in transport have reduced the importance of geographical distance in containing the spread of disease. Because main transport routes have distinct focal points, places of maximum accessibility, with the highest levels of connectivity, are often key locations in the development and spread of infection.

Electro-magnetic fields

A number of studies have established a statistical link between transmission masts, power lines and mobile phone masts on the one hand and leukaemia and other types of cancer.

Key term

Accessibility — a measure of the ease with which people can reach features (human and physical) in the wider environment.

Case study: Vadodara City, India

As India has progressed from an LEDC to an NIC, the country has witnessed considerable economic and social progress. However, there have been negative aspects to development such as environmental degradation and an increase in the incidence of degenerative and respiratory diseases. This has particularly happened in urban areas.

Vadodara is the largest city in the state of Gujarat. A high rate of population increase has led to considerable shortfalls in the potable water supply and in the sanitation system. This has had an impact on water-borne disease in particular, although there are very large variations within the urban area (Figure 36.4). There is a very strong relationship between the prevalence rates of gastroenteritis and infective hepatitis and socio-economic grouping. For example, Fatepura, Gajrawadi and Panigate, the wards with the highest rates for both diseases, all have large slum populations. Disease rates are also high in Shiyabaug and the City where population densities are very high alongside environmental degradation, inadequate water supply and poor sewerage infrastructure. Elsewhere both population density and slum populations are lower.

A recent article entitled 'Development, Environment and Urban Health in India' (*Geography*, 2007, pp158–9) concluded that 'The poorer sections of society can either not afford to take care of their physical and other needs or are unaware of the need to do so, the result being unclean living areas.'

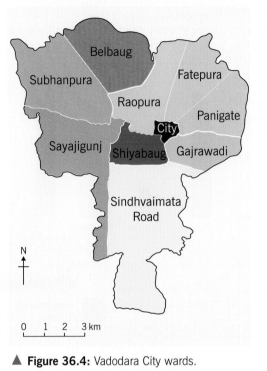

▲ **Figure 36.4:** Vadodara City wards.

Taking it further

Find the article entitled 'Development, Environment and Urban Health in India' (*Geography*, 2007, pp158–60) for a more detailed consideration of Vadodara City and urban health in India in general.

Environment

The characteristics of the environment can have a big influence on infection. Many diseases that thrive in tropical areas have very limited impact in temperate regions.

How models help in the understanding of health risk causes and patterns

Models can help in the understanding of health risk causes and patterns. The Swedish geographer Hagerstrand identified diffusion waves when he studied the spread of agricultural ideas in Sweden in the 1950s (Figure 36.5). Although the spread of disease is more complicated than the diffusion of technological knowledge and understanding, Hagerstrand's basic concepts have provided a platform for later research.

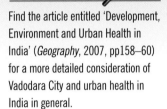

1) **Expansion diffusion**

→ = spread
X = place of origin; whatever is spread remains here, while spreading at the same time
2 = measure of distance

two types:
a) contagious diffusion (spread by direct contact) - influenced by distance from place of origin. Risk lessens with distance.

b) hierarchic diffusion - spread through a class or group (e.g. different sizes of settlement)

2) **Relocation diffusion**

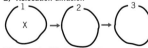

Whatever is diffusing shifts to a new place in time

3) **Expansion/relocation combined**

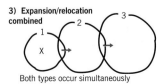

Both types occur simultaneously

▲ **Figure 36.5:** Types of diffusion.

(a)

S: susceptible population;
I: infective population;
β: rate of infection.

Assumptions: the model is aspatial, the population mixes evenly, everyone has the same opportunity of catching the disease, the population falls into two groups - susceptibles and infectives.

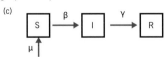

(c)

μ: birth rate of the population

Assumptions: the susceptibles population will grow in size as more people are born, allowing repeating waves of infection to spread through the population.

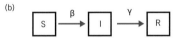

(b)

R: recovered population;
γ: recovery rate.

Assumptions: a new group - recovereds - is introduced.

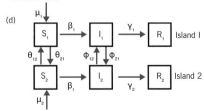

(d)

θ and φ: migration rates to and from each island

This model is more like reality, it looks at how infection will spread between two island populations.

▲ **Figure 36.6:** The four Hamer-Sopel models.

Figure 36.6 shows the four Hamer-Soper models which examine the spread of disease in relation to fertility, mortality and migration. The models begin with the example of one island. The final stage looks at how infection spreads between two islands.

Kilbourne saw influenza spreading out around the world in waves (Figure 36.7), with a much higher incidence in winter than in summer. As the population becomes immune to one strain the magnitude of the waves decreases and eventually the strain dies out.

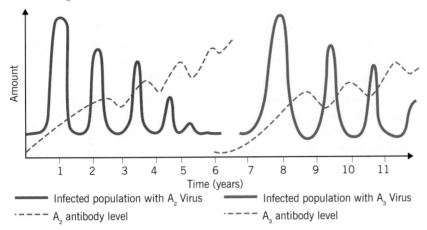

▲ **Figure 36.7:** Kilbourne's model: the spread of influenza.

However, the virus has the ability to change its antigens, so that the body's defence mechanism does not recognise it. Thus, a new strain may begin with a wave pattern similar to the original strain of the virus.

The core–periphery model (Figure 36.8) has also been used to help explain the spread of disease. With its larger and more dense population, the core has much greater mixing rates than the sparsely populated periphery. However, at times the focus or source of an epidemic is in the periphery. The infection may then travel to the core before spreading to other peripheral areas.

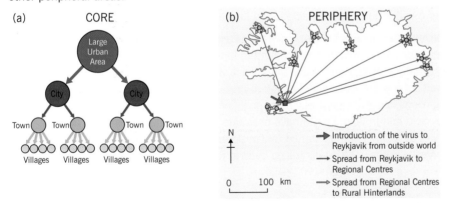

▲ **Figure 36.8:** The core–periphery model.

Summary

In this chapter you have learnt:

- about the different causes of health risk including pollution.
- about the relationship between health patterns and variations in economic standard of living.
- about the influence of geographical features on the development and spread of infection.
- about the use of models in understanding the causes and patterns of health risk.

Key terms

Diffusion — the spread of a phenomenon over time and space.
Model — a simplification of reality.

Examiners' tip

Remember that a model concentrates only on major characteristics and processes. It makes understanding easier at the start of the learning process. However, once clear about the framework of a situation or process, it is then not too difficult to unravel the detail.

Key terms

Core — a region of concentrated economic development and high population density.
Periphery — a region of low economic development where population density is sparse relative to the core.

Taking it further

Look at 'The Geography of New Diseases' (Geofile Online, No. 481, Sept 2004) for an analysis of the spread of SARS (Severe Acute Respiratory Syndrome).

CHAPTER 37 What is the link between health risk and pollution?

Key terms

Externality
Externality field
Incidental pollution
Pollution fatigue
Sustained pollution
Toxicity

Key term

Toxicity — a measure of the degree to which something is poisonous. It is often expressed as a dose–response relationship.

Learning objectives

After studying this chapter, you will be able to discuss these ideas and concepts and provide located examples of them:

• The link between different types of pollution and the health of societies.
• The relative health risks associated with incidental and sustained pollution.
• The link between pollution, economic development and changing health risks.
• The role of pollution fatigue in reducing health risk.

Different types of pollution and health

Figure 37.1 shows the considerable global variations in deaths from urban air pollution. Compare the relatively low incidence in western Europe with the very high level in China and a number of other Asian countries. According to the World Health Organisation, diseases caused by air pollution kill 650,000 Chinese every year. This is the highest incidence in the world. Two of the world's most polluted places on earth are in China – Linfen and Tianying. A recent study in China has revealed that children exposed to highly polluted air while in the womb had more changes in their DNA, and a higher risk of developmental problems, than did those whose mothers breathed cleaner air during pregnancy. Apart from the direct effects on health of pollution there are considerable indirect economic effects which include: the cost of healthcare for pollution-related illnesses; interruptions to the education of children which may cause them to leave school with lower qualifications than expected; and lost labour productivity.

Virtually every substance is toxic at a certain dosage. The most serious polluters are the large-scale processing industries which tend to form agglomerations as they have similar location requirements (Figure 37.2). The impact of a large industrial agglomeration may spread well beyond the locality and region to cross international borders. For example, prevailing winds in Europe generally carry pollution from west to east. Thus the problems caused by acid rain in Scandinavia have been due partly to industrial activity in Britain. Dry and wet deposition can be carried for considerable distances. For example, pollution found in Alaska in the 1970s was traced back to the Ruhr industrial area in Germany.

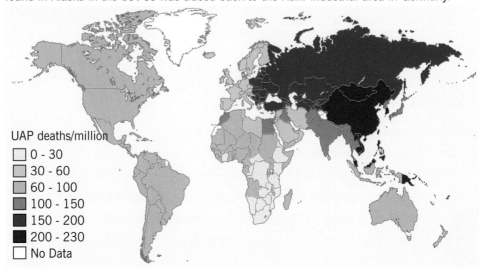

UAP deaths/million
☐ 0 - 30
☐ 30 - 60
☐ 60 - 100
☐ 100 - 150
■ 150 - 200
■ 200 - 230
☐ No Data

▶ **Figure 37.1:** Global distribution of deaths from urban air pollution.

Industrial sector	Examples
Fuel and power	Power stations, oil refineries
Mineral industries	Cement, glass, ceramics
Waste disposal	Incineration, chemical recovery
Chemicals	Pesticides, pharmaceuticals, organic and inorganic chemicals
Metal industries	Iron and steel, smelting, non-ferrous metals
Others	Paper manufacture, timber preparation, uranium processing

◀ **Figure 37.2:** Table of most polluting industries.

Pollution is the major externality of industrial and urban areas. It is at its most intense at the focus of pollution-causing activities, declining with distance from such concentrations (Figure 37.3). For some sources of pollution it is possible to map the externality gradient and field. In general, health risk is greatest immediately around the source of pollution and the risk decreases with distance from the source. However, atmospheric conditions and other factors can complicate this pattern.

Exposure to pollution can result in health effects (Figure 37.4) that range from fairly minor to severe. These include:

- skin irritation
- nose irritation
- fatigue
- breathing problems
- changes in behaviour
- changes in immune system response
- headaches
- blood disorders
- cancer.

Cancer is an example of a delayed health problem that may be a result of long-term exposure to a chemical.

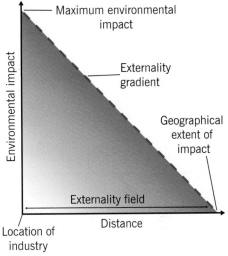

▲ **Figure 37.3:** Externality gradient and field.

Key terms

Externalities — the side effects, positive and negative, of an economic activity that are experienced beyond its site.
Externality field — the geographical area within which externalities are experienced.

	Major sources	Health effects	Environmental effects
SO_2	Industry	Respiratory and cardiovascular illness	Precursor to acid rain, which damages lakes, rivers and trees; damage to cultural relics
NOx	Vehicles; industry	Respiratory and cardiovascular illness	Nitrogen deposition leading to over-fertilisation and eutrophication
PM	Vehicles; industry	Particles penetrate deep into lungs and can enter bloodstream	Visibility
CO	Vehicles	Headaches and fatigue especially in people with weak cardiovascular health	
Lead	Vehicles (burning leaded gasoline)	Accumulates in bloodstream over time; damages nervous system	Fish/animal kills
Ozone	Formed from reaction of NOx and VOCs	Respiratory illness	Reduced crop production and forest growth; smog precursor
VOCs	Vehicles; industrial processes	Eye and skin irritation; nausea; headaches; carcinogenic	Smog precursor

◀ **Figure 37.4:** Major sources and health and environmental effects of air pollutants.

Noise and light pollution

Not all pollution involves inhalation, ingestion and absorption. Noise and light pollution are increasing hazards in developed societies. The increase in air traffic is one of the major contributors to noise pollution. A large area is currently affected by aircraft noise from Heathrow airport stretching from the southern outskirts of Maidenhead in the west to the edge of Camberwell in the east. 600,000 people are affected by noise levels of 55 decibels or over. People living close to the airport are affected by noise levels of 75 decibels. Significant annoyance from aircraft noise begins at 50 decibels.

The proposed third runway at Heathrow will increase the number of flights from 420,000 a year to 700,000 and will bring far more people into the area affected by aircraft noise. A recent study has highlighted the link between exposure to noise and ill-health, noting in particular exposure to night-time aircraft noise and high blood pressure. The latter can lead to heart attacks and strokes.

Light pollution is an externality of a developed society. It can impact on human health causing fatigue, loss of sleep, headaches and loss of amenity.

Pollution control in the developed world

Considering the intense use of energy and materials, levels of pollution are relatively low in the developed world because:
- in recent decades increasingly strict environmental legislation has been passed in developed countries. This is the beginning of a process to make polluters pay for the cost of their actions themselves rather than expecting society as a whole to pay the costs.
- industry has spent increasing amounts on research and development to reduce pollution – the so-called 'greening of industry'.
- the relocation of the most polluting activities, such as commodity processing and heavy manufacturing to the emerging market economies.

Thus the expectation is that after a certain stage of economic development in a country the level of pollution will decline.

The relative health risks of incidental and sustained pollution

It is important to consider the different impact on health between one-off pollution incidents (incidental pollution) and longer-term pollution (sustained pollution). The former is mainly linked to major accidents caused by technological failures and human error. Causes of the latter include ozone depletion and global warming.

Incidental pollution: major causes

Some of the worst examples of incidental pollution are shown in Figure 37.5.

Major examples of incidental pollution such as Chernobyl and Bhopal can have extremely long-lasting consequences which are often difficult to determine in the earlier stages. The effects of both accidents are still being felt more than two decades after they occurred.

It is usually the poorest people in a society who are exposed to the risks from both incidental and sustained pollution. In the USA the geographic distribution of both minorities and the poor has been found to be highly correlated to the distribution of air pollution, municipal landfills and incinerators, abandoned toxic waste dumps, and lead poisoning in children. The race correlation is even stronger than the class correlation.

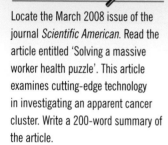

Taking it further

Locate the March 2008 issue of the journal *Scientific American*. Read the article entitled 'Solving a massive worker health puzzle'. This article examines cutting-edge technology in investigating an apparent cancer cluster. Write a 200-word summary of the article.

Examiners' tip

Remember that both incidental and sustained pollution can cover a wide range of impacts from minor to major.

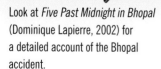

Taking it further

Look at *Five Past Midnight in Bhopal* (Dominique Lapierre, 2002) for a detailed account of the Bhopal accident.

Location	Causes and consequences
Seveso, Italy	In July 1976 a reactor at a chemical factory near Seveso in northern Italy exploded, sending a toxic cloud into the atmosphere. An 18 km² area of land was contaminated with the dioxin TCDD. The immediate after-effects, a small number of people with skin inflammation, were relatively mild. However, the long-term impact has been much worse – increased numbers of premature deaths from cancer, cardiovascular disease and diabetes.
Bhopal, India	A chemical factory owned by Union Carbide leaked deadly methyl isocyanate gas during the night of 3 December 1984. The plant was operated by a separate Indian subsidiary which worked to much lower safety standards than those required in the USA. It has been estimated that 8,000 people died within two weeks and a further 8,000 have since died from gas-related diseases. The NGO Greenpeace puts the total fatality figure at over 20,000. Bhopal is recognised as the world's worst industrial disaster.
Chernobyl, Ukraine	The world's worst nuclear power plant accident occurred at Chernobyl, Ukraine in April 1986. Reactor number four exploded, sending a plume of highly radioactive fallout into the atmosphere which drifted over extensive parts of Europe and eastern North America. Two people died in the initial explosion and over 336,000 people were resettled. In total 56 direct deaths and an estimated 4,000 extra cancer deaths have been attributed to Chernobyl. The estimated cost of $200 billion makes Chernobyl the most expensive disaster in modern history.
Harbin, China	An explosion at a large petrochemical plant in the north-east Chinese city of Harbin released toxic pollutants into a major river. Benzene levels were 108 times above national safety levels. Benzene is a highly poisonous toxin which is also carcinogenic. Water supplies to the city were suspended. Five people were killed in the blast and more than 60 injured; 10,000 residents were temporarily evacuated.

▲ **Figure 37.5:** Major examples of incidental pollution.

Unequal environmental protection undermines three basic types of equity:
- Procedural equity – the extent to which planning procedures, rules and regulations are applied in a non-discriminatory way.
- Geographic equity – the proximity of communities to environmental hazards and locally unwanted land uses such as smelters, refineries, sewage treatment plants and incinerators.
- Social equity – the role of race and class in environmental decision-making.

Ironically some government actions have created and exacerbated environmental inequity. More stringent environmental regulations have driven noxious facilities to follow the path of least resistance towards poor, over-burdened communities where protesters lack the financial clout and professional skills of affluent areas, or the prospect of bringing in much-needed jobs justifies the risks in the eyes of some residents.

Sustained pollution: ozone depletion and skin cancer

The ozone layer in the stratosphere prevents most harmful UV radiation from passing through the atmosphere. However, CFCs and other ozone-depleting substances have caused an estimated decline of about 4% a decade in the ozone layer of the stratosphere since the late 1970s. Depletion of the ozone layer allows more UV radiation to reach the ground, leading to more cases of skin cancer, cataracts and other health and environmental problems. The widespread global concern resulted in the Montreal Protocol banning the production of CFCs and related ozone-depleting chemicals.

▲ **Figure 37.6:** Polluting industry next to poor working class area in USA.

Skin cancer is the fastest growing type of cancer in the USA. In the UK it is the second most common cancer in young people aged 20–39. Over-exposure to UV radiation is the major cause. Skin cancer generally has a 20- to 30-year latency period. Figure 37.7 shows that there is a significant relationship between skin cancer and latitude in the USA and Canada. However, the use of tanning salons has also come under the microscope with a number of studies linking the high use of artificial tanning to skin cancer.

Sustained pollution, such as that caused by ozone-depleting substances, usually takes much longer to have a substantial impact on human populations than incidental pollution, but it is likely to affect many more people in the long term. Likewise, tackling the causes of sustained pollution will invariably be a much more difficult task as the sources of incidental pollution are more localised compared with the ubiquitous nature of sustained pollution.

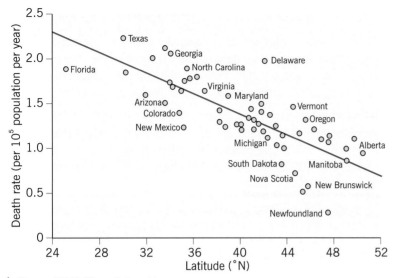

▲ Figure 37.7: The relationship between skin cancer and latitude in the USA and Canada.

Pollution, economic development and changing health risks

Types and amounts of pollution change with economic development. In low-income economies where primary industries frequently dominate, pollution related to agriculture and mining often predominates. As countries industrialise, manufacturing industries, energy production and transport become major polluters. The focal points of pollution will be the large urban–industrial complexes. The newly industrialised countries of the world are in this stage. In contrast, the MEDCs have experienced deindustrialisation as many of their major polluting industries have filtered down to NICs. This has resulted in improved environmental conditions in many MEDCs in general although pollution from transportation has often increased.

Figure 37.8 shows changing air pollution trends in developed and developing countries between 1990 and 2000. It shows a slow but steady decline in developed countries and a very significant rise in developing countries from the mid-1990s.

The Kuznet curve

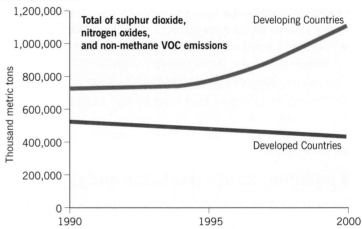

▲ Figure 37.8: Air pollution trends in developed and developing countries, 1990–2000.

▲ Figure 37.9: The Kuznet curve.

The Kuznet curve (Figure 37.9) is a graph representing Simon Kuznet's theory. Here economic inequality increases over time as a country develops. Then, after a critical average income is reached, inequality begins to decrease. However, the curve has also been applied to environmental health indicators such as water and air pollution. The rationale for the environmental Kuznet curve is:

- In the early stages of industrialisation the focus is on economic development with little concern for the environment. Pollution levels increase rapidly.
- After a certain standard of living is reached and pollution is at its highest, attitudes to pollution change and there is now a general desire to tackle the problem.
- With increasing environmental investment, pollution levels fall.

The Kuznet curve works well for some environmental health concerns, but is not particularly valid for others such as landfill sites and biodiversity.

Figure 37.10 is an example of how health risks can change with development in more

Traces of potentially dangerous medicines may be contaminating tap water and putting unborn babies at risk, scientists have warned.

There are growing concerns that powerful and toxic anti-cancer drugs are passing unharmed through sewage works and finding their way back into the water supply.

The Government is taking the threat so seriously it has asked scientists to start testing untreated river.

Although the levels of individual prescription medicines are thought to be too low to pose a direct threat to health, some researchers are concerned that a mixture of drugs could be harmful to foetuses.

Experts will meet in the next few weeks to decide which five drugs to test for and where sampling will take place. The Thames Valley is the most likely location.

Doctors are most concerned about 'cytotoxic', or cell-killing, cancer drugs. They are taken by 250,000 Britons.

The drugs are easily dissolved in water and are flushed from the body and into sewers largely unaltered, remaining highly toxic. They are hard to destroy in water treatment plants.

The trials will also test for anti-inflammatory sedatives and at least one illegal drug such as cocaine or heroin.

A spokesman for the Drinking Water Inspectorate, which will run the pilot trial, insisted that the tests were precautionary.

▲ **Figure 37.10:** Is our water being poisoned with a cocktail of drugs?

advanced countries. Here, medical advance has created a range of powerful new drugs which bring a welcome increase in life expectancy. However, the impact of such drugs on the water supply is causing increasing concern.

China's 'cancer rivers'

China's rapid economic growth has led to widespread environmental problems. Pollution problems are so severe in some areas that the term 'cancer villages' has become commonplace. In the village of Xiditou, south-east of Beijing, the cancer rate is 30 times the national average. This has been blamed on water and air contaminated by chemical factories. Tests on tap water have found traces of highly carcinogenic benzene that were 50% above national safe limits. In the rush for economic growth local governments eagerly built factories, but they had very limited experience of environmental controls.

• The Chinese government admits that 300 million people drink polluted water.
• This comes from polluted rivers and groundwater.
• 30,000 children die of diarrhoea or other water-borne illnesses each year.
• The River Liao is the most polluted, followed by waterways around Tianjin and the River Huai.

Pollution fatigue

The amount of information, discussion and education about environmental pollution has increased rapidly in recent decades. This has occurred to such an extent that many people have become weary of the issue. The constant debate about so many environmental issues, accompanied by what seems to be very limited progress, appears to be turning many people off environmental issues. At the same time many people feel that government at different levels has failed to manage pollution problems effectively. An example is recycling: local councils in the UK expect high standards of recycling from residents, but often fail to keep track of the materials collected when they leave local authority collection points.

Taking it further

To look at how the development of a country can bring both benefits and problems, read 'Reducing air pollution in Bangkok' on your Student CD-ROM.

Taking it further

Look at the World Resources Institute website – www.wri.org – to examine in more detail the link between pollution, health and development.

Summary

In this chapter you have learnt:

• about the types and sources of pollution and their impact on health.

• about the differing impacts of one-off incidents and longer-term sustained pollution.

• about the changes in type and amount of pollution with economic development.

  • about the link between pollution fatigue and the backlash from the public to pressurise for effective management.

MCQ

CHAPTER 38 How can the impacts of health risk be managed?

Key terms

AIDS
Depression
Diabetes
Healthcare sustainability
Health system
Horizontal health programme
Obesity
Preston curve
Vertical health programme

Learning objectives

After studying this chapter, you will be able to discuss these ideas and concepts and provide located examples of them:
- The socio-economic and environmental impacts of health risk.
- Differing management strategies and policies for reducing health risk.
- The role of different agencies involved in health risk.
- Which health risks can be managed effectively and which cannot.
- The role of sustainability.

Key term

Health system — all the activities whose primary purpose is to promote, restore or maintain health.

The socio-economic and environmental impacts of health risk

'Health gaps between countries and among social groups within countries have widened. Social, demographic and epidemiological transformations, fed by globalisation, urbanisation and ageing populations, pose challenges of a magnitude that was not anticipated three decades ago.'

The World Health Report, 2008

Infection and disease can have varying impacts on people and communities, resulting in short- and long-term economic and social burdens on society. Chronic disease, disability and early death are destructive forces for both individuals and whole communities. As populations age, the prospect of so many more people at risk from the degenerative non-communicable diseases such as those of the circulatory system, cancers and diabetes is a challenge to healthcare and welfare systems worldwide.

Healthcare is a major cost in all countries, irrespective of the level of development. Globally healthcare spending accounts for 8% of GDP, a considerable increase on the 3% of 1948. In many countries, the total amount spent on health is insufficient to fund access for all to even a very limited package of essential healthcare.

Health systems are funded in a variety of ways which include:
- taxation
- state social insurance schemes
- employers' contributions to workers' insurance schemes
- private health insurance schemes
- direct payments from patients
- NGOs and other sources of aid.

The socio-economic impact of health risk

Figure 38.1 shows how (a) women using malaria prophylaxis and (b) full basic immunisation coverage vary by income group in selected countries. For most countries and for most indicators, infection and disease impact more heavily as income declines. Higher income is associated not just with the ability to pay, but also with greater knowledge and understanding of the importance of health prevention measures.

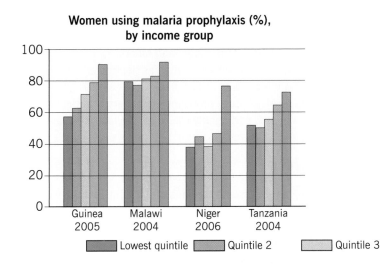

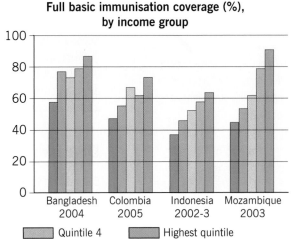

▲ **Figure 38.1:** The relationship between healthcare and income group.

Income has a major impact on the quality of housing to which people can aspire. Studies in the USA and the UK in particular have examined those aspects of housing which have adverse impacts on health. These include lack of an indoor toilet, the sharing of basic domestic facilities, overcrowding, nitrogen oxide and carbon monoxide emissions from poorly functioning gas appliances, damp and low temperatures in the main rooms of the dwelling. A recent study in the UK concluded that to target poor-quality housing in areas of harsh climate was the best way to tackle respiratory health and to narrow health inequalities.

Short- and long-term economic burdens on society

Infection and disease result in clear economic costs. Some costs can be viewed as short-term while others have a much longer time scale (Figure 38.2). The human and economic cost of illness and premature death is huge in the developing world. It is a major impediment to the development process. Various studies have shown how the level of health can impact on countries in terms of:

* labour supply
* labour productivity
* savings and investment
* education.

Short term	Long term
Interruption to schooling	Can reduce skill levels and qualifications of a significant proportion of the population, thus reducing national income
Cost of hospitalisation and immediate drug care	Cost of long-term disability and care. Alzheimer's and dementia are rapidly rising cost factors in many MEDCs
Reduction in household wages for periods of illness	National costs of absenteeism due to illness
Temporary loss of key personnel	Long-term skills shortages due to disability and death from HIV/AIDS, etc.
Lost short-term productivity	
	Death of a household member increases the probability of depression, alcoholism, etc.
	Increasing the real dependency ratio as those who are economically active reduce in number
	Health problems reduce national savings and investment

◄ **Figure 38.2:** Economic consequences of infection and disease on society.

Management strategies and policies

Some health risks and environments are harder to manage than others, for example, indirect spin-offs from modern societies and consumerism such as depression, obesity and diabetes. It is proving difficult to tackle the causes of these health risks as the numbers affected continue to rise. The highest levels of these problems are generally in the most advanced countries, but many other nations, particularly the NICs, are recording rapidly rising figures.

Diseases of modern society

Depression is likely to be one of the greatest disease burdens of the 21st century. It already costs health systems large amounts of money, but this is almost certainly going to increase. Depression causes much suffering and a substantial number of deaths. Depression is more common in women than men, although suicide is more common in men.

'The Depression Report' published in 2006 stated that mental illness accounts for over a third of the burden of illness in Britain. About 40% of all disability is due to mental illness (Figure 38.3). However, depression and anxiety attract only about 2% of NHS expenditure. The total loss of output due to depression and chronic anxiety is about £12 billion a year. This amounts to about 1% of total national income.

Surveys have shown that 2% of the population suffer from pure depression at any one time while another 8% suffer from a mixture of anxiety and depression. The lifetime rate of depression is 8% for men and 12% for women. Depression is now more frequently diagnosed in younger people than it was previously. Depression becomes chronic in 10–20% of cases. The modern management of depression combines social, psychological and pharmacological approaches.

Obesity is associated with various diseases, particularly cardiovascular diseases, type 2 diabetes, certain types of cancer and osteoarthritis. It reduces life expectancy. Most cases of obesity are due to excessive caloric intake, lack of physical activity and genetic susceptibility.

Obesity has been likened to a health time bomb. Patients being overweight or obese cost the UK's National Health Service £4.2 billion in 2007, which could rise to £6.3 billion by 2015. These figures come from the recent 'Healthy Weight, Healthy Lives Toolkit: A Toolkit for Developing Local Strategies'. This publication advises local professionals on how they can help people in their areas to eat more healthily and be more active. Every year 9,000 people in the UK die prematurely because of obesity. In the USA, obesity is the second leading cause of preventable death after smoking.

Diabetes is rapidly becoming one of the world's most common diseases. A recent study in the USA put the total cost to the country at $218 billion in 2006. This included all direct medical costs plus indirect costs such as lost productivity, disability and early retirement. The death rate from diabetes in the USA continues to rise.

It is estimated to cost the National Health Service in the UK about £1 million per hour. This disease affects as many as 2.75 million people in the UK. It accounts for one-tenth of the annual NHS budget. There are numerous complications associated with diabetes including heart disease, kidney failure, blindness and amputation.

International agencies

A range of agencies, both national and international, are playing an increasing role in managing health risk and pollution. The World Health Organisation is the directing and coordinating authority for health within the United Nations. It has existed since 1948.

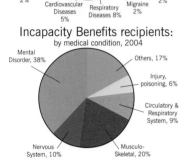

Causes of Disability

Depression 17%
Other Psychiatric Conditions 12%
Other 36%
Alzheimer's 8%
Alcohol Addiction 8%
Cancer 2%
Drug Addiction 2%
Cardiovascular Diseases 5%
Respiratory Diseases 8%
Migraine 2%

Incapacity Benefits recipients: by medical condition, 2004

Mental Disorder, 38%
Others, 17%
Injury, poisoning, 6%
Circulatory & Respiratory System, 9%
Nervous System, 10%
Musculo-Skeletal, 20%

▲ **Figure 38.3:** The UK: causes of disability and incapacity benefit recipients.

The WHO's main responsibilities are:

- Providing leadership on global health matters
- Shaping the agenda for health research
- Setting norms and standards
- Providing evidence-based policy options
- Providing technical support to countries
- Assessing health trends.

These core functions are set out in the publication/programme 'Engaging for Health', covering the 10-year period 2006–2015. The WHO's policies are directed by the principle of equity, whereby access to life-saving or health-promoting interventions should not be denied for unfair reasons. Thus, priority should be given to poor, disadvantaged and vulnerable groups of people. Attainment of the health-related Millennium Development Goals, preventing and treating chronic diseases and addressing the neglected tropical diseases, are the cornerstones of the WHO's health and development agenda.

At the Sixtieth World Health Assembly in May 2007, the member countries of the WHO discussed health protection from climate change. The importance of strong health systems as the front-line defence against the impacts of climate change was emphasised.

The United Nations Children's Fund (UNICEF) funds programmes to (a) prevent childhood illnesses and death, (b) make pregnancy and childbirth safer, (c) encourage care and stimulation for young children, and (d) help with girls' education and female equality.

NGOs have played an increasing role in managing health risk in targeted locations in terms of long-term policy and in disaster areas where immediate relief is required.

Which health risks can be managed effectively and which cannot? and the role of sustainability

Although shorter-term planning is vital when unexpected circumstances occur, the emphasis for health management needs to be on longer-term sustainable planning for a better health environment. This can be applied more easily to some health risks than others. Diseases which have been entirely eradicated from large areas show how effective health planning can be in certain circumstances. The global eradication of smallpox is an example of such success. In contrast, the current battle against HIV/AIDS is proving much more difficult.

According to the World Health Report 2008, 'Higher spending on health is associated with better outcomes, but with large differences between countries.' The Preston curve is often used to show the relationship between health and wealth (Figure 38.4). The curve has shifted upwards over time:

- An income of $1,000 was associated with a life expectancy of 48.8 years in 1975.
- In 2005 it was almost four years higher for the same income.
- The evidence suggests that improvements in nutrition, education, health technologies and management now allow for the greater production of health for the same level of wealth.

▶ **Figure 38.4:** GDP per capita and life expectancy at birth, 1975 and 2005 (the Preston curve).

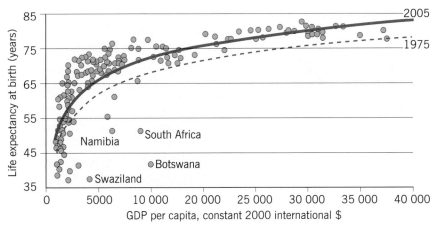

Is HIV/AIDS spending sustainable?

HIV/AIDS is an example where longer-term sustainable planning is required. From the UN and other major organisations there is agreement that the best way to prevent people from catching AIDS is education and testing while the best way to keep infected people alive is anti-retroviral drugs. Data on HIV/AIDS is collected from a variety of sources. The most detailed data is gathered using demographic surveillance systems whereby an initial study and follow-up studies of a population are carried out in a defined area over time.

Figure 38.5(a) shows how the total available funds to tackle AIDs have increased since the late 1990s, while Figure 38.5(b) illustrates three different projections to 2015. There are clearly concerns about the sustainability of targeting such large sums on a single disease. Many sub-Saharan countries have been hard hit by the medical, social and economic burden of HIV/AIDS. There is some concern that the funding of AIDS and other single disease projects, known as 'vertical' health programmes, is taking much-needed money away from broader 'horizontal' health systems which prevent and treat all forms of illness. The Global Fund to Fight AIDS, Tuberculosis and Malaria is the world's largest source of funds for health projects. Its annual disbursements are planned to rise to $8 billion by 2010.

Key terms

AIDS — stands for 'acquired immune deficiency syndrome', while HIV stands for 'human immunodeficiency virus'. The underlying cause of AIDS is infection with HIV-1 or HIV-2.

Vertical health programmes — concentrate on tackling a single disease.

Horizontal health programmes — aim to prevent and treat all forms of illness.

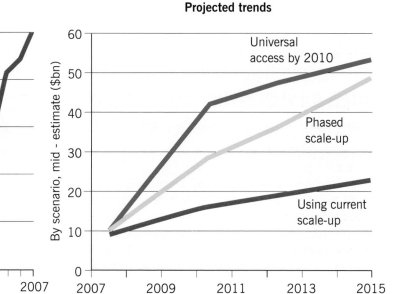

▲ **Figure 38.5:** Resources to fight AIDS.

Taking it further

Look at the UNAIDS website (www. unaids.org) for the latest global statistics on HIV/AIDS.

HIV uses up more than one-fifth of all global health aid. However, it accounts for only one-twentieth of the burden of disease in low- and middle-income countries. HIV is particularly costly because of:

• sophisticated equipment
• expensive medicines
• heavy demands on medical staff.

In comparison, more modest resources could have a very significant impact on relatively neglected conditions such as trachoma and bilharzia.

Many vertical health programmes are funded by individual donors. This can:
• create wasteful administrative costs
• draw much-needed medical expertise away from weak state health systems.

However, supporters of vertical programmes highlight the measurable results such programmes provide. The WHO is encouraging donors, recipients and agencies to reflect on how best to limit any negative impact from vertical programmes.

In reality there have been few studies to illustrate:
- which models work best
- which organisations are best able to distribute and spend money.

Shorter-term planning for emergency disaster relief

Virtually every year major disasters occur somewhere in the world which have significant health implications. Emergency disaster relief operates at two levels of planning:
- General strategic planning whereby governments and major NGOs have personnel and procedures in place to respond quickly to emergencies
- Detailed short-term planning with regard to the particular location in question.

Players	Actions	Futures
World Health Organisation	Working with its 193 member states to combat disease in all its various forms	Trying to ensure that the health communities in different countries are ready to respond effectively to the additional risks posed by climate change
The United Nations Children's Fund (UNICEF)	Working to improve the health and welfare of children worldwide	Setting targets for future improvement
Non-governmental organisations (NGOs) such as WaterAid	Targeting the poorest communities in the least developed countries	Attempting to put in place projects which are sustainable so that they can move on to other communities/countries in need
National Health Service (UK)	To provide free healthcare for UK citizens at the point of delivery	The increasing expectations on the NHS could result in a funding crisis
Global Alliance on Vaccines and Immunisation	Delivering a range of childhood vaccines to poor countries	Aiming to extend the scheme to more people in the developing world
Global Fund to Fight AIDS, Tuberculosis and Malaria	Largest multilateral funder of health projects	Projected annual disbursements of $8 billion by 2010

Summary

In this chapter, you have learnt:
- about the varying impact of infection and disease on people and communities.
- why some health risks and environments are harder to manage than others.
- about the increasing role of international agencies in managing health risk and pollution.
  - about the contrasting needs for longer-term sustainable planning and shorter-term planning for emergency disease relief.

MCQ

CHAPTER 39 The growth of leisure and tourism landscapes

Key terms

Active and Passive activities
AONB
Disposable income
Leisure
Mass tourism
National Park
NNR
Pleasure periphery
Rural–urban continuum
Rural–urban fringe
SSSI
Tourism
Wilderness
World Heritage Site
World Biosphere Reserve

Learning objectives

After studying this chapter, you will be able to discuss these ideas and concepts and provide located examples of them:
• Why leisure pursuits and tourism are increasing and the pleasure periphery is widening.
• The range of rural landscapes that are used for leisure and tourism activities.
• Attitudes towards the use of rural landscapes vary.
• The use of rural environments for leisure and tourism activities can lead to conflicts.

Growth in leisure and tourism

Tourism and leisure combined form the world's largest industry. It has seen unprecedented growth over the last two decades (Figure 39.1), but with the recent downturn in economies worldwide it will be interesting to see how individuals and the industry adapt. What has led to this growth in leisure and tourism? Throughout the 20th century, in developed nations, there was an increase in the amount of paid holiday entitlement. (The anomaly is the USA where annual paid leave is still usually only two weeks a year.) Linked to this was the increased availability of free time due to using machines to carry out repetitive daily tasks such as laundry and having a family car, reducing the time spent travelling to and from work.

On average, the disposable income of households has increased – meaning that after money for all the household expenses has been put aside, there is more money left over each week that can be used for other purposes. Overall, populations in the developed world, including the newly industrialised countries like China, are now better educated and are more aware of other countries. This has been aided by television travel shows and documentaries about distant lands. This, plus the advent of individual internet booking, has led to the development of niche tour operators offering holidays such as exotic wildlife safaris. There have also been developments in transport, such as wide-bodied jet aircraft which can carry more passengers and therefore reduce flight costs to the individual.

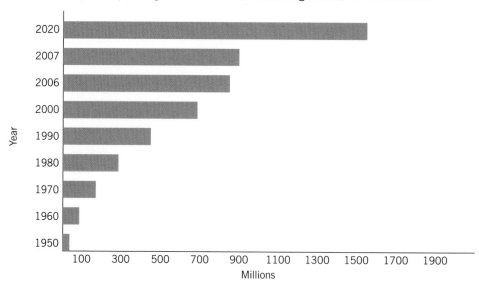

▶ **Figure 39.1:** Graph of growth in number of international tourists.

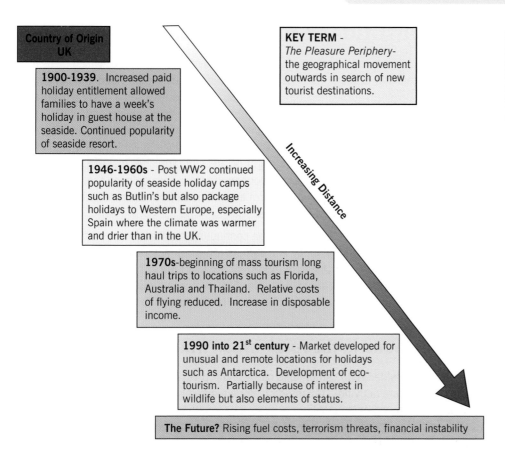

Country of Origin
UK

1900-1939. Increased paid holiday entitlement allowed families to have a week's holiday in guest house at the seaside. Continued popularity of seaside resort.

1946-1960s - Post WW2 continued popularity of seaside holiday camps such as Butlin's but also package holidays to Western Europe, especially Spain where the climate was warmer and drier than in the UK.

1970s-beginning of mass tourism long haul trips to locations such as Florida, Australia and Thailand. Relative costs of flying reduced. Increase in disposable income.

1990 into 21st century - Market developed for unusual and remote locations for holidays such as Antarctica. Development of eco-tourism. Partially because of interest in wildlife but also elements of status.

The Future? Rising fuel costs, terrorism threats, financial instability

Increasing Distance

KEY TERM -
The Pleasure Periphery- the geographical movement outwards in search of new tourist destinations.

▲ **Figure 39.2:** The expansion of the pleasure periphery in the UK.

Key terms

Leisure — all activities that are carried out in non-work time for recreation; includes tourism and sport.
Tourism — travel away from home, normally for at least one night.
Passive leisure activities — relaxing at home, e.g. watching television.
Active leisure— sport and activities such as fell walking or non-competitive swimming.
Mass tourism — when large numbers of tourists travel to the same destination — closely allied to the rise of the package holiday.

During the 20th century in the developed world, the majority of the population was able to have some time to enjoy leisure activities and holidays.

The tourism industry has continued to grow as new sources of tourists enter the industry. The rapid development of China has resulted in a huge number of its population now having the money and time to travel (with similar developments in India). With millions of people having increased leisure time and the capacity to travel abroad, there are increasing pressures on destinations to cope without damaging the landscapes that the visitor has come to see. Many active leisure pursuits, such as walking, skiing, mountain biking, boating and fishing, take place in rural or semi-rural locations and a considerable amount of tourism activity utilises rural areas, even if just to view open landscapes through a car window. Rural landscapes do not have the infrastructure to cope with huge flows of people and as these areas are increasingly accessed for leisure and tourism worldwide, they are under pressure to change in order to accommodate the recreational demands of the urban populations.

Taking it further

Find out how farmers are responding to pressures on the landscapes they manage in the UK. Read 'Farm diversification' on your Student CD-ROM.

Case study: Penguin Place, New Zealand

On the Otago Peninsula on South Island, New Zealand, it has become difficult to make a living from livestock farming alone. Many farms offer accommodation to supplement their income, but one farm has virtually stopped all of its livestock rearing to concentrate on conserving, but also using as an income source, the daily visits to their land of one of the rarest penguins in the world, the Yellow-eyed Penguin. On this farm there is a system of hides and tunnels along which visitors walk in order to get really close to the birds without disturbing them. Penguin Place is now an extremely popular visitor spot in a very rural area. Guided talks and walks are given and photographers can get within a few metres of the birds. Not only is an income provided for the farming family, but also for further conservation efforts on their land to encourage more breeding pairs of this endangered species. Find out more at www.penguinplace.co.nz.

Taking it further

Find out why the rural fringe is important by accessing the following site and reading the article 'Unlocking the potential of the rural–urban fringe': www.arthurrankcentre.org.uk/projects/rusource_briefings/firm04/111.pdf.

What constitutes a rural landscape?

Rural is a difficult concept to define and often an index of rurality is used, which takes a number of factors into account, such as land use, level of services provided and density of population. Generally rural areas have a low population density and a larger percentage than the national average of people working in primary industries, mainly agriculture. However, the reality is often more complex with the range of rural landscapes varying from those areas on the edge of urban areas in the rural–urban fringe to wilderness areas where the impact of humans is minimal. There might be areas of farmland, managed forests, reservoirs and country parks in between. There are no clear lines defining these changes between areas and they are often said to form a continuum: from the rural–urban fringe through other rural landscapes to wilderness.

Apart from where they are on the rural–urban continuum, rural landscapes differ widely due to factors such as geomorphology and climate (physical factors) and cultural practices and economic level (human factors). In 2008, for the first time in history, the majority of the world's population became urban with over 50% of people now living in towns and cities. This increases the appeal of the more open landscapes of rural areas for leisure activities and tourism.

Activities found in the rural–urban fringe

The areas just outside urban settlements come under pressure from further development, but also from leisure activities. Horse riding along marked bridleways can take place in these areas and many riding stables are located here within easy access of the population. Apart from the impact of buildings to stable the horses (often converted from farm buildings or new wooden structures that are not visually intrusive) and the use of the bridle paths, horse riding does not vastly alter the landscape. This is not the case with golf courses, which are also often found within the rural–urban fringe. Here there is a monoculture of grass, fertilised using chemicals and in some climates such as in the arid south-western states of the USA (e.g. Arizona), millions of litres of water are used to keep them green. Sports centres and facilities, such as BMX tracks, are often located in this semi-rural landscape as they need their customers to have relatively easy access.

▲ **Figure 39.3:** Golf course within rural–urban fringe.

Beyond the fringe

Further out from urban settlements, farmland, especially in developed countries, is being used to offer activities to attract tourists. This increases the number of people using rural infrastructure such as roads which were not designed to cope with the amount of traffic generated by the leisure developments. Areas of forest create a different rural landscape, but now in developed countries they are largely multipurpose; meaning that they provide timber as a product, they support certain natural habitats and they offer paths for walking and cycling, e.g. the Coed-y-Brenin Forest in Mid Wales. The presence of trees means that such sites have a higher carrying capacity as the tree roots hold the soil together.

Rural village landscapes, such as those found in the Cotswolds in the UK, attract tourists to their built environment, although they are in a rural setting. In wealthier countries, the more affluent citizens often wish to access the countryside regularly during weekends and holidays, so they buy houses as second homes in rural communities in their home country or abroad. Rural villages in attractive areas (such as the Lake District in the UK and the Dordogne region of France) have seen a large number of houses being bought for this use.

Areas with attractive landscapes attract a large number of tourists, perhaps just for sightseeing, but many will wish to walk trails and get nearer to nature. Dovedale in the Peak District, with its mix of attractive views and limestone dales, attracts a huge number of visitors especially at weekends and during school holidays. Alpine regions can attract visitors all year with skiing and other sports during the winter and sightseeing and walking during the warmer months.

Yet further out along the continuum, the Grand Canyon in Arizona, USA, attracts more than 4 million visitors a year, even though it is many miles away from major settlements. Many people stop only for a couple of hours to view the canyon before getting back into their holiday coach, but a large investment in infrastructure has had to be made in the way of roads, toilets, shops and accommodation in a very rural, wilderness region.

How different people and groups view the rural landscape

Many different people and organisations access the countryside for the purposes of leisure and tourism, but they can have very varied attitudes towards it. In developed countries the traditional role of rural areas as purely for agricultural production is changing. Increasing demands for leisure use are altering our view of the countryside, including the rural areas of developing countries where tourists are attracted by exotic wildlife and cultures. The perception of rural space alters depending on the role an individual or organisational body wants it to play.

 Figure 39.4: Amazonia at the edge of the pleasure periphery.

Examiners' tip

In your report, make it clear what type of rural area you are referring to (where on the continuum) and whether it is in a developed or developing country.

Exclusively conservationist	Conservation dominant	Balanced conservation and exploitation	Exploitation dominant	Exclusively expoitative
e.g. wilderness preserve. Severely limited human access.	e.g. National Nature Reserve – public access	e.g. National Parks	e.g. forestry plantations where timber is main function or shooting moors	e.g. quarry

▲ **Figure 39.5:** How different groups view the rural landscape.

International level

At an international, global level, the attitude is mainly one of protecting fragile landscapes in order that they should survive for future generations. The World Tourism Organisation (WTO) is part of the United Nations and has drawn up a code of conduct that encourages ethical and responsible tourism both by the individual, but also by the tourism organisations of the 154 participating countries. UNESCO (United Nations Educational, Scientific and Cultural Organisation) is involved in drawing up World Biosphere Reserves which help to protect globally important regions, conserving their wildlife while also allowing sustainable development. An example is the Bialowieza Forest in Poland, which has ancient woodland of the type that once covered much of Europe. Conservation is the most important factor in its designation, but tourism provides an income.

Within the European Union much research is conducted on rural areas as many are areas of decline, both in population and in terms of economy. Due to their lack of infrastructure, rural areas do not develop as fast economically as more urban areas, but therein lies their attraction for tourists. SPRITE is an EU organisation that supports and promotes integrated tourism in the rural areas of Europe that are lagging behind. Its view of rural is an area that can be managed and supported to create a wider job base and be more economically secure. The EU also provides support for rural areas through Leader grants which help to revitalise communities and support new initiatives.

An example is the youth hostel at Langdon Beck in the Peak District which is now the first truly green hostel, having used the Leader funding to install solar energy panels to provide electricity.

Taking it further

For an illustration of the edge of the pleasure periphery and the far end of the rural–urban continuum, read 'The British Schools Exploring Society' on your Student CD-ROM.

Taking it further

Find out more about the UK's 'Breathing Spaces' in our National Parks at www.nationalparks.gov.uk. Which is our most visited National Park and how is it managed for wildlife?

Taking it further

Go to your Student CD-ROM and read 'Abel Tasman National Park in New Zealand' for an illustration of how attitudes towards a rural landscape can change over time. Additionally use the following website to investigate how the Department of Conservation in New Zealand makes decisions about rural landscapes and ecosystems: www.doc.govt.nz.

Governmental level – national and local

In the UK much rural development is the responsibility of DEFRA (Department for Environment, Food and Rural Affairs). Part of its aim is to promote sustainable development of the UK's countryside and this includes development for tourism and leisure. One way this is carried out is by supporting farmers in their quest towards diversification. In some European alpine areas there is help for marketing tourist activities, such as walking trails with accommodation being provided by farms in remote areas.

Natural England is a governmental body whose aims include 'to conserve and enhance the natural environment for its intrinsic value, wellbeing and enjoyment of people and the economic prosperity it brings'. This gives rise to potential conflicts as the countryside is to be preserved and yet also to be financially sound. Natural England manages 222 National Nature Reserves and 36 AONBs (Areas of Outstanding Natural Beauty), as well as over 4,000 SSSIs (Sites of Special Scientific Interest). These designations have the potential to attract tourists, but must do so in such a way that the original landscapes are not damaged.

The National Parks concept now operates worldwide with 6,000 parks, covering 12% of the earth's surface. In the UK there are 14 National Parks and their remit is very similar to that of Natural England, to 'conserve and enhance the natural beauty, wildlife and cultural heritage of an area' and also to promote understanding of the qualities that make up a particular National Park. National Parks are accessed by millions of visitors in the UK for whom they are an important recreational destination. Some National Parks are so popular, especially those that are within the catchment area of several cities such as the Peak District National Park, that they are in danger of 'being loved to death'.

Local level

On a local level the countryside is viewed as a leisure resource with many towns having local country parks within the rural–urban fringe that provide a managed, yet informal, landscape for people of all ages to enjoy. Linked to these is the national network of footpaths that give access to much of the British countryside and are viewed as Rights of Way. Local authorities now have Biodiversity Action Plans (BAPs) which guide how landscapes and wildlife can be conserved now and in the future.

Conservation bodies

Some charitable organisations operate nationally in the UK, such as the National Trust, which is responsible for a large number of stately homes located in the countryside as well as great swathes of countryside itself. Landscapes are protected, but there is a certain tension as to whether they should be preserved (kept exactly as they were historically) or conserved (maintained in a sustainable manner). Other NGOs (non-governmental organisations) in the UK include the Wildlife Trusts, which operate in all counties and manage local nature reserves, most of which allow access to the walker or birdwatcher. For the trusts, a healthy, viable countryside is necessary in order to support the full range of wildlife species.

Landowners — including farmers

Landowners need their land to provide enough profit to repay their investment of time and money and to support them and their families. However, many landowners have a deep understanding of their land and its ecology and want to support its continued existence as long as it does not interfere too much with their profits. They are important tourism providers and include:

- hotels – can provide a wider employment base in a rural area. Sometimes difficult to get planning permission for development
- rural theme parks such as Oakwood in Carmarthenshire or Acton Scott Working Farm in Shropshire
- specialist providers such as shooting or fishing concerns
- community schemes such as Village Ways in India (see Chapter 41).

Individuals

Views inevitably vary widely between individuals and will impact on their decisions as to how to use the countryside. The sportsman may view rural areas as the habitat for the game, such as pheasants, he wishes to shoot. He wants the countryside to be managed to produce these birds specifically. This involves gamekeepers whose job it is to protect the birds from predators and provide artificial feeding to ensure the birds reach a healthy adulthood. The conservationist wishes to protect the natural, wild areas, as does the walker, although he requires access to the area. In developing countries such as Nepal, the large number of tourists walking the trails in the Himalayas has impacted negatively on the footpaths. Elsewhere tourists wish only to view scenic countryside; others wish to become involved with it through sports such as skiing or orienteering. Some activities require a greater infrastructure and this has an impact on the landscape.

Conflicting views

With so many different views about rural areas it is no surprise that conflicts arise between decision-makers. Rural areas need to be managed in order that those residing in them can make a living and yet protect valuable (in the broadest sense) landscapes, so they will continue to exist in the future. There is often a tension between conservation and exploitation. On Salisbury Plain in Wiltshire much of the land is under military ownership for manoeuvres and firing ranges, yet the Plain is also the habitat for a diverse ecosystem which is protected. In fact, as the military use is intermittent, much of the ecosystem survives well as there is no public access.

Conflicts can change over time. The little village of Port Isaac in Cornwall is a relatively isolated settlement. Tourism is an important part of its economy, but until recently it was low key with visitors attracted by its scenery and location. The TV series *Doc Martin* was filmed there, calling the village Port Wenn, and since then the number of tourists has increased. This has been good for the local cafes and pubs, but many of the residents are not happy about the increasing crowds in the summer months of people wishing to see the locations from the series. It is feared that traditional visitors will be put off from visiting because of the village seeming more crowded. Older people often choose to retire to a quieter rural/coastal area, but in order for services such as pubs to survive visitors are needed to spend money within the community. Conflicts can arise as the view of a rural area changes due to circumstances outside the location, in this case, a television series.

Taking it further

To look at a case study that shows how conflicts can arise with multiple uses of a rural location, read 'Lyth Hill Country Park' on your Student CD-ROM.

Taking it further

For whom should such areas of open space be managed? What form should the management take? Investigate fair trade in tourism. Find out how fair trade values can be applied within the tourism industry and lessen some conflicting needs. Do you think it can work? Go to: www.tourismconcern.org.uk.

Summary

In this chapter you have learnt:
- that there is an increasing interest in rural areas for leisure and tourism.
- that rural locations can be located along a continuum from semi-urban to wilderness.
- that different groups have different approaches to rural landscapes and this can impact on the ecosystems and amenities of rural regions.
  - that different approaches can lead to conflicts between different users of rural areas.

MCQ

CHAPTER 40 Rural landscapes explored

Key terms

Carrying capacity
Environmental quality
Endemism
Fragility
Leakage
Red Data Book
Resilience
Vulnerability

Key term

Endemism — when species of plants and animals are found nowhere else in the world.

Taking it further

To learn more about the elements of the rural landscape that attract tourists, read 'Kenya and safari tourism' on your Student CD-ROM.

Learning objectives

After studying this chapter, you will be able to discuss these ideas and concepts and provide located examples of them:
- Why some rural landscapes are particularly important.
- That some landscapes are fragile and why this is so.
- The threats to rural landscapes and how these can be measured.
- How some of the measurements/assessments can be used in helping to protect rural landscapes.

As we have seen, the term rural covers a wide range of locations, but some are more important than others due to their landscape and ecological values. These values are becoming increasingly significant as many rural areas are changing from landscapes of production (mainly agriculture) to landscapes of consumption, via leisure pursuits and tourism. This change is farthest advanced in developed countries, although developing countries are realising the potential of some of their landscapes as tourism becomes more important globally.

Some rural landscapes are of global importance because of the ecosystems they support and many of these are in developing countries. The Galapagos Islands with their unique animal and bird species (high level of endemism) are a notable example. This location attracts a large number of tourists wanting to experience exotic wildlife in unspoiled settings. Rural areas hold many spectacular landscape features that are important attractions, such as the Blyde River canyons in South Africa or the arid area of rock formations that makes up Monument Valley in Arizona.

Rural areas that can support leisure and tourism range along the continuum from isolated wilderness like Alaska to the Cotswold Water Park situated a few miles outside Cirencester in the UK, but the capacity of rural areas to cope with tourism pressure may vary according to how vulnerable its ecosystems and cycles are.

However, it is sometimes the landscapes of production that are important, such as the South Downs in the UK where the clearance of woodland many hundreds of years ago and the rearing of sheep have led to the typical downland scenery of gently rolling hills of grazed grassland. The Downs support their own specialised ecology that is partly dependent on the maintenance of the agricultural system. On the island of Bali in Indonesia, the spectacular rice terraces cut into the sides of hills millennia ago are part of the landscape that attracts tourists.

Fragile rural landscapes

At the rural far end of the rural–urban continuum, in locations classed as wilderness, natural systems operate largely without human interference. Most wilderness locations are regarded as being at the edge of the pleasure periphery as, by their very nature, they have limited infrastructure and more effort has to be made by tourists to access them.

As human activities impinge more on rural areas, natural systems are disrupted, such as in East Anglia in the east of the UK, which is an important cereal-growing region. It is largely rural, but many of its natural systems have been altered because it is an intensively farmed and highly productive area. Its large prairie-like fields growing a monoculture of wheat aided by chemical fertilisers now lack the traditional hedgerows of the typical English farmscape.

▲ **Figure 40.1:** South Downs landscape, UK.

Eutrophication of water courses has resulted from the over-use of artificial fertilisers rich in nitrogen. Such changes have led to a more impoverished landscape in terms of ecosystems and intensively farmed areas are not usually associated with tourism although the Norfolk Broads, an important tourist destination, has suffered from eutrophication. Tourists are more attracted to areas such as the Lake District where landscapes are more in balance with the natural ecosystems.

Factor	Example of tourist location	Reason
Wide biodiversity	Iwokrama, Guyana	Complex food webs with highly specialised niches. Relatively easy to destroy a plant species in an area and its dependent insects. Clearing for tourist infrastructure has to be done carefully.
High levels of endemism	Galapagos Islands	High numbers of flora and fauna found in one location only, therefore if tourism activities are not well managed, it could be devastating for species. Large numbers of visitors could affect breeding patterns of e.g. birds.
Spectacular landscape	Grand Canyon, Arizona, USA Fiordland, New Zealand	These are landscapes with high visual/aesthetic value. Any human structure such as a visitor centre or access roads impact on this. Need, in planning, to allow landscape to dominate.
Fragmentation	Rural–urban fringes Coastal forests of SE Brazil	Semi-rural areas broken up by human activities such as golf courses. Impacts on surrounding natural ecosystems and green corridors needed to allow species to move across areas of human activity. Some forested areas being fragmented by multiple uses including tourism activities.
Geology/soils	Peak District and Lake District National Parks, UK	Thin soils on impermeable rock make them more susceptible to footpath erosion as numbers of visitors rise. Can cause gullying and habitat removal in extreme cases.
Sand dunes	Newborough Warren, Anglesey	Without human activity the system is in balance. Human activity affects paths through the dunes, allowing winds to erode further back. Removal of stabilising vegetation opens up system to erosion.
Intensive farming systems	East Anglia Forests of Sabah, Malaysia (change from forest to palm oil plantations)	Alters the natural systems that often survive, albeit in a restricted form, when traditional, less intensive farming methods are used. Intensive farming using chemical fertilisers and pesticides alter landscapes and ecosystems and are less attractive for tourism.
Traditional way of life, well-established communities linked to the natural ecosystem	Masai, Kenya Maori, New Zealand	When tourism arrives, more consumer-oriented activities. Dances and festivals often put on for visitor rather than as natural part of their year. Can weaken/destroy community structures unless carefully managed.

▲ **Figure 40.2:** Factors affecting fragility.

In the rural–urban fringe tourism and leisure activities add to the human impact on the natural ecosystems. Many of the activities require considerable infrastructure such as shooting ranges or golf courses. Although the latter changes the natural ecosystem, they can support quite a large number of common birds. Country parks with wooded areas and open glades are usually much more biodiverse that the surrounding farmland and can offer a refuge and breeding area. Just outside towns in the UK there has often been a change from intensively farmed fields to less intensively used fields to graze horses as this can generate more income. This is good for the natural systems as chemical fertilisers are no longer used and grass and wild flowers can go to seed, producing a more natural, stable ecosystem.

It is possible to utilise fragile ecosystems for tourism, but great care has to be taken in order that the effects are minimised.

Threats to rural landscapes

Increasing populations wanting space for leisure and tourism are upping the pressures on rural landscapes. Figure 40.3 summarises some of those threats. Research carried out into those threats has led to several models being developed to assess them and also to help decide on levels of protection for a rural area.

Carrying capacity and resilience

The model for carrying capacity is used when considering ecologically important areas. It aims to assess the level of use an area can sustain without the landscape and natural systems deteriorating and leading to a reduction in the quality of visitor experience. It can be seen as a threshold of environmental quality below which tourism might totally collapse or change in type.

Key terms

Fragility — easily damaged.
Vulnerability — the degree to which an area is susceptible to damage. There is considerable overlap between the two terms.
Leakage — money generated by tourism which returns to the country where the company is located and is not available to be reinvested locally.

Taking it further

To discover the impact of leakage on tourism profits in developing countries, read 'The problem of leakage' on your Student CD-ROM'.

Case study: Iwokrama Project, Guyana

This case study illustrates a low-level impact of tourists within a pristine environment. Although there is great pressure in Guyana to increase the rate of the commercial logging of its tropical rainforest, there is also a greater awareness of the sustainable use of the forests for tourism. The International Centre for Rainforest Conservation and Development is located 300 km away from Georgetown, the capital and only settlement of any size.

The Project covers an area of 360,000 hectares and aims to promote conservation, but also sustainable development, including tourism. As a pristine rainforest, all its natural systems, such as the hydrological cycle, are intact, but at the same time they are fragile and easily disturbed. Low-level, ecotourism is encouraged and runs alongside scientific research.

There is some basic infrastructure such as access roads, but accommodation is designed to use minimal amounts of locally produced energy. Visitor numbers are small so that impacts are kept low. The latest development was a canopy walkway that allows tourists safe and easy access to the rainforest canopy in order to see the birds and mammals.

The ecosystem of the rainforest is fragile as it is so complex and there are many interactions. A small area of forest may have 200 tree species with different organisms dependent on each species, therefore damaging or removing one tree can have an immediate effect on some creatures and reduce the biodiversity. Management plans for Iwokrama do not envisage large increases in tourism as there is the realisation that it would be all too easy to unbalance this increasingly rare ecosystem. Consequently the carrying capacity for visitors is low. You can find out more on the Iwokrama Project at www.iwokrama.org.

Taking it further

Find out about assessing wilderness areas in the USA on the website www.wilderness.net.

Taking it further

For a case study about how landscape created by human activity can be highly valued and yet under threat from tourism activities, read 'The Lake District' on your Student CD-ROM.

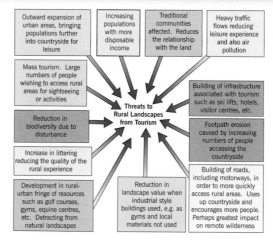

▲ **Figure 40.3:** Threats to the rural landscape.

Some activities have a greater impact than others — walking, horse riding and canoeing generally have a lower impact than mountain biking or off-roading in four wheel drive vehicles. This gives rise to different carrying capacities for different activities and also for different locations. Factors that affect the carrying capacity, apart from the fragility of the natural systems, include visitor perceptions, the activity undertaken and the age of

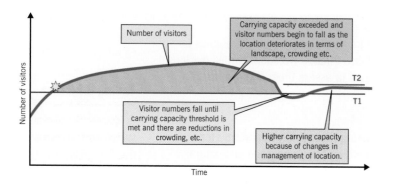

▲ **Figure 40.4:** Carrying capacity.

the visitor. A party of young school students is likely to have a greater impact on carrying capacity than a party of birdwatchers.

Another concept is that of resilience. This is the ability of a location to recover from increased activity. Some systems can cope, at least for short periods, with higher numbers and the quieter months allow a certain amount of recovery. Others are less resilient to higher numbers of visitors, such as some sand dune areas, and need help in order to recover.

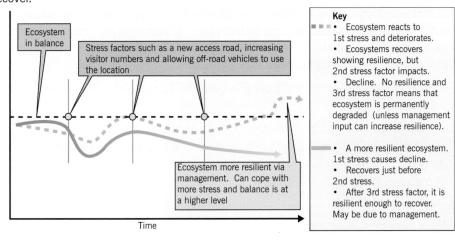

◀ **Figure 40.5:** Resilience model.

Both of these models are only approximations of reality and with so many variables, they offer useful, yet not definitive, guidelines. Not all human impacts cause damage and the level of damage is often a subjective assessment. The concept of carrying capacity needs to incorporate elements of the natural environment, but also the visitor's perception of the experience and the impacts on the host community. Resilience can be difficult to assess and it is hard to know whether an ecosystem has been damaged or not.

Deciding what and where to protect

In order to protect fragile rural areas from human activity that damages them, the quality of the natural environment first needs to be assessed. Continual monitoring of visitor impacts is also required so that carrying capacities are not exceeded and ecosystems are not degraded. Environmental quality surveys investigate a range of factors, some of which are subjective.

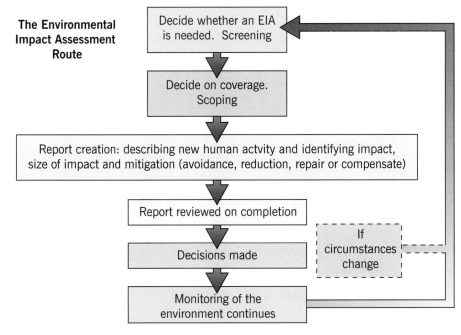

▲ **Figure 40.7:** Environmental Impact Assesment process.

Quantitative assessment (clearly measurable)
- Air quality: compared with national/international targets
- Number of species of flora and fauna
- Presence of Red Data Book species (those assessed as rare or endangered)
- Noise levels of human activity
- Number of visitors
- Visitor density
- Means by which the area is accessed: car, bike, coach, train, on foot.

Qualitative assessment (subjective)
- Level of visual intrusion of e.g. visitor facilities
- % land left without human influence
- How much noise levels impact on level of enjoyment
- Value for quality of the scenery
- How crowded a location feels
- Level of visitor ability to experience peace and solitude.

▲ **Figure 40.6:** Quantitative and qualitative assessments.

Taking it further

For a case study detailing the Conservation Area Project in Nepal, read 'The Annapurna Conservation Area Project (ACAP)' on your Student CD-ROM.

Taking it further

To investigate the problem of carrying capacity, read 'The Jurassic Coast of the UK' on your Student CD-ROM.

Environmental Impact Assessments (EIA) can be carried out to assess what might be the impact of a new activity within the landscape or if a factor were to change, such as an increase in visitor numbers. EIAs follow a general path (Figure 40.7) and they aim to identify the consequences for a landscape, and the physical, social and economic environments that form it, of implementing new activities. Examples might be the construction of a visitor centre or the conversion of a disused quarry into a nature reserve. EIAs are now an important part of the planning process.

Impacts of an activity can be identified using checklists, surveys of flora and fauna, network analysis, quantitative methods and matrices. Network analysis recognises that environmental systems are complex and tries to factor in this complexity. However, it does not give an idea of size or significance of the linkages.

◀ **Figure 40.8:** Visitors to the Grand Canyon.

Wilderness component	How it is measured (Scale of 1–5 with 1 being least natural, most polluted, etc. and 5 most natural, least polluted, etc.)	How the Grand Canyon measures up
Natural composition	Using past records of flora, fauna and geology Satellite imagery and GIS Land use maps	Large biodiversity Elements of 3 out of 4 of American desert types Endemic species, e.g. Kaibab squirrel Long geological record
Unaltered structure	Largely unaltered structure of the Canyon Huge proportions: 1219–1828 m deep, 466 km long and 24 km wide at widest point	Maps showing infrastructure and settlements Land use maps
Lack of pollution	Maps of dumps, nuclear sites Records of air quality City light pollution Noise measurements	Clear night skies Limited air pollution (mainly blown in from Los Angeles) Generally clean air
Solitude	Maps of population density Records of visitor numbers on trails	11 km from nearest settlement, which is Tusayan 755 km from Los Angeles Away from Grand Canyon Village, can experience solitude
Remoteness	Map distance of each km² to nearest road	Access roads and meandering rural roads along rim Rest largely accessed on foot or by horse
Uncontrolled processes	Maps of river dams Land use maps	Some control upstream on the Colorado at Glen Canyon Dam Some controlled burning, but less than in past (to control bushfires) Otherwise, natural processes uncontrolled
If TOTAL = 30 then completely wild, if TOTAL = 6 then not at all wild.		

▲ **Figure 40.9:** Measuring the wildness of the Grand Canyon.

Case study: The Grand Canyon, Arizona, USA

This case study shows why the Grand Canyon was designated as a National Park and also why it is classed as wilderness.

In 1908 the Grand Canyon was protected by being made a National Monument, followed by being designated a National Park in 1919. As it is a globally significant landscape, it was given the protection of a World Heritage Site in 1979. Almost all of the park is wilderness, scoring highly on wildness, although there is considerable tourism development at places along the South Rim, such as Grand Canyon Village, and there is a continual challenge to maintain the wilderness experience when 5 million visitors come every year. The Grand Canyon scored highly on the wildness assessment, but some subjective elements that are important for the location cannot be measured, such as its spiritual qualities. Once away from the honeypot site of Grand Canyon Village and Bright Angel Trail, all the components of the wildness can be experienced.

Other assessments

The Recreational Opportunity Spectrum (ROS) is used to help create an integrated planning approach, which is used to set guidelines and limitations for tourism activities. The components of a visitor's experience of a location are mapped — the physical resource, the opportunities for public use and the management carried out to meet the conditions at the location. Inconsistencies are identified between the experience that visitors have and the need for conservation. Conflicts are recognised and mitigation processes put in place. Regular monitoring is carried out so that plans can be updated. It is a useful tool for planning, but all managers must agree on the indicators used if it is to work.

The ROS further developed into the Limits of Acceptable Change (LAC). Here planning begins with identifying the resource conditions and levels of impact and deciding on the actions needed to achieve those conditions. It is a useful process with clear limits, but it is based on issues and concerns that might change. There is a need for continuous monitoring.

Visitor Activity Management Process (VAMP) often incorporates elements of ROS and LAC and produces a clear decision-making process, analysing opportunities and impacts, but it does not lead to clear zoning policies.

Taking it further

To learn more about ROS, LAC and VAMP, read 'The Recreational Opportunity Spectrum' on your Student CD-ROM.

Summary

In this chapter you have learnt:
- that some rural landscapes are more important ecologically than others.
- that fragility can come about due to a number of factors.
- that landscapes can support only a certain number of visitors and that this number must be taken into account when planning for the future.
- that there are several measures of landscape quality, and also of usage of rural environments for leisure and tourism.

MCQ

CHAPTER 41 What are the impacts on rural landscapes of leisure and tourism?

Key terms

Biodiversity
Ecological damage
Heritage tourism
Tourism hotspot

Learning objectives

After studying this chapter, you will be able to discuss these ideas and concepts and provide located examples of them:

- The range of negative and positive impacts that leisure and tourism activities can have on the rural landscape.
- How impacts, both positive and negative, can alter over time.
- The threats and opportunities posed by tourism in areas at different levels of development.

Synoptic link

For links with this chapter look at Edexcel AS Geography Unit 2 Chapters 16 and 18.

Key term

Biodiversity — the number of species an area can support.

What are the negative impacts of leisure and tourism on rural landscapes?

Although the leisure and tourism industries are very important to some areas, their existence is not without negative impacts on landscapes. Figure 41.1 summarises some of these negative impacts. The danger is that by allowing visitor numbers beyond the carrying capacity of the location, the visitors end up destroying the very landscape components they have come to see.

Tourism that has developed to serve the needs and wishes of visitors from developed nations such as the UK and the USA puts huge pressures on the natural systems within developing countries or areas of the world that are particularly fragile. In the peak summer season, these tourists demand air conditioning and this puts pressure on what are often elementary electricity generating systems; however it is the local people's supply that suffers power cuts rather than the hotels. It has been estimated that a holiday-maker in the Mediterranean area consumes 440 litres of water a day, including all uses. This is double the amount of a Spanish citizen. In a country that is experiencing a long-term drought, this is devastating for the natural environment and in some areas is impacting on the biodiversity.

Visual impacts are more subjective. If you are a skier, removing coniferous trees to build a ski lift might seem a sensible decision. However, as well as the visual intrusion into the alpine landscape of the infrastructure, the removal of the trees means that settlements located below have less protection against avalanches.

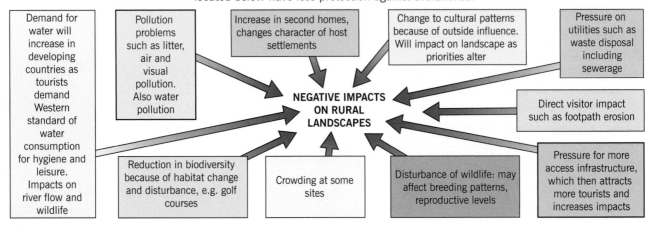

▲ **Figure 41.1:** Negative impacts on rural landscapes.

A growth in visitor numbers to upland areas, which often have quite thin soils, is leading to an increase in footpath erosion.

Case study: Footpath erosion in the Lake District National Park

This case study looks at a common problem in areas that are accessed by a large number of visitors.

As people in the UK have more leisure time, many more are taking to the hills in locations such as the Peak District and the Lake District. This concentration of people has led to some paths being used to such an extent that not only is the vegetation removed, but soil is being carried away in the runoff as the rain has easy access to it. Over time small channels are formed and these allow even more soil to be washed away. When paths are in this state not only do they look unsightly, but they are difficult to walk on. Without work being carried out to stabilise them, the eroded paths detract from the natural lakeland landscapes and the scars can be seen from a distance. Human factors that affect the rate of erosion are:

• the number of visitors using the route each day

• how the tourists are accessing the path, i.e. whether on foot, pushing a child's buggy or cycling

• how well grazed the area is (heavier grazing means the path will have lower resilience to trampling)

• how near the path is to tourist facilities.

The issue of eroded paths is such a problem that the Upland Path Restoration Project was set up to repair all paths identified as suffering from erosion over the period 2002–11. Find out more about paths in the Lake District National Park by accessing the following website: www.lakedistrict.gov.uk/lake_district_docs95/path_erosion_factsheet.pdf.

▲ **Figure 41.2:** A Lake District footpath suffering from erosion and showing the effect of gullying.

Another negative impact is the problem of litter that detracts from the quality of the landscape for everyone. The National Trust does not provide litter bins on most of the land it owns, except directly outside its cafes. It encourages people to take all litter back home to dispose of it and this has generally been successful.

Case study: Snowmobiles in Yellowstone

This case study illustrates the problems caused by trying to minimise the negative impacts of inappropriate access.

Yellowstone National Park has over 3 million visitors a year attracted by the landscapes, geothermal features and wildlife. The majority of visitors is during the high summer season, but 130,000 come during the winter when the roads are closed, many because they wish to travel using snowmobiles. Numbers had grown to 750 a day and the impacts were not conducive to the quiet enjoyment of the park. A total ban on their use was put in place in 2001, but was overturned two years later because of a lawsuit filed by the snowmobile manufacturers, maintenance centres and the snowmobilers themselves.

The Park does not encourage snowmobile use as many of the 185 miles of track run alongside water courses and there is the concern about pollution from particulates in exhausts. However, the average snowmobiler spends $4,000 a year on his sport and the towns around the park have developed businesses to support the activity. Snowmobiles are allowed on all State Forest trails and the National Park still questions the right of snowmobilers to access lands that are primarily for conservation. Find out more by accessing the resources at http://serc.carleton.edu/research_education/yellowstone/snowmobiles.html.

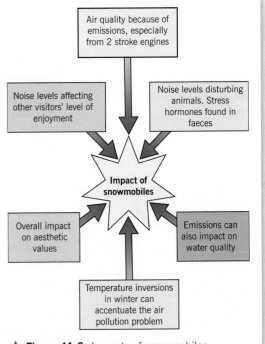

▲ **Figure 41.3:** Impacts of snowmobiles.

What are the positive impacts of leisure and tourism on rural landscapes?

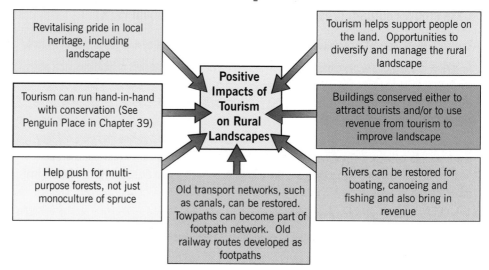

▶ **Figure 41.4:** Summary of some of the positive impacts on rural landscapes of leisure and tourism activities.

Tourism and leisure can impact positively on rural landscapes by providing funds to protect the resource that visitors come to see and also by providing confirmation to the local populations of the value of their local landscape. Figure 41.4 summarises some of the positive impacts tourism can have on rural landscapes. These positive impacts can have a knock-on effect forming a multiplier effect.

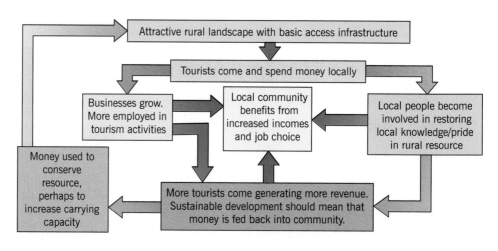

▶ **Figure 41.5:** The multiplier effect of tourism.

Taking it further

To look at a case study on how a previously run-down settlement can be revitalised by tourism, read 'Arrowtown, South Island, New Zealand' on your Student CD-ROM.

The conservation of special rural landscapes enables local communities to maintain their cultural values by maintaining their base: the landscape. The landscape that originally attracts the tourist needs to be conserved, whilst at the same time allowing people access to it for leisure and tourism, whether it is the traditional hill farming uplands of the Lake District or the mesa and butte landscape of the Navajo tribe in Monument Valley, Arizona, in the USA. Heritage tourism is based on cultural, natural and historical assets of a landscape. An example of this would be Stonehenge on the Salisbury Plain in Wiltshire. Its image is globally recognised and great efforts are now being made to preserve the Neolithic (Stone Age) landscape on which it stands, as well as conserving the associated ecosystems. In recognition of its global importance Stonehenge has been designated as a World Heritage Site and it attracts about 1 million visitors a year, so it is important that the attraction and its setting do not further deteriorate.

In developing nations tourism can provide income but also, if sustainably managed, confirm and enhance the value of the indigenous culture as the following case study shows.

Case study: The Hideaway Resort and the village of Tagage

This case study shows how tourism can have positive impacts on the rural landscapes of the south coast of Fiji's main island.

The village of Tagage is located on the Coral Coast, to the south of Fiji's largest island. The village chief gave permission for the development of a small resort within an old coconut plantation. This has led to long-term benefits for the village, apart from jobs and a wider economic base. Tourists visit partly because the resort has used traditional housing design and has had a minimal visual impact on the Fijian landscape, but also because of the reef that fronts the development. The reef had been degraded by unsuitable fishing techniques and also coral bleaching (a problem that occurs when coral are stressed). The resort managers and the chief have made the reef taboo, which means that no fishing can take place on it and access to the reef for viewing its marine life is limited to high tide. Tourists pay for guided reef walks and glue pieces of live coral onto the damaged part of the reef in order to help repair it.

The relationship between the village and the Hideaway Resort is symbiotic: it is to the advantage of both parties.

Activity linked to tourism	Positive impact on landscape
Building of resort in old coconut plantation.	Keeps original land use. *Bures* (cottages) built amongst the trees, so little visual impact.
Visits to village by tourists. Voluntary contributions.	Income to village. Enables village to have electricity and a TV. Young men more likely to stay in village than migrate to towns. Landscape will be maintained. Also realise that traditional culture has a value: that people want to come and participate.
Tourists pay for reef guides and pay to repair reef. Covers cost of growing the coral in coral farm.	Reef maintained. Fish stocks increase so fishing is again a viable occupation. Keeps young in the village and increases job opportunities.
Resort's existence.	Offers wider job opportunities near to village. Encourages training and linked craft industries.
Kula Eco Park: set up near the village. Money from UK and Fijian governments. School visits are free, sponsored by overseas visitors. Also houses a research institute.	Aims include that every child experiences a day of ecology at the centre so that they know why their ecosystems are worth protecting. Future development is more likely to be sustainable if the majority understand their ecosystems and their own impact upon them. Research is being carried out into maintaining the remaining areas of rainforest and its indigenous species.

▲ **Figure 41.6:** Activities linked to tourism and positive impacts on the landscape.

Changing impacts

Tourism and leisure activities have become more important parts of our lives during the 20th and into the 21st centuries, but the impacts are changing. This is partly because of changes in fashion as to where we go and why, but also because we have become more aware of our impact when we travel and on our destinations. Butler's model shows how a tourism destination can go through a number of stages and at each stage the impacts would be different. Figure 41.7 shows the model.

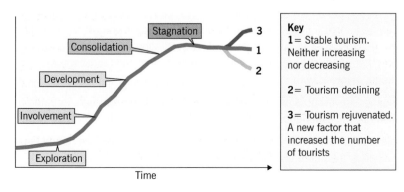

◀ **Figure 41.7:** Butler's model.

Case study: European Alps

This case study looks at the changing popularity and impacts on the rural landscapes of the Alps linked to Butler's model.

Stage in Butler's model	Type and amount of activity	Impacts on landscape
Exploration: 19th century	In the 19th century the Alps were accessed for walking holidays and mountaineering.	Minimal. Visitors tended to use houses and inns that were already in existence.
Involvement: late 19th into 20th century	Walking, mountaineering and sightseeing grew in popularity. Skiing towards the end of the 19th century.	Guesthouses opened to cater for the increasing number of visitors. Lakeside hotels also adjacent to small villages (at the time), such as Kitzbühel, Austria.
Development: 1960s	'Lakes and Mountains' holiday packages for mass tourism. Skiing becomes more important.	Hotel construction. Increase in skiing infrastructure: creation of pistes and ski lifts. Road tunnels enable easier access. Air pollution from vehicles begins to be a problem.
Consolidation: 1970s–1990s	Skiing becomes a mass tourism activity. Sightseeing and walking in summer.	Increasing amount of skiing infrastructure. Purpose-built ski resorts in e.g. Val d'Isère. Overseas visitors buying or renting ski chalets. Removal of coniferous trees above settlements in order to build ski lifts. Cafes on tops of mountains. Disturbance of wildlife. Seasonally huge numbers of visitors on upper slopes.
Stagnation: 1990s–present day	Skiing holidays in winter, but low amounts of snow, possibly linked to global warming, for several years. Crowding on slopes in some locations.	Limited new developments and ones that are built tending to cater for mass market to try to keep up income. Use of artificial snow to keep resorts functioning and new ski lifts to access glaciers to ski on. Increasing incidence of avalanches impacting on skiers.
Decline: late 1990s	People responding to crowding on the slopes and going elsewhere such as Transylvanian Alps in Romania or abroad to e.g. Lake Louise, Canada.	Some under-used infrastructure, but still within the landscape. Fewer visitors may improve the overall experience and return the area to a steady state.
Rejuvenation: 2000 onwards in some areas	Specialist resorts for snowboarding, keeping some resorts exclusive and therefore their slopes less crowded, e.g. Klosters in Switzerland. Others concentrate on family skiing parties. Change to nature tourism.	More aware of impacts, but difficult to balance with need for tourism industry for the economy of the areas.

▲ **Figure 41.8:** Table of European Alps according to Butler's model.

When there were small numbers of people skiing, the impacts were minimal and the Alps were well within their carrying capacity for this activity. Today this has been exceeded and the infrastructure for skiing has a strong negative impact on the landscape. Nature tourism is being put forward as a means for tourism to continue, but with less impact. The Parc Naturel Régional du Queyras is located in the French Alps near the Italian border and contains 11 villages with a total population of 2,400 people. This area did not benefit from the skiing industry and farming was declining.

The Parc developed the idea of an integrated protected area, encouraging visitors, whilst supporting the natural landscapes and occupations that depended on them. A bottom-up approach was used, involving the community. A carefully focused marketing strategy was devised, aiming for tourists who would enjoy the peacefulness and beauty of this alpine region and not require a heavy investment in infrastructure. Individual internet booking has been promoted and local crafts and produce encouraged. The idea is to maintain the natural landscape, encourage local involvement and to have minimal impact on the natural ecosystems. It's a sustainable way of using the alpine region for tourism, returning to the original activities for which people visited the Alps.

Coping with tourism

Tourism can be a force for good and can help support people in rural environments, allowing rural landscapes to be maintained. However, some developments are too large-scale, or in other ways inappropriate, and can detract from the landscape that visitors have travelled to get involved with.

In other locations a resource can prove too popular and sheer numbers threaten the resource itself or the experience (see section on carrying capacity in Chapter 40).

An example would be Dovedale on a Sunday in the summer when the numbers of visitors make the location feel more like an urban park.

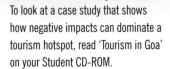

Taking it further

To look at a case study that shows how negative impacts can dominate a tourism hotspot, read 'Tourism in Goa' on your Student CD-ROM.

A tension exists between gaining economic benefit from the landscape and keeping it largely in its natural state. Governmental decisions may be swayed by a need to provide more jobs and attract foreign direct investment, so it is important that the views of the people who live in an area are listened to, whether in a developed or developing country.

Tourism hotspots exist in both developed and developing countries and in these locations it is easy for negative impacts to dominate. A tourism hotspot is an area that is experiencing a rapid increase in visitor numbers. Look at the Taking it further activity on Goa to investigate the tension and problems that can arise in a tourism hotspot. However, it is possible to develop tourism on a small and sustainable scale, involving local people in the decision-making and having positive impacts on people and landscapes.

Taking it further

To look at a case study exploring the costs of tourism, read 'The planned development of the Menie sand dunes' on your Student CD-ROM.

Case study: Village Ways – a walking company in northern India

This case study shows how low-impact tourism in an area that has not yet experienced tourism can help in a less developed region and bring positive impacts.

The Kumaon area of Uttaranchal in northern India is a mountainous region with rushing streams and flower meadows where subsistence agriculture dominates. By the late 1990s it was found that many of the younger people were migrating out of the area in search of jobs and that Kumaon was declining. A new Anglo-Indian walking company called Village Ways was set up with the aim of giving tourists a more authentic view of northern India, but also to involve the local communities in a new industry that would not negatively impact on their landscape. Initially five villages around the Binsar Wildlife Sanctuary were involved and Village Ways gave interest-free loans to have guest houses built. Most of the profits go back into the communities. In 2007 Village Ways won Best Overseas Tourism Project, awarded by the British Guild of Travel Writers, and in 2008 the project was extended into the nearby Saryu Valley. Find out more about Village Ways and its recent expansion on www.villageways.com.

OPPORTUNITIES	THREATS
Guesthouses built by locals using local materials and methods. Meals cooked by local people. Ingredients supplied by local farmers. Craft skills encouraged to make local souvenirs. Guides are local – new jobs for younger people, making them less likely to leave. Environmental awareness for locals and for visitors. Realise importance and beauty of local landscapes. Cultural interchange, but where locals take the lead in what is provided.	The project may develop too much and begin to impact negatively on landscapes and/or local culture. Interaction with Western tourists may tempt younger people away to sample life elsewhere.

▲ **Figure 41.9:** Opportunities and threats created by Village Ways.

Summary

In this chapter you have learnt:

- that tourism and leisure activities will impact on landscapes, especially as visitor numbers increase, but it does depend on what type of activity.
- that negative impacts are often outweighed by benefits to the rural communities and therefore to their landscapes.
- that pressures to develop an important landscape area for tourism still occur within MEDCs.
  - that involving local communities helps mitigate negative impacts.

MCQ

CHAPTER 42 How can rural landscapes be managed for leisure and tourism?

Learning objectives

After studying this chapter, you will be able to discuss these ideas and concepts and provide located examples of them:
• Whether or not rural landscapes should be managed.
• The advantages and disadvantages of a range of management strategies.
• How and why conflicts can occur between users and managers.
• Investigating management strategies in different locations.

To manage or not to manage

With more of the world's population travelling for pleasure it is almost impossible for a region or country to decide that tourism will not be part of their economy and culture. As the pleasure periphery expands, more parts of the world are affected by the tourism industry and, if it is not managed, it is likely that rural landscapes will suffer from the negative impacts we looked at in the previous chapter. Without management, foreign interests may move in and the majority of the profits may be leaked back to the country where the company is based. This means less of the profit is available to be fed back into the host country's economy.

If an area such as the Lake District were to be left without management, it would change drastically and would probably be less appealing to the visitor. However, in more wild landscapes, some feel that no management might be better as it would allow natural systems to return to their former state before human influence changed them. With biodiversity under threat rural landscapes could support a large number of wildlife, but inevitably, with an increasing number of people wanting to access these environments, not having any management or control could easily lead to the destruction of the landscapes.

Case study: Upland areas of the UK

This case study looks briefly at some of the possible outcomes for UK upland landscapes if they are not managed.

The upland areas of the UK are the result of natural and human-induced processes. Although we refer to them as wild, they are the result of thousands of years of human intervention and the resulting landscapes are amongst our most attractive. However, with hill farmers struggling to make a living, there is a real worry that the landscape will change, plant succession will occur and it would make the area difficult to access on foot. Without the grazing of sheep the moorlands would revert to having scrubby oak and birch woodland on them and the bird and insect communities would alter. The dry stone wall boundaries would not be maintained and people would leave the area due to lack of employment. This would have a knock-on effect on, e.g. provision of guesthouse accommodation often run as an extra job alongside farming. Overall, the landscape would be less attractive to the tourist. The UK government has plans to extend the financial help they offer to hill farmers who help to maintain traditional upland landscapes, so that they can continue to attract visitors and their spending power.

At present some upland areas are so popular that there are problems of traffic congestion on narrow roads and inadequate parking for accessing attractions. This popularity can lead to negative impacts on the landscape such as unattractive and extensive car parking areas. Too many tourists can be a problem and visitor flows require management if people are to have a positive experience and continue to spend money within an area's economy.

The need is for a balance as we move away from landscapes of production towards a landscape of consumption through our leisure use. If we are not careful, the landscapes we thought of as permanent will disappear without some form of caretaking and this needs clear leadership and management.

How to manage the rural landscape

In most rural places visited by tourists, there has been some form of management of the location, but it will vary from being led nationally to being small-scale such as a local country park. Attitudes have changed over the years and decision-makers are less likely to want just to preserve a landscape. In the past, many rural landscapes were solely used for food production (landscapes of production), but now they are also used for leisure and tourism (landscapes of consumption) or this use dominates, depending on the location. There is a tension between balancing the needs for conservation with those for recreation. Figure 42.2 summarises some of the management strategies employed by decision-makers when considering landscapes for tourism and leisure.

One of the newer schemes to support and encourage sustainable development initiatives in tourist locations is the Green Globe. Set up in 1994 it aimed to try to implement the principles defined by Agenda 21 of the Rio Earth Summit. Over the years since its inception, it has developed from being mainly concerned with raising awareness about environmental issues in tourism to an accreditation/certification scheme. These are at three levels and the organisation can use its accreditation in its marketing, showing that it is committed to sustainable development within the industry. It includes sections on environmental management, but also stakeholder consultation that would include local communities. Awards are also given annually for outstanding achievement within the Green Globe programme.

Maintaining a balance

Previously we looked at how conflicts can arise between different users of the rural landscape. However, there can also be conflicts between the managers of the location and the users. If a management strategy is focusing on conservation of wildlife and limited tourist access, there will be a conflict with those users who have hunted there, perhaps for generations. Management of a lake, e.g. Windermere in the Lake District, might mean that speedboats are banned for the good of tourism as a whole and to maintain a more natural feel to the area. It may prove popular with the general tourist, but will upset those who own or rent speedboats (generally younger visitors) and have a knock-on effect on boat hire and maintenance businesses.

▲ **Figure 42.1:** The North York Moors, UK.

Key term

Agenda 21 — this came out of the Rio Earth Summit of 1992 and is summarised by the phrase 'Thinking globally, acting locally'. It is a blueprint for environmental management of the earth's resources and encourages thinking and decision-making at a local level.

Taking it further

Access the Green Globe website at www.greenglobeint.com and investigate what a location has to do in order to achieve a Green Globe certification. What are the likely outcomes for landscapes of this accreditation?

Case study: The Galapagos Islands

This case study looks at the conflicts that can arise when tourism is developed in a fragile and isolated location.

The Galapagos Islands are situated in the Pacific Ocean, about 1,000 km off the coast of Ecuador. These remote, volcanic islands and their unique wildlife are attracting an increasing number of tourists. People come here to see animals, such as the giant tortoise and the marine iguana, which are endemic to the islands. In the past nature tourism became very popular and there was an influx of immigrants from mainland Ecuador hoping to take advantage of the jobs and money that tourism or fishing would bring. Until the 1970s the population was only a few thousand, but it is estimated that it is now nearly 40,000. The islands cannot support a large population as there is very little drinking water and the poor, thin soils do not support much agriculture, so the economy is mainly based on tourism and fishing. Unregulated use of the islands' resources had led to real worries about whether such a unique location could survive into the 21st century. A system of protective zones was drawn up. Find out what are the main threats to the landscapes of the Galapagos Islands at www.darwinfoundation.org.

Before the zoning strategy there was pressure from too many tourists wanting to visit fragile areas and local businesses being happy to take them despite the disturbance this caused for the wildlife. The strategy aimed to allow some resource extraction and tourist access, but also to protect what it was that visitors were coming to see. Alongside the zoning strategy, recent migrants were encouraged to return to Ecuador to try to reduce human pressures on the islands. Another change to the management strategy is that the local people are consulted much more and are part of the integrated decision-making process. This means they feel that they have ownership of the islands and, by being included, are encouraged to help conserve them for the future, working as partners with the scientists.

Strategy	Description	Advantages	Disadvantages
Preservationist approach	Aims to keep a landscape exactly as it was into the future. Limit human use of these landscapes if they cause change, e.g. National Trust maintenance of grounds at Attingham Hall, Shropshire and similar.	Keeps landscape in original form – at least at time decision is taken. Can be shown to present generation as historical landscape.	Does not allow changes which might be better in long term. Frozen in time.
Conservationist approach	Sometimes used interchangeably with preservation but has a more open approach. The landscape survival is paramount along with its biodiversity but can adapt modern thinking to the problem of maintaining rural landscapes. At Llanddwyn Island on Anglesey, ponies are used as grazers to keep the vegetation cover as grass and prevent plant succession. Keeps the footpaths and the views open.	Preserving what is good/beneficial for ecosystems and landscape but allowing new approaches if it means landscape is protected, e.g. allowing more people to access an area by using public transport instead of car.	May not take on board the wishes of the local community if they conflict with conservation.
Stewardship	This goes hand in hand with conservation and sustainable development but it focuses more on individual responsibility for rural landscapes. It is our responsibility to see that the landscapes survive relatively intact for the next generation and even though we may not own the landscapes, we need to care about them and be involved in decisions about their management. Natural England is a steward in looking after areas of great natural importance such as the National Nature Reserves.	Can be applied at all levels, from the individual up to governmental level. Encourages thinking of landscapes as only being lent to us to look after and to pass on to the next generation.	Relies on people taking responsibility and is only fully successful when legislated for.
Ecotourism	This was developed in the 1980s and is tourism usually based on the natural world and only involving small groups of visitors. Aims to have lower impact on local resources than mass tourism.	Using the attraction of the natural world to encourage visitors. This then leads to tourism locations ensuring that the natural world is protected for people to come and view. Facilities provided should have minimal impact on natural systems.	Some ecotourism projects are not well planned and have negative impacts on the natural systems such as water resources.
Sustainable management	This can include elements of all of the above but the overriding aim is to manage that the resource (the rural landscape) is used in such a way that it does not compromise the ability of future generations being able to utilise the resource. For it to be successful, sustainable tourism must work with local communities and be integrated into their economy. An example would be the management of Iwokrama (see Chapter 40).	When all elements of sustainability are covered – social, economic and environmental – and there is local involvement in the planning of the tourism enterprise, then the tourism development should be able to make use of today's resources without reducing the ability of future generations to use the same resources (rural landscapes).	To be truly sustainable all elements need to be present. Often local involvement is limited and without this any development is likely to fail.
Cultural tourism	More of a theme than a management strategy but the aim is for tourists to engage more with local cultures. Includes following cultural routes such as the Silk Road from Tashkent, Uzbekistan through to Beijing, China.	Encourages local people to take a pride in their culture. Can devise tours that take in a range of locations within rural landscapes. Souvenirs can be based on traditional crafts. More likely to help maintain traditional landscapes.	Might degenerate into performing for tourists rather than tourists seeing for themselves what life is like. Local people may focus on tourism to detriment of local landscapes.
Tourist enclave	This is a form of management where tourists are kept apart from the local culture. They take the form of resorts with only limited contact with life outside although dance troupes may come in to give a performance of local dances. All facilities and attractions are within the site and many tourists never go beyond the resort other than to and from the airport. Examples are the Sandals resorts on e.g. St Lucia in the Caribbean.	Tourists all in one place. Easy to manage and can put in place all necessary facilities. Keeps Western tourists away from local people – less chance for tourists to offend through behaviour or dress.	Can change landscape of a rural coastal area (but it is limited). Very limited interaction with the culture that has created the landscape. Tourist will not return home with clear idea of the destination he has just visited.

▲ **Figure 42.2:** Table of management strategies.

The Protected Area Network (PAN) parks use tourism as a tool for nature and landscape conservation. PAN parks form a network of protected natural landscapes in Europe and aim to give tourists access to wildlife whilst protecting habitats and minimising the environmental impact of tourism. It was started in 1997 under the auspices of the World Wide Fund for Nature (WWF) in order to create a certification for sustainable tourism. Parks in the network aim to create balance between local users, tourism and recreation and nature conservation and to avoid potentially conflicting activities. To be part of PAN, the park needs to be large and have outstanding landscapes and/or ecosystems along with sound management.

The Rila National Park is part of the network and covers a large mountainous area of Bulgaria where there are attractive landscapes and large animals such as bears still roaming free. The management involves several stakeholders including tourist service providers, NGOs (non-governmental organisations like the WWF), local authorities and the park managers. They take into account the national, regional and local plans for sustainable tourism development in order to develop a Sustainable Tourism Development Strategy (STDS) for 2008–13. With all local communities being represented, issues can be addressed before they become problems.

Several local businesses, such as guesthouses, have made a commitment to work with park managers to provide a quality tourism product that does not harm the environment and have become PAN parks business partners. In this way the environment is protected, income is brought into the community via the tourism that the park attracts and local communities are maintained.

Synoptic link

For links with this chapter look at Edexcel AS Geography Unit 2 Chapters 16 and 18.

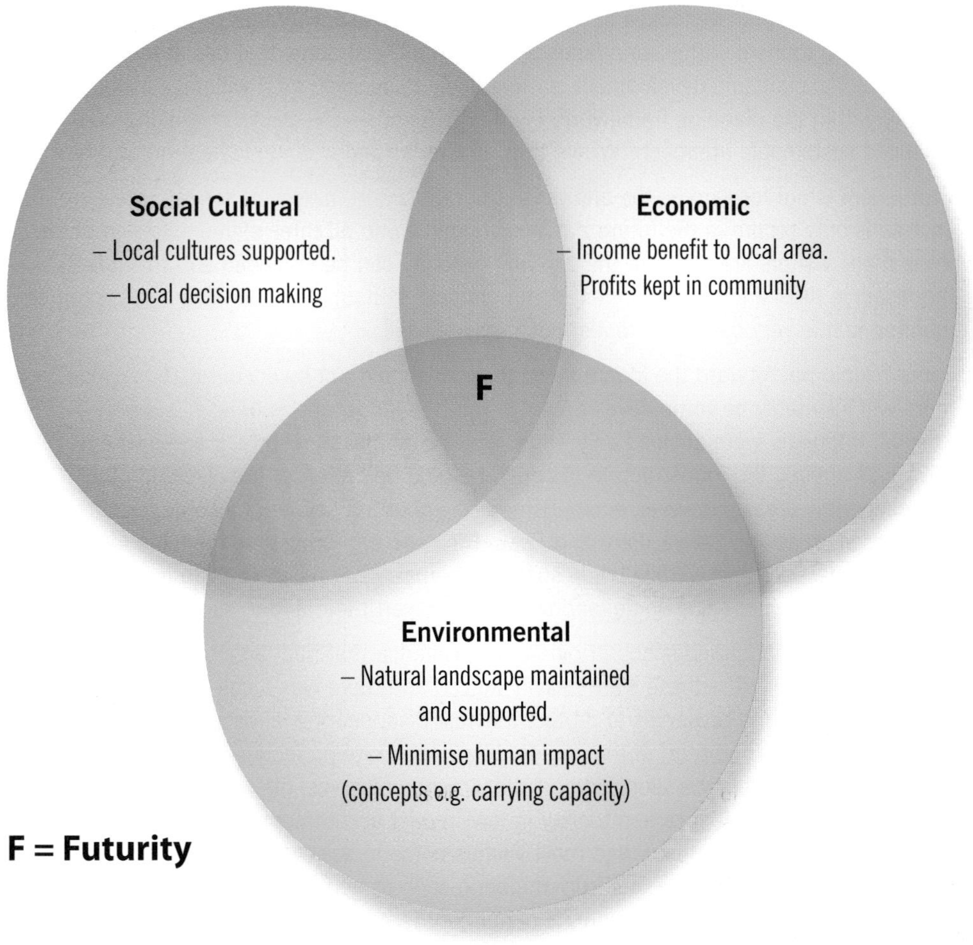

Social Cultural
– Local cultures supported.
– Local decision making

Economic
– Income benefit to local area.
  Profits kept in community

F

Environmental
– Natural landscape maintained and supported.
– Minimise human impact (concepts e.g. carrying capacity)

F = Futurity

Figure 42.3: Elements making up a balanced sustainable approach.

Case study: Snowdonia

This case study looks at how Snowdonia National Park is trying to encourage its visitors to reduce their impact on the environment.

Snowdonia National Park, an area of mountains, valleys, lakes and waterfalls, attracts visitors of all ages throughout the year. Recently the park has tried to highlight ways in which we can reduce our individual impact on this special landscape and yet still enjoy it. In publicity material physical health is linked to seeing Snowdonia on foot or by bicycle. The park managers have made it easier to access walking tracks and facilities by running Snowdonia Green Key. Sherpa buses run all year round and take visitors to the base of all the six major footpaths and also along the major valleys as part of a push to try to get visitors to go 'car-free'. There are several free walking and

▲ **Figure 42.4:** Snowdonia National Park.

biking leaflets and information on how to access accommodation using public transport. The National Cycle Network runs through the park which gives greater access to cyclists. Altogether these travel initiatives have meant that visiting the park can now be done in a more sustainable way.

Taking it further

To find out other ways in which visitors can reduce their impact, go to www. green-snowdonia.co.uk.

Comparing approaches

Earlier in this chapter we looked at the advantages and disadvantages of various strategies for managing tourism within rural landscapes. Overall, a strategy that has at least some elements of sustainable development is more likely to succeed as it will have aspects of futurity within the planning framework. Figure 42.3 shows the elements making up a balanced sustainable approach. Where they all overlap there is an element of futurity.

Ecotourism is put forward as the answer to the problem of increasing tourism pressure, but an area is only secure in the future if it is sustainable and all three elements are in place. If too many visitors are allowed, the carrying capacity can be exceeded and this affects the resource itself and the dependent communities. Without clear planning and continual monitoring it is very easy for a tourist destination to fail.

Some people put forward the idea that ecotourism should not be encouraged because there will inevitably be some development within the landscape in order to support tourists. If tourists were allowed only in well-developed beach resorts or areas where there was already the infrastructure to cope, it would be better for the wildlife in the less accessible areas. However, ecotourism is an important source of income for many countries such as Fiji, Kenya, Peru and Costa Rica and can bring great benefits to the local people, landscapes and wildlife when sustainably managed. As ecotourism is shown to be profitable, it is encouraging some landowners to convert their land to such activities.

Taking it further

For more information on ecotourism, visit the website www.ecotravelling. co.uk/CarbonOffsetting.html.

Costa Rica is a mountainous country in Central America that had large tracts of tropical rainforest. In the 1940s these were heavily logged and there was a call for the creation of national parks and preserves to protect this fast disappearing landscape and its biodiversity. Nearly one-third of the country has some state protection and today the national parks and refuges, alongside privately owned reserves, offer the chance for visitors to see a range of landscapes and to stay in low-impact accommodation. Tourism is Costa Rica's most important industry and most visitors come to see its wildlife and protected forests and are happy to stay in accommodation such as eco-lodges, which can be based on the local dwelling design or simply a permanent tented camp and have limited facilities.

The Santa Elena Cloud Forest Reserve is a community-managed reserve, which was opened in 1992. The community benefits from the proceeds of entrance fees, guided tour payments and the selling of souvenirs. This money is either reinvested into the reserve or the local school. At present, there are plans to extend forest corridors from the central core of the reserve to encourage more of the larger animals such as the ocelot, puma and jaguar as these animals require more extensive territories. Here tourism revenues are providing jobs and expanding the conservation of the landscape.

It would seem that the most successful tourism management is based on the ideas of sustainability, but when tourism relies on long-haul flights, can it ever be truly sustainable? Tourists are more aware of environmental impacts of their travel, especially air travel, and can offset them by paying for the planting of trees or supporting projects in less developed countries.

However, there is also an increasing number of tourists who wish to maintain their standard of living as they travel. They want high-quality hotels with air conditioning, imported foods with which they are familiar, large swimming pools and easy access to attractive rural landscapes. These demands will inevitably impact negatively on the rural landscapes and communities in which they occur.

Summary

In this chapter you have learnt:

• that management is needed for all rural landscapes in order for them to be passed on to future generations.
• that there is a range of management strategies and that they all have something to offer in the way of maintaining viable rural landscapes.
• that conflicts can occur between users of the landscape and the view of managers as to how it should be used.
• that management strategies that are successful in developed or developing country locations tend to be based on sustainable development.

MCQ

Exam Practice – Unit 4

Topic 1: Tectonic Activity and Hazards

Research focus:

Explore the meaning of response ❶ and the range of responses ❷ to tectonic hazards ❸ and evaluate how technology ❹ and research ❺ have contributed to changing responses.

Research: a range of case studies which show the impacts ❻ of tectonic hazard events ❼ and how response to these has affected impacts.

Unpicking the research focus:

1. Researching the meaning of response including modifying loss burden, modifying the event and modifying human vulnerability.
2. Researching the different ways in which people attempt to cope, before, during and after hazard events. Examining models of response such as Parks and the Hazard Management Cycle.
3. Considering the range of tectonic hazards, including earthquakes and volcanoes. You must not be unbalanced by only considering one or the other.
4. Examining the role technology can play in response. This could include prediction of events such as volcanic eruptions, or technology used as part of evacuation and warning. Technology might be used to mitigate against some hazards such as a seismic building design in earthquake zones.
5. Research is driving at the idea of increasing scientific understanding of tectonic hazards and how this might feed through into improved response. Note that 'changing response' implies a shift, perhaps an improvement.
6. Different hazards produce different impacts – there are contrasts between impacts in the developing and developed world, and in different locations based on their tectonic setting. You will need to research contrasting hazard case studies to ensure you have the range needed to answer the question in sufficient breadth and depth.
7. You will need to relate your ideas on technology and research to your case studies, and make sure they are integrated. There will need to be contrasts to show that in some cases technology and research have led to an improved response, which has reduced impacts. You may be able to show that for some hazards this is more true than for others.

For more information on the question, student plan, essay and mark scheme for this assessment go to your Student CD-ROM.

Topic 2: Cold Environments – Landscapes and Change

Research focus:

Explore the characteristics ❶ of cold environments in high latitudes ❷ and determine how far ❸ they are important locations for economic ❹ and research activity. ❺

Research a range of contrasting locations ❻ which show varying degrees of human activity and exploitation. ❼

Unpicking the research focus:

1. Characteristics of cold environments could include all details of climate, such as temperature, precipitation and seasonality. It also refers to the physical landscape including relief, landforms and dominant physical processes. The nature of ice is also relevant – such as the periglacial versus glacial environments.

2. Note that the research focus does state high latitudes; this is important as it is asking you to focus on the Arctic and Antarctic. If you were to drift away from this focus you would not get credit for it.

3. There is a clue in the research focus as the phrase 'determine how far' suggests that you will have to evaluate or decide 'to what extent'.

4. Economic activities could be very wide-ranging and include farming (unlikely in high latitude cold environments), resource exploitation such as drilling, mining and quarrying and possibly activities such as tourism and transportation.

5. The 'research activity' part of the research focus is a little obscure but it is driving at the idea of science and research as an important part of life in the high latitudes.

6. Contrasting locations could be as simple as the Arctic versus the Antarctic. However, you would need to consider other alternatives such as glacial versus periglacial or perhaps even inland versus coastal. You need to consider carefully if the examples you choose are truly high latitude and be prepared to explain and justify your choices.

7. There is a strong suggestion that you should consider and research some areas with limited (or even no economic activity) and some areas which are more heavily exploited – note the 'varying degrees' phrase in the research focus.

For more information on the question, student plan, essay and mark scheme for this assessment go to your Student CD-ROM.

Topic 3: Life on the Margins: the Food Supply Problem

Research focus:

Explore the physical and human processes ❹ which lead to desertification ❶ and evaluate how it can increasingly ❸ threaten livelihoods in dryland ❷ areas.

Research a range of case studies which illustrate the extent to which desertification both threatens the lives of communities living on the margins ❼ yet at the same time farming ❺ methods can exacerbate ❻ desertification.

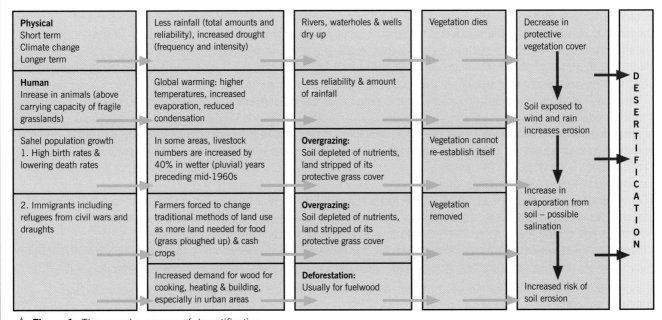

▲ **Figure 1:** The complex causes of desertification.

Unpicking the research focus:

1. Research definition of desertification – revise distribution map of areas currently vulnerable to desertification, UNCCD definition 'Land degradation in arid, semi-arid and dry sub-humid regions resulting from a variety of factors, including climatic variation and human activities'.

2. Research drylands, i.e. areas with limited inputs of rainfall, and few other sources such as groundwater – hence those living there (subsistence farmers and nomads) are almost totally dependent on conserving rainfall to use for their water needs. Dryland areas (see a map such as that obtainable from www.greenfacts.org) are therefore all at high risk from desertification, and the people living in them experience a high risk of food insecurity (note key areas such as Sahel, drylands of E/S Africa, NE Brazil, SW USA, Central Asia, etc).

3. Think about increasingly – could this be the impact of more frequent droughts, loss of glacier-fed water supplies, and increasingly climatic variation (in the Sahel) brought about by short-term climate change (global warming/El Niño – La Niña oscillation).

4. Re-research processes leading to desertification – ideally prepare a diagram which shows how physical and human processes interlink. List factors such as drought, salination, soil erosion, over-farming (over-grazing and over-cultivation), deforestation, etc. and sort them into physical and human factors.

5. In the information on case studies there is another clue as many researchers now think that the type of farming, such as over-grazing, or over-cultivation in response to food insecurity in developing countries, or salination from irrigation to increase food supplies in developed areas, accelerates the desertification process. This is clearly an argument you have to rehearse well before the exam.

6. Develop your case studies to cover a range of countries at different levels of economic development, for example SW USA/ Western Australia, Sahel and then other less researched areas (the text studies Guatemala and Uganda, both of which are good options).

7. Read back in the specification to consider what living on the margins actually means.

For more information on the question, student plan, essay and mark scheme for this assessment go to your Student CD-ROM.

Topic 4 : The World of Cultural Diversity

Research focus:

Explore the concept of cultural globalisation ❶ and its meaning to a range of different groups ❷; the degree ❸ to which cultural globalisation may be leading to negative consequences ❹ for some cultures and their landscapes. ❺

Research a range of contrasting cultures ❻ and the degree to which change has affected them ❼, and how well they have adapted ❽ to the challenges of cultural globalisation.

Unpicking the research focus:

1. Cultural globalisation is mentioned several times in the research focus so it is clearly going to be important to define this term in detail. You should be very clear in your mind what it means and how it links to different areas of the specification.
2. 'Different groups' is a strong steer towards different cultures. The differences could be based on nationality, religion or ethnicity – they clearly need to be cultural differences rather than say, differences in wealth.
3. Phrases such as 'the degree to which' in a research focus point towards the idea of assessment and evaluation. They hint at particular command words and phrases which you should expect in the question.
4. Notice the focus on negative consequences, which could point towards threats and problems resulting from cultural globalisation.
5. It is important to consider landscapes as well as people ('cultures') – you should ensure that you consider the constructed landscape and how cultural globalisation has affected it, as well as people.
6. Consider researching a range of contrasting cultures. The clearer the contrast the better, so move towards cultures from different parts of the world, those with differing religions and those which have been heavily influenced by the modern world compared with those for whom the globalisation process is just beginning.
7/8. The phrase 'how well they have adapted' is a good clue – it may be the case that some cultures have adapted to the negative consequences of cultural globalisation very well, whereas other cultures are under threat.

For more information on the question, student plan, essay and mark scheme for this assessment go to your Student CD-ROM.

Topic 5: Pollution and Human Health at Risk

Research focus:

Explore the complex causes of health ❷ risk from pollution ❶ and consider how they vary between ❸ and within countries across the world and why.

Research a range of case studies of health risks from various pollution types to show how the risks vary spatially ❹.

Unpicking the research focus:

1. Define pollution and explain how it can be a risk to human health. Differentiate between sustained pollution risks such as persistent smog/low air quality and asthmas, and incidental or point pollution resulting from an accident or explosion (Chernobyl/Bhopal) or emissions from a chimney of a smelter (e.g. a copper smelter).

2. What are links?
   • They may be **direct** (e.g. poor air quality and lung/heart asthma problems)
   • **indirect** (e.g. pollution from greenhouse gases leading to an increase in spread and development of diseases such as malaria)
   • **short term** (e.g. polluted water from an incident such as a sewage leak leading to an outbreak of dysentery or cholera)
   • **long term** (e.g. ozone depletion leading to skin cancers and cataracts).

3. The issue as to why variation occurs is for a variety of reasons. Clearly the location of the pollution sources has an impact as most of the pollution does affect local areas. The source will determine what type of pollution occurs. Other types of pollution are regional, for example acid rain, and some are even global such as GHG impacts and ozone depletion so less differentiation. Levels of risk from pollution can also relate to states of development, for example the **Kuznet curve**. Hence countries enjoying economic take-off such as China are likely to experience very high levels of pollution especially in urban industrial areas such as Chonquing.

4. The action carried out nationally and locally to manage and control pollution will also be important. Research ways of managing health risks from pollution such as education and screening programmes.

5. Create case study cards from your research file, and try to fit them into a framework (see 2).

For more information on the question, student plan, essay and mark scheme for this assessment go to your Student CD-ROM.

Topic 6: Consuming the Rural Landscape for Leisure and Tourism

Research focus:

Explore the concept of the pleasure periphery (key word) in order to evaluate (command word) its relevance in increasing tourism pressure.

Research a range of case studies which illustrate over time how the periphery has extended spatially, rationale.

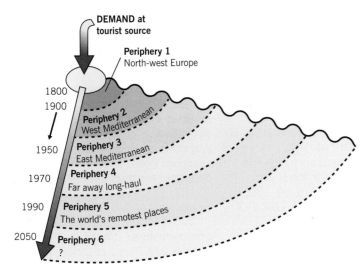

▲ **Figure 1:** The expanding pleasure periphery, from a European perspective

Unpicking the focus:

1. Find reference to the pleasure periphery in the specification – essentially the spread over time of tourist destinations further away from tourism source centres of Europe, North America and more recently the Far East. This is for both active and passive tourism.
2. Research reasons why the periphery has extended.
3. Explore the threats and opportunities the extension of the periphery poses to a range of environments to consider whether it does increase tourist pressure especially in remote, fragile, semi-pristine environments.
4. Devise case study rationale to look at when and how the pleasure periphery extended. Use the selected case studies to assess impacts.

Use UK as a source	19th century Resort and spa tourism	1
	Early 1930s–60 – parts of Europe, French Riviera	2
Pressure ✔	Rise of mass tourism 1960s Costa Brava 1970s Costa del Sol and Canaries	3
variable ✔ variable ✔	Extension across Europe – Greek Islands, Turkey Beginning of long-haul flights – Maldives, Far East, Australia	4
Beginning to be ✔	Extension for adventure tourism – Galapagos	5
A threat ✔	Extension to remote areas – Arctic, Antarctica	6
Not yet ✘	Plans for space tourism	7

◀ **Figure 2:** Case studies

For more information on the question, student plan and mark scheme for this assessment go to your Student CD-ROM.

Index

Published by Pearson Education Limited, a company incorporated in England and Wales, having its registered office at Edinburgh Gate, Harlow, Essex, CM20 2JE. Registered company number: 872828

Edexcel is a registered trademark of Edexcel Limited

Text © Pearson Education Limited 2009

First published 2009

12 11 10 09
10 9 8 7 6 5 4 3 2 1

British Library Cataloguing in Publication Data
A catalogue record for this book is available from the British Library
.
ISBN 978 1 846903 66 3

Designed by Ian Foulis
Illustrated by, Ian Foulis, Nick Hawken and Tony Wilkins
Indexed by Indexing Specialists (UK) Ltd
Picture research by Alison Prior
Development edited by Helen Farrell and Lucy Hyde
Permissions by Rachel Naish
Printed and bound in Great Britain at Scotprint, Haddington

The publisher would like to thank the following for their kind permission to reproduce their photographs:
(Key: b-bottom; c-centre; l-left; r-right; t-top)
Alamy Images: B&C Alexander 192r, 202l; Blickwinkel 68; Cliff Le Sergent 182l; Dave Pattison 182r; David Crausby 246b; Eitan Simanor 54; Imagebroker 193; Jacky Palmer 139; John Birdsall 216; John Sylvester 201; John Warburton-Lee Photography 66; Mary Evans Picture Library 258; Nagelestock.com 127; Pacific Press Service 176; Quentin Bargate 297; Robert Harding Picture Library 192l; Ron Niebrugge 202r; Russell Kord 195; Sean Sprague 117; The Photo Library Wales 300; The Print Collector 142l; Vario Images GmbH.co.KG 208; **CartoonStock Ltd**: 131; **Corbis**: Igor Kostin/Sygma 27; Jamal Nasralleh 22; Jim Zuckerman 58; John Bartholomew 269; Larry Lee Photography 14; Mohammed Berno/Document Iran 17; Reuters 172; Roger Ressmeyer 8, 178; Stephen Frink 63; **Getty Images**: AFP 4, 74; Axiom Photographic Agency 284; Daniel Beltra 281; Digital Globe 159c, 159t; Hugh Sitton 288; Michael Turek 291; Sylvester Adams 280; Time & Life Pictures 219; **GNU Free Documentation license:** 184l, 184r; **iStockphoto:** 77; Lynn Graesing 147; Michael Hoefner 134; **Oxfam:** Ger Murphy 224; **STILL Pictures The Whole Earth Photo Library:** Biosphoto/Delfino Dominique 78; Fred Bruemmer 197; Mark Edwards 222; McPhoto 60; Sean Sprague 255, 259; **Tony Waltham/Geophotos:** 170; **USGS:** 158, 159b
All other images © Sally Garrington, Garrett Nagle & Viv Pointon

Every effort has been made to contact copyright holders of material reproduced in this book. Any omissions will be rectified in subsequent printings if notice is given to the publishers.

The websites used in this book were correct and up to date at the time of publication. It is essential for tutors to preview each website before using it in class so as to ensure that the URL is still accurate, relevant and appropriate. We suggest that tutors bookmark useful websites and consider enabling students to access them through the school/ college intranet.

This material has been published on behalf of Edexcel and offers high-quality support for the delivery of Edexcel qualifications.
This does not mean that the material is essential to achieve any Edexcel qualification, nor does it mean that it is the only suitable material available to support any Edexcel qualification. Edexcel material will not be used verbatim in setting any Edexcel examination or assessment. Any resource lists produced by Edexcel shall include this and other appropriate resources.

Copies of official specifications for all Edexcel qualifications may be found on the Edexcel website: www.edexcel.com